LEOPAI

TURNING THE PAGE

Mark Mazour

· Cambridge 1994 ·

LEOPARD II

TURNING THE PAGE

Essays, Memoirs, Fiction, Poetry, and One Sermon

Edited by Christopher MacLehose

HARVILL
An Imprint of HarperCollinsPublishers

First published in 1993 by
Harvill
An Imprint of HarperCollins*Publishers*
77/85 Fulham Palace Road,
Hammersmith, London W6 8JB

1 3 5 7 9 8 6 4 2

A CIP catalogue record for this title is
available from the British Library

ISBN 0 00 272174 0

Photoset in Linotron Galliard by
Rowland Phototypesetting Ltd, Bury St Edmunds, Suffolk
Printed and bound in Great Britain by
Cromwell Press, Melksham, Wiltshire

CONTENTS

ACKNOWLEDGEMENTS

The Publisher thanks the following for permission to reproduce the texts in this anthology:

Nadine Gordimer: *Turning the Page*. First broadcast by BBC Radio 4 in the series *Beloved Country* © Nadine Gordimer.

Yunna Moritz: *Russian Literature Today* © Yunna Moritz 1993. English translation by Frank Williams © HarperCollins*Publishers* 1993.

Robert Hughes: *Columbus Day Sermon* © Robert Hughes 1993.

Richard Ford: *My Mother, in Memory* © Richard Ford. First published in *Harper's* Magazine, USA.

Lydia Chukovskaya: *The Akhmatova Journals* 1938–41 © Lydia Chukovskaya 1993. English translation by Milena Michalski and Silva Rubashova © HarperCollins*Publishers* 1993.

Aleksandr Kushner: *Lidiya Ginzburg* © HarperCollins*Publishers* 1993. English translation by Alan Myers © HarperCollins*Publishers* 1993.

Yulia Pyanitskaya: *The Diary of a Bolshevik's Wife*. First published in Russian as *Dvevnik jeny bolchevika* by Chalidze Publications, Vermont, USA © Chalidze Publications 1987. Copyright in languages other than Russian © Editions du Seuil 1992. English translation by David Floyd © HarperCollins*Publishers* 1993.

George MacDonald Fraser: from *Quartered Safe out Here*. First published by Harvill 1992 © George MacDonald Fraser 1992.

Andrei Bitov: from *A Captive of the Caucasus* © Andrei Bitov 1969, 1986, 1989. English translation © Susan Brownsberger 1991. Reprinted by permission of Farrar, Straus & Giroux, Inc, New York, and Weidenfeld & Nicolson, London.

Anna Akhmatova: *There Are Four of Us* from Anna Akhmatova: *Selected Poems*, Harvill 1973, 1989. Reprinted by permission of Little, Brown & Co. Inc, New York. English translation © Stanley Kunitz with Max Hayward 1973.

Osip Mandelstam: *Tristia* English translation © Robert Tracy 1993.

Marina Tsvetaeva: *An Attempt at Jealousy*. English translation by Peter Norman © HarperCollins*Publishers* 1993.

Boris Pasternak: *Night* English translation © Craig Raine 1993.

Anna Akhmatova: *Boris Pasternak*. English translation by Peter Norman © HarperCollins*Publishers* 1993.

Claudio Magris: *A Different Sea*. First published by Garzanti, Milan, 1991, as an *Un Altro Mare* © Garzanti Editore, SPA 1991. English translation by Stephen Spurr © HarperCollins*Publishers* 1993.

EDITOR'S PREFACE

*Leopard** is an occasional review dedicated to writers in all languages which concerns itself with the political struggle of writers, their lives and work, and with aspects of the work of publishers. *Leopard*'s first issue, *Dissonant Voices*,† was exclusively Russian: Oleg Chukhontsev's anthology of the new Russian fiction. His collection of twenty-six stories, none hitherto translated into English, is the best anthology of its kind.

This second issue, which takes its title from Nadine Gordimer's essay on African writers in the twenty-first century, brings into a single volume essays and fiction, prose and poetry from an exceptional array of writers. Yunna Moritz's provocative study of the vanished Russian reader was written for this issue; George MacDonald Fraser's description of battle is reprinted from his recollection of the Burma Campaign, *Quartered Safe out Here*, and demands an even wider readership; Robert Hughes' sermon was given on Columbus Day last year in Grace Cathedral in San Francisco; Yulia Pyanitskaya's *Diary*, of which we print an extract, is one of the saddest documents of the twentieth century and was only lately discovered in Moscow; in short, these essays derive from a variety of sources. *Leopard* will as gladly reprint valuable works (as Richard Ford's memoir or as John Ryder's classic study, *The Case for Legibility*) as it will introduce new writers or work-in-progress from established writers. And, as in the case of the four greatest Russian poets of the century, we will, if we can come by them, publish outstanding new translations. There are two American short-story writers in this collection: Joy Williams, who read her story for the first time in London in the spring of 1992, and Julian Mazor who has chosen to remain unpublished since a brilliant debut twenty-five years ago. All of the other stories and work-in-progress are translated. There must be little argument as to their standing in their own countries. Our view is that in translation they make a magnificent company.

*The leopard, which is the emblem of the publishers of this review, is a tribute to Giuseppe Tomasi di Lampedusa. The creature itself was made for Harvill by Richard Shirley-Smith, the English engraver.

†A list of the contents of *Dissonant Voices* appears at the end of this volume.

Harvill now publishes work in translation from twenty-two languages and is proud to bring those writers into English alongside its English-language authors, in book form or in *Leopard*. Our debt to our translators cannot be overstated. Their knowledge of foreign tongues, literatures and cultures makes them indispensable to our work. They form, as do our authors, a wider editorial board on which this small imprint imposes. To each of them and to the contributors to this *Leopard* the publisher is happy to make plain his gratitude.

CCML

NADINE GORDIMER

Turning the Page

African Writers and the Twenty-first Century

Writers in Africa in this century now coming to an end have inter-
preted the greatest events on our continent since the abolition of
slavery.

We have known that our task was to bring to our people's consciousness and that of the world the true dimensions of racism and
colonialism beyond those that can be reached by the newspaper column and screen image, however valuable these may be. We have
sought the fingerprint of flesh on history.

The odds against developing as a writer able to take on this huge
responsibility have been great for most of our writers. But as Agos-
tinho Neto, Angolan poet and president said, and proved in his own
life: "If writing is one of the conditions of your being alive, you create
that condition."

Out of adversity, out of oppression, in spite of everything . . .

Looking forward to the twenty-first century, I think we have the
right to assess what we have come through. Being here; the particular
time and place that has been twentieth-century Africa. This has been
a position with particular implications for literature; we have lived
and worked through one of those fearful epochs Brecht has written
of when "to speak of trees is almost a crime". Our brothers and sisters
have challenged us with the Polish poet Czeslaw Milosz's cry: "What
is poetry which does not serve nations or people?" And we have taken
up that challenge. Inevitably, the characteristic of African literature
during the struggle against colonialism and, latterly, neo-colonialism
and corruption in post-colonial societies, has been engagement –
political engagement.

Now, unfortunately, many people see this concept of engagement
as a limited category closed to the range of life reflected in literature;

it is regarded as some sort of upmarket version of propaganda. Engagement is not understood for what it really has been, in the hands of honest and talented writers: the writer's exploration of the particular meaning his or her being has taken on in this time and place. For real "engagement", for the writer, isn't something set apart from the range of the creative imagination. It isn't something dictated by brothers and sisters in the cause he or she shares with them. It comes from within the writer, his or her creative destiny as an agency of culture, living in history. "Engagement" doesn't preclude the beauty of language, the complexity of human emotions; on the contrary, such literature must be able to use all these in order to be truly engaged with life, where the overwhelming factor in that life is political struggle.

While living and writing under these conditions in Africa some of us have seen our books lie for years unread in our own countries – banned – and we have gone on writing. Many writers have been imprisoned. Wole Soyinka, Ngugi wa Thiong'o, Jack Mapanje, Jeremy Cronin, Mongane Wally Serote, Breyten Breytenbach, Dennis Brutus, Jaki Seroke and a host of others. Many, such as Chinua Achebe and Nuruddin Farah, have endured the trauma of exile, from which some never recover as writers, and some do not survive at all. I think, among too many, of Can Themba and Dambuze Marechera.

What do we in Africa hope to achieve, as writers, in the new century? Because we are writers, can we expect to realize literally, through our work, that symbol of change, the turning to a fresh page?

What are the conditions under which we may expect to write – ideological, material, social?

It seems to me that these are the two basic questions for the future of African literature. I think it's generally agreed that consonance with the needs of the people is the imperative for the future in our view of our literature. This is the point of departure from the past; there, literature played the immeasurably valuable part of articulating the people's political struggle, but I do not believe it can be said to have enriched their lives with a literary culture. And I take it that our premise, in Africa, is that a literary culture is a people's right.

We all make the approach from our experience in the twentieth century. We all hazard predictions, since we do not know in what circumstances our ambitions for a developing literature will need to be carried out. We have our ideas and convictions of how literary development should be consonant with the needs of our people; we cannot know with what manner of political and social orders we shall have to seek that consonance.

I think we have to be completely open-eyed about the relation between our two basic questions. We have to recognize that the first – what we hope to achieve in terms of literary directions – is heavily dependent on the second: the conditions under which we shall be working as writers. A literary culture cannot be created by writers without readers. There are no readers without adequate education. It's as simple – and dire – as that. No matter how much we encourage writers who are able to fulfil, according to their talents, the various kinds and levels of writing that will take literature out of the forbidding context of unattainable intellectualism, we shall never succeed until there is a wide readership competent beyond school-primer and comic-book level. And where there are readers there must be libraries where the new literature we hope to nurture, satisfying the need of identification with people's own daily lives, and the general literature that brings the great mind-opening works of the world to them, are easily available to them.

Will these potential readers find prose, poetry and non-fiction in their mother tongues?

If we are to create a twenty-first century African literature, how is this to be done while publishing in African languages remains mainly confined to works prescribed for study, market-stall booklets, religious tracts? We have long accepted that Africa cannot, and so far as her people are concerned, has no desire to, create a "pure" culture in linguistic terms; this culture is an anachronism when for purposes of material development the continent eagerly seeks means of technological development from all over the world.

We all know that there is no such workable system as a purely indigenous economy once everyone wants computers and movie cassettes.

Neither, in a future of increasing intercontinental contact, can there be a "pure" indigenous culture. We see, a plain fact all over Africa, that the European languages that came with colonial conquest have been taken over into independence, *acquired* by Africans and made part and parcel of their own convenience and culture. The brilliant examples of this acquisition are there to be read in the work of some black African writers. (Whites, of course, have never had the good sense to do the same with African languages . . .)

But we writers cannot speak of taking up the challenge of a new century for African literature unless writing in African languages becomes the major component of the continent's literature. Without this one cannot speak of an African literature. It must be the basis of the cultural cross-currents that will both buffet and stimulate that literature.

What of publishing?

We write the books; to come alive they have to be read. To be available, they have to be competently distributed, not only in terms of libraries, but also commercially. Many of us in Africa have had experience of trying to meet the needs of the culturally marginalized by launching small, non-profit publishing ventures in African literature. We find ourselves stopped short by the fact that the distribution network, certainly in the Southern African countries (I don't imagine there is much difference in countries to the North) remains the same old colonial one. Less than a handful of distribution networks make decisions, based on the lowest common denominator of literary value, on what books should be bought from publishers, and this handful has the only means of distributing books widely to the public, since they own the chain book stores which dominate the trade in the cities, and are the only existing book stores in most small towns. In South Africa, for example, in the twentieth century there have been and are virtually *no* book stores in the vast areas where blacks have been confined under apartheid.

Another vital question: what will be the various African states' official attitude to culture, and to literature as an expression of that culture? We writers don't know, and have every reason to be uneasy. Certainly, in the twentieth century of political struggle, state money has gone into guns, not books; literature, culture, has been relegated to the dispensable category. As for literacy, so long as people can read state decrees and the graffiti that defy them, that has been regarded as sufficient proficiency. As writers, do we envisage, for example, a dispensation from a Ministry of Culture in South Africa to fund publishing in African languages, and to provide libraries in rural communities and in the shanty towns which no doubt will be with us, still, for a long time? Would we have to fear that, in return for subvention, writers might be restricted by censorship of one kind or another? How can we ensure that our implicit role – supplying a critique of society for the greater understanding and enrichment of life there – will be respected?

Considering all these factors that stand between the writer's act of transforming literature in response to a new era, it seems that we writers have, however reluctantly, to take on contingent responsibilities that should not be ours. We'll have to concern ourselves with the quality and direction of education – will our schools turn out drones or thinkers? How shall we press for a new policy and structure of publishing and distribution, so that writers may write in African languages and bring pleasure and fulfilment to thousands who are cut off from literature by lack of knowledge of European languages? How shall we make the function of writers, whose hand held out to contribute to development is in the books they offer, something recognized and given its value by the governing powers of the twenty-first century? We have to begin now to concern ourselves with the structures of society that contain culture, and within which it must assert its growth.

And there is yet one more problem to be faced by the naked power of the word, which is all we have, but which has proved itself unkillable by even the most horrible of conventional and unconventional weaponry. Looking back, many well-known factors inhibited the growth of a modern African culture, an African literature, in the century whose sands are running out through our fingers. One hardly need cite the contemptuous dismissal of all African culture by frontier and colonial domination; the cementing-over of African music, dance, myth, philosophy, religious beliefs and secular rituals: the very stuff on which the literary imagination feeds. The creativity of Africa lay ignored beneath the treading feet of white people on their way to see the latest Hollywood gangster movie or to pick up from the corner store a comic with bubble text in American. And soon, soon, these were joined by black people in the same pursuit, having been convinced, since everything that was their own was said to be worthless, that this was the culture to acquire. The habit of chewing cultural pulp is by now deeply established among our people. And it is so temptingly cheap to be bought from abroad by our media, including the dominant cultural medium of our time, television, that literature in Africa not only has to express the lives of the people, but also has to assert the beauty and interest of this reality against mega subculture – the new opium of the people . . .

Surely the powers of the imagination of our writers can be exerted to attract our people away from the soporific sitcom, surely the great adventures that writers explore in life can offer a child something as exciting in image and word as the cumbersome battle between Japanese turtles? We in Africa don't want cultural freedom hijacked by the rush of international sub-literature into the space for growth hard-won by ourselves in the defeat of colonial culture. that is perhaps the greatest hazard facing us as we turn the page of African literature and write the heading: Twenty-first century.

YUNNA MORITZ

The Great Russian Readership: Where has it Gone?

Drama's Vitallest Expression
is the Common Day.
EMILY DICKINSON

The communist empire was home to the second principle of thermo-
dynamics – in closed systems entropy is progressive and irreversible.
The Bolsheviks seized one sixth of the world, took over an empire
with immense natural wealth and human potential, then set about
carving out with fire and sword, with hammer and sickle, a new reality
and a new man, sealing off the borders and replacing information
with propaganda. In seventy years the Bolshevik elite annihilated tens
of millions of their fellow citizens, spent everything to the last (literally!) rouble on arms in the struggle to be the predominant super-
power. When finally confronted by the hollowness of their ambitions,
they abandoned all pretence, dumped their slogans and threw in their
lot with the barons of the shadow economy, funnelling state resources
into their own private enterprises.

An exhausted and exploited populace was told it had only itself to
blame. It had squandered the benefits of free health care, free education and prices way below world market levels. Since only Bolsheviks could possibly be at the forefront of progress, the Party, in
the person of its General Secretary, launched *perestroika* and ordered
a nationwide movement forward to a new economic order based on
free market prices. The masses were offered a new consensus, a "socialist choice" within the framework of a "pluralism of opinion".

When Edith Piaf was a young street performer, pickpockets used
to work the crowds she drew. A roughly similar thing happened when

the truth was allowed for the first time in seventy years and Party
hacks in what used to be a reactionary official press succumbed to
glasnost, pushing the ideas of the dissidents (many of whom were still
rotting and dying in the camps) as their own. Round about this time
the first commercial organizations were formed. They bought up at
state prices goods which were totally unavailable in the shops and
re-sold them at commercial prices, so pumping ordinary people's
savings into their own pockets. Without producing a thing, the "communist capitalists" of the "new economy" acquired vast property for
next to nothing, long before vouchers and privatisation laws secured
them a legitimate future.

Today the atmosphere here is one of uselessness. Useless impoverished pensioners, useless children fainting from hunger and inadequately clothed, a useless governing apparatus which fears a
useless population, a useless retrograde parliament which is frightened of being thrown off the gravy train, a useless over-educated
intelligentsia unwilling to soil itself with commerce and which
emigrates as proof of its uselessness. A population with guns,
a disintegrating army, armouries stripped of weapons, ethnic
conflicts and cleansings, clan feuds, streams of refugees, bands of
mercenaries, lawlessness and a complete paralysis of authority, all
this is endemic.

Yet when foreign visitors come to see our nightmare, where a
student stipend or an old age pension comes to between $3 and $5
a month and a professor is paid $20, many of them ask, without the
slightest irony: "What's happened to the great Russian reader, the
greatest reading public in the world (GRPW)?"

Today a writer cannot afford books! Fortunately I have never lost
the childhood skill of reading a book in a shop while appearing to
browse. The reader, meanwhile, has his own private war to wage –
for sheer physical survival. The war is all around him, there is no front
and no supply line from the rear. There is no time left for reading,
people are done with that.

There is an old Islamic legend according to which the fabulous
horse that was carrying the Prophet to heaven let fall a pitcher of
water. But when the Prophet came back to earth and picked up the
pitcher, he found that not a drop had been spilt.

In the fifties, during the Thaw years, Akhmatova, Pasternak,
Zabolotsky, Tvardovsky were all still alive. But it was Yevtushenko,

Rozhdestvensky and Akhmadullina the public really wanted to hear. Some years later at readings by the sixties generation there were always squads of mounted police on hand to keep out the crowds of ticketless fans. In the hall, a poet or a group of poets, sometimes as many as twenty of them, would come out on stage and demand: "Let all those people out on the street in!" It used to bring the house down. It was just what the faithful readers out in the street expected of their writers. The crowd would surge into the hall, squatting on steps, perching on window sills, standing on tip-toe in the crush, all agog, applauding every note of defiance wildly. The second trump card was to put a "Sold Out" sign on the door before a single ticket had gone on sale; the hunt was on!

Imagine a performance in the sixties (if such a thing were possible) by Blok, Akhmatova, Gumilev, Tsvetaeva, Mandelstam, or Pasternak. None of them would have filled a hall, let alone a stadium, and would have been a huge disappointment – so little defiance, such boring delivery, such total lack of charisma. There would have been none of the standing ovations that rewarded the sixties generation.

Akhmatova had a poor opinion of the group I refer to as the State-sponsored sixties generation (S-SSG) – "Poets are they? . . ." – of their public adulation and of the GRPW. They were their readers, not hers. Her reader could not be massed in a stadium, her reader preferred to be one to one . . . When Pasternak stepped up on stage at one of the first public readings of the Thaw, he said he would recite three poems. And the public, which the new generation had provoked into calling "Bravo! Encore! More!", did not dare challenge him, did not dare turn the Poet into their plaything by demanding more. He delivered what he promised, no more, no less. It was a lesson in dignity and the hall gave him a standing ovation.

When the fashion switched to song, to the bards, who sang their own lyrics and other verse, the S-SSG had to move over. The bards, out of favour and underground, unauthorized and, therefore, uncensored, won a huge following. Tapes of their songs circulated in millions of copies. For a long time (and to their huge advantage) they were banned, official venues were closed to them and they performed wherever they could find a welcome: private flats (often belonging to "enlightened" up and coming members of the Party leadership), artists' studios, scientific and design institutes. The bards themselves were often young scientists, engineers and members of the liberal professions. The quality of the poetry they sang ranged from the sublime to the awful. It was a nomadic affair of the heart between poetry and the guitar. Eventually the caravan rolled to a halt in the vast official concert halls where everybody knew the words by now. As a result the only poetry the GRPW knew was what they heard sung to a guitar. Right until *perestroika* bards could fall out of official favour and find their concerts banned by the censor. For example, somebody somewhere sang bits from Marx's *Das Kapital*. It was hilarious and a tape was made, until somebody informed . . . Along with the audience for the S-SSG, the huge public for the parade of bards, undoubtedly charming and heartwarming as they were, helped reinforce the myth of the greatest culture-consuming public in the world. But the bards had their own axe to grind with the sixties generation. The S-SSG had been admitted to all the official creative unions, while the bards were not allowed within a mile of either the Composers' or the Writers' Unions.

On the anniversary of the bard Vysotsky's death, a concert was held in his memory at the Luzhniki stadium in Moscow. Yevtushenko, the first poet anywhere to fill a soccer stadium, was booed off stage. Anyone else would have had a bellyful of these recitals, but to him they were meat and drink. And when he heard that whistling, he physically felt he was a victim of repression – in all seriousness – and he let the world know that a poet's life was in danger. The sixties poets as a whole made great play of the tragic fates of Tsvetaeva and Mandelstam, measuring their own lives against theirs – Tsvetaeva's suicide and Mandelstam's cruel end in the camps – knowing full well they would never be arrested, never even be deprived of their Peredelkino dachas.

Sitting in a stadium, or theatre, or factory Palace of Culture to hear the S-SSG perform, our representative of the GRPW did occasionally hear of other "forbidden poets", so anti-Soviet they would never be seen in public, but whose words had been set by some bard or other to music. But it took too much effort, the snatches they heard were sufficient, and it was so much easier to pick up from hearsay rather than actually discover the magnificent poetry out there, even if it was beyond the reach of most of Moscow, let alone the rest of the USSR. This was the S-SSG's reader, the GRPW, reading by ear and feeding off rumours of literature.

Meanwhile excellent books could be had, photocopied, microfilmed or manually typed. In the seventies and eighties you could, for a price, buy practically any forbidden book: confiscated copies of Tsvetaeva, Mandelstam, Akhmatova, Pasternak, Kuzmin – everything that was published in the West. The West saved us with those books. A network of inexpensive photocopying gradually developed across the country. I bought a four-volume Gumilev, books on philosophy and religion, all of Solzhenitsyn, Shalamov and more besides published like this.

On the one hand the cultural vacuum was quietly being filled by increasingly good private libraries – good books were published officially, too, and the second-hand bookshops were full of treasures. On the other hand, books became a popular form of investment, a type of hard currency. The right book could obtain you a bed in a hospital, a good job, a train or air ticket, a room in a hotel where there were no vacancies. A butcher at a Moscow market famously remarked: "Get me some good books. Good books never go down in price. Besides, when they arrest us they don't confiscate our libraries."

In the most "bourgeois", pragmatic households, books were not for reading but for decor, collected for the colour of the binding and the format. Even so, children grew up in them, picked something up and read it, and in the cafés of the elite they could hear the S-SSG arguing over whether Brodsky was too literary and whether he used the word "culture" too often in his poems.

People would stand night and day in a twenty degree frost to subscribe to a multi-volume edition of Dostoyevsky or a dictionary. To join the subscription list you had to have coupons and to get coupons you had to collect tons of waste paper, very often the classics of socialist realism. And despite all the privations associated with obtaining decent books, they did their work, opening new perspectives, new mentalities, new values, the strange tongues of strange thought processes.

For the S-SSG Gorbachev's arrival on the political scene was the second high point in their careers. They snatched at the last prizes awarded by the dying Soviet Union as their just reward. The whole business of *perestroika* looks like a calculated attempt by the politically influential elements of the S-SSG and "enlightened" elements of the Komsomol and Party leaderships to take power into their own hands. The August putschists wrecked their plans. Nothing, though, had been left to chance, and a host of new committees, associations, unions, congresses, forums and assemblies had been put in place to bolster the old and, of course, the new elite. "The press department of the President reports: a new government decree calls for the introduction of legislation to provide additional material support to persons who have rendered Russia special service." (A recent newspaper cutting.) Sakharov rendered special service, so did Solzhenitsyn, Shalamov, Akhmatova, Tsvetaeva, Mandelstam, Andrey Tarkovsky, Vadim Sidur, Petr Grigorenko, Anatoly Marchenko, Rostropovich, Natalya Gorbanevskaya, Yuli Daniel, Andrey Sinyavsky, Vassily Grossman, Nabokov, Brodsky, Academician Likhachev, Tvardovsky, Sergey Kovalev, Bukovsky, Alec Ginsburg, Alfred Shnittke, Yury Galanskov . . . Who else? We'll see when we read the lists proposed by the various "cultural advisers" from the various "creative unions".

It would be nonsense to suggest that the lives and personalities of the sixties generation resemble each other any more than those of any other representatives of the various species, both four- and two-legged, herbivore and carnivore, denizens of earth and ocean. The age difference between them can be astonishingly great, sometimes as much as twenty years. Some of them were wounded during the war, others were born during it. Some of them had been in the camps, others put people there. Some founded the dissident movement, *The Chronicle of Current Events*, created great literature, art and science. Others took from them what little the authorities would allow and made themselves careers as "liberal" patrons. Some were paupers in a wealthy land, others wealthy in a pauperised one. Some enjoyed the acclaim of the GRPW, others' readership was only a drop in this great ocean, but this drop would never spill even from an overturned vessel – lift it upright and the vessel would still be full.

However, politics and a literature at the service of politics marked out and labelled as "the sixties generation" a very specific caste of people, divided in roughly even proportions into left, right and centre. And regardless of what happened in the outside world, their interests always seemed to coincide, enjoying a degree of indulgences from the censors and the whole gamut of privileges approved by the Central Committee – where they had a very special readership – for the "especially talented". For decades they blocked the way of a new generation.

Today the challenge – to a bare-knuckle fight (Get out, move over, you pigs!) – comes from infantile, rude thirty- and forty-year-old psychopaths, cynical, hard young pragmatists. It will do no good. The S-SSG will stay state-sponsored regardless of who has power. Because whatever they say about any government or regime, no matter how outspoken, cannot disguise the S-SSG's awareness of acquaintance and mutual self-interest as a source of money and fame, of the importance of being on first-name terms, knowing which door to kick, how to influence and be influenced, to feel the "spiritus rector", the guiding hand of those who hold the reins of power.

In the old days people knew the only things worth reading were what the press denounced and the customs confiscated. Huge quantities of unbought books by Party literary hacks were transported to the Gobi desert, to satisfy the cultural needs of our Mongolian brothers, or placed in every barracks library. A year later new editions of the same rubbish would appear in a glossier cover, in a fatter format. Authors were paid by the line.

But as soon as the Party's *perestroika* merchants rushed into the marketplace to launder Party funds by publishing expensive books printed on cheap state-owned presses with cheap ink and cheap paper at cheap state prices – as soon as the profits started to pour in from the first wave of "commercial" editions, reprints of the anti-Soviet and émigré books buried in the special depositories of the state libraries – as soon as serious money was being made and we were up to our eyes in all the things that had not appeared over the past seventy years plus the porno-psycho-UFO-sado market offerings of the Party publishing wizards – it was then the whole elitist structure came crashing down to howls of: "What's happened to the GRPW? Stop publishing dead authors! All that stuff is dead and buried! Enough cheap, corrupting Western popular trash!"

There is some good news: newspapers occasionally report thefts of books; burglars risk life and limb dropping onto balconies to make off with suitcases full of books, thieves drill through walls to steal books worth half a million roubles.

At one time little Estonia used to publish its poets in editions as big as those in Russia . . . Estonia never published its literary officials in quantities destined for the Gobi. Food was in as short supply as in Moscow, Minsk, Kiev or Leningrad, which Estonia used to supply with meat and dairy products. But only in Estonia could a new author without connections or influence publish a first novel at 17, be famous by 20, and feel himself a European without any complexes. There was no mass readership in Estonia, thank God, and disgraced Russian writers went there to publish their books, artists to show pictures that would have been bulldozed into the mud in Moscow ... Five thousand copies for a population of one and a half million or a hundred thousand copies for two hundred million – where's the bigger readership?

So how are Russian writers getting along in the market economy, without their guaranteed royalties and rest homes? That is a question I sometimes hear asked by Western writers or Russian émigrés, warm in their colleges and universities, secure in their jobs in radio, television, the press, supported by their various creative awards and grants.

Food for thought. Leaving aside Union and Party functionaries and those with friends in high places (Central Committee and Ministry of Culture), no decent Russian writer ever fed his family on his books alone. In cases of extreme hardship or serious illness a writer might receive, by special dispensation, up to two interest-free loans in any one year of $25, making a total of $50 or 400 roubles, exactly the cost of 24 days at a writers' rest home, plus the train fare. A decent writer could never find work as a university lecturer, let alone have his own programme on the radio with the right to read his own work, could never write regularly for magazines or newspapers, expect a creative grant for a year, let alone get a loan to buy an apartment.

All my friends were penniless and homeless. Help came from scientists, doctors and the good Lord. To make ends meet a decent writer made translations or reviewed manuscripts, or did lecture tours organized by a helpful literary magazine, or gave badly paid readings, if he/she was allowed to. Profitable undertakings, such as writing scripts for television documentaries or for radio or films, only went to safe candidates prepared to offer a cut to the dispensing Union functionary. If it had been decided to starve a particular writer of oxygen altogether and deprive him of all income, his only chance was to work as a stoker or janitor, write for the desk drawer and wait for better times, which would come, just to spite him, after he was dead and gone. And even if his time came after his death, his heirs' rights expired after twenty-five years and the state was then free to publish his books with a "balanced foreword", not paying a penny to his relatives and pocketing all the proceeds from worldwide sales.

All those stories about the Russian writer's privileged position, enjoying special facilities and fine dachas, snugly housed by a caring state which protected him from the rapacity of the market and the need to be a wage slave, were a snare and a delusion, if not a cynical deception.

These days the writer is told: "Find a rich sponsor and we'll publish". If the author can find the $500 the book will come out, nicely produced as well. Since being a writer is still prestigious in Russia, our nouveaux riches are always opening publishing houses to bring out books of their own, as good, in their opinion, as any of the other stuff, plus the efforts of their friends and relations. For some reason they always seem to prefer writing for children, their memoirs or on the occult. Bring out two books, find two sponsors, and you're in the Writers' Union and have a brand new image – to be a writer and a businessman in these difficult times is both fashionable and up-to-date.

Many non-commercial books bear little relation to literature. Equally, many commercial books are great literature. But people's ideas are totally confused because some publishers made millions out of pornographic trash and spy thrillers, and everybody has come to believe that this is what commercial literature is. We have not even begun to bring criteria of taste to the market. Our critics cannot bring home the distinctions. We are a country at war. We do not even know how much a loaf of bread will cost tomorrow. And all this so-called commercial literature bothers the GRPW very little. The front is all around, there is no rear. Just the time to be writing for the desk drawer – our traditional genre and one that will continue to serve us well. The main thing is for your reader to come back from the front alive.

"There are no schools, only conscience." Vladimir Sokolov's line is bitter as gall. We were born in a country where all literary schools were wiped out, exterminated, napalmed out of existence. Now we are buried under the shards of schools old and new, plotting every last contour of the social landscape, the poisoned river of language, the dead bones of a cruel utopia. Literature wants to vomit, and it chooses that most ancient of emetics: two fingers down the throat of history and up it all comes, a great gut-wrenching heave, a method as aristocratic as they come. A test to make you feel at home – spleen, booze, pus, tears, shit and sentimentality, sex in a puddle under a street-lamp, just the thing! With dollops of half-remembered quotes thrown in: snatches of songs and slogans, Pushkin and Khrushchev, Gogol and Brezhnev, Dostoyevsky and Andropov. And if it relates the joys of cannibalism, vampirism, eating your mother or tearing at the flesh of some tender child, the sense of catharsis is simply a knock-out. What more is required for a sure-fire hit? The book, no matter what the contents, must cost about as much as a yacht on the Med., so only a select few can afford it, so it is a sign of being one of the select few.

We are sickened, literally sickened, by fascists, communists, democrats, deputies, advice from Nobel prizewinners, great project lies, hunger, gluttony, fear, coffins – they force children in boarding schools to make them – we are sickened by this wretched war. Daniel Kharms, *The Unsuccessful Play*: "Daddy has asked me to tell you all that the theatre is closing. We all feel sick." Curtain.

Absurd as it may seem, the new literature is extremely politicized, its apoliticism is over-rehearsed. Sex phobia and sex mania, parody of the Soviet way of life, on the Soviet classics, on ethics and aesthetics, all the wild japes come straight from the menu at the Post-Perestroika Elite Hotel. It is a revolt of slaves given absolute freedom. Absolutely everything is grist to the mill: one shouts that he despises politics, another that he cannot live without it, he cannot live without its restrictions and constraints, whence spring his fondest hopes of quick fame and fortune. The old tradition is reproduced in a faithful likeness: young and old, the disgraced and would-have-beens rushing – where? – to the West and into the Writers' Union, both at once, hopefully. Many have made it. Avant-gardists and Zen Buddhists have proved no less adept at this business than the old generals of Soviet literature.

And yet . . . Given the impoverished state of literature in Russia, the number of magazines and anthologies featuring interesting new work by little or unknown writers is incredible. The regime has collapsed, but literature is alive. It is crazy, delirious, self-advertising and exhibitionistic, it spits on the tyranny of middlebrow taste.

"By this art you may contemplate the variation of the 23 letters . . ."
The worst thing about this writing is that it provides in huge quantities "samplers" of prose, poetry and language – not language, but a "sampler" of language, a text as a "sampler" of poetry or drama. Nobody wants to be seen to be provincial, everybody wants recognition in the West, to reach Western middle-class standards and earn

a decent living, to show the abyss they have leaped, the distance they have come to become a Western intellectual, a professional writer. Does this mean that Russia has or is about to become provincial? What a nightmare for one's self-esteem that would be! It's so humanly understandable, touching in a way.

It is a commonplace that literature is a living organism. Sometimes it smells bad, burps, farts, pulls faces, becomes senile or infantile or manic, gets depressed, renews its senses, finds fresh form in the most perverse ways. But it can never equal the depravities of politics and political regimes, and bears as much responsibility for their actions as the Great or Little Bear. Nor does it go into the dustbin with the regime.

As an interesting example of self-perception, I saw in a tiny magazine called *Urbi* published in the provinces, in Nizhny Novgorod, an article called "The Word Is Superfluous". It was written by a poetess, Ry Nikonova-Tarshis, from a town called Eisk, who has for many years been in contact with other concrete poets from the West. The article described her idea of "vacuum" poetry: literature's most intimate concern is its own absence, but a vacuum is not emptiness, while freedom from literature is the freedom of the reader to suggest his own text. "I believe that competition between the vacuum and the text improves the quality of literature as a whole." This kind of piece could never find its way into one of the "independent" metropolitan journals. It is too far out of the framework of conventional taste. The provinces have more imagination, take more risks, nurture that very rare talent – the ability to air differences of opinion in a way that gives birth to new forms, to something alive with an extraordinary awareness of self and place.

The country is going its way, let literature go its – it doesn't seem to be at home, call later, it's gone for a walk, not back yet. Out there they don't have a sense of where literature ends.

The horror of mass psychology for the writer is that he knows exactly what is expected of him. Churning it out is as easy as falling off a log. There is no strength to resist. The new writer longs for recognition, publications, money, reviews, fame all at once and then off to the West. The Russian émigré, on the contrary, comes to be published here where he could not be published before, and then rushes back in horror. From the point of view of simple common sense and normal psychology, everybody should have left – now, then,

and later, on the spot, immediately, Platonov and Mandelstam and
Tsvetaeva and Akhmatova and Shalamov and Pasternak and . . .

It is not just that the stress and pressure of the market is nothing
in comparison with the pressure of ideology. Those writers for whom
the writer's prestigious status was the only thing in life are now
thoroughly miserable. And I have every sympathy with them. For the
rest little has changed. Literature is as rough as life. If you choose
you can end it all. But life cannot. High time to write for the desk
drawer, if you can . . . some people do not even have the luxury of a
desk.

> Tell all the Truth but tell it slant –
> Success is circuit lies
> Too bright for our infirm Delight
> The Truth's superb surprise
> As lightning to the children eased
> With explanation kind
> The Truth must dazzle gradually
> Or every man be blind –
>
> EMILY DICKINSON

Translated from the Russian by Frank Williams

ROBERT HUGHES

A Columbus Day Sermon

This is the Columbus Day sermon, and I offer it with some trepidation. To say anything favourable, or even neutral, about the mariner
of Genova cuts very little ice with many Americans, and it seems that
the further West you go the less it cuts. It is a task roughly equivalent
to rising in a synagogue to deliver a panegyric on Columbus' patrons,
Ferdinand and Isabella of Castile, who by an unhappy coincidence of
history chose exactly the same year, 1492, to expel the Jews from
Spain. For Columbus, for reasons I will soon come to, is widely
regarded by many Americans as the primal demon of American history, the occasion of its fall. For thousands of years, by their account,
the continent lived in prelapsarian bliss; then, five hundred years ago
today, European man emerged from the caravels, and the rest was
misery – not, indeed, for the invaders, but for every native culture
from the tip of Patagonia to the Aleutians.

So the air of celebration is muted in 1992. The feeling was very
different a century ago. Then, both Europeans and white Americans
celebrated a cult of Columbus that, as cults do, exceeded the bounds
of history and crossed the borders of myth. Columbus was seen as
the prototypical discoverer; the man for whom nothing was impossible, and who added the Americas, as the phrase then went, to the
sum of human knowledge. By crossing the Atlantic he set in train a
process which, in your ancestors' opinion, was then passed to the
European settlers of America to complete: Columbus' act wound up
the inexorable clock of Manifest Destiny, and those who went West
to California were all, in some sense, Columbians. He thus became
the secular saint of an imperial America, from the Atlantic to the
Pacific, and what he did in the Caribbean pointed forward to what
would be enacted in Manila Bay in 1898, when by seizing the Philip-
pines America took over the last of the Spanish Empire and thus
closed the cycle that Columbus' voyages had begun. He was, in short,

an honorary American – your man, though temporarily working for Spain.

Naturally, others disagreed, both then and since. The Italian historian Paolo Taviani remarked that he "symbolizes the creative genius of Italy shaping the beginning of the modern age"; and at one time or another Columbus has been presented as Castilian, Catalan, Corsican, Majorcan, Portuguese, French, English, Greek and even Armenian, depending on the nationality of the writers. He was, however, certainly Italian. There are now twenty-eight monuments to Columbus in the United States, ten in the Caribbean, nine in Spain, seven in Italy, five in South America, three in France, and two in Mexico – a grand total of sixty-four Columbuses, of which the one on the harbour front of Barcelona, standing 187 feet from the ground to the bronze hat of the Discoverer, or Encounterer, is by far the biggest, though due to the inconvenient lay of the Mediterranean coast he is pointing out to sea in the general direction of Libya, rather than to America. Almost all of these were planned and done around 1892. None of them are recent, and there are, as far as I know, no plans to create any more. Iconographically speaking, Columbus is a dead duck.

Nor has the 500th anniversary turned up much in the way of new knowledge about either Columbus or his voyages. The first European settlement in the Americas is in Haiti. There, in 1492, Columbus left the crew of the wrecked Santa Maria to fend for themselves – they were all dead when he returned the next year. Archaeologists have found some shards of Venetian glass at the site, and the bones of a fifteenth-century pig. But to expect dramatic discoveries to appear on cue for 1992 is unrealistic. The Holy Grail of Columbus studies would be the long-lost original log of his first voyage to what he called "the Indies", which exists only in a badly garbled abridgement made after his death by the Spanish priest Bartolome de las Casas. It is full of errors that have caused endless dispute about such basic matters as Columbus' course on his historic sail, and where his little fleet of three ships made landfall. Candidates for this honour include the islands of San Salvador, Grand Turk, East Caicos, Conception Island, and half a dozen others. In these as in a myriad other matters, we don't know enough about Columbus and probably never will.

Nor do we know all that much about his character and personality. This, in our own ludicrously subjectivized times, where the self is our sacred cow and confession has become the pseudo-sacrament and binding ritual of popular culture, strikes many people as irksome.

But we do know some things about him, not all of them agreeable.

He was an obsessed man, determined to transcend his humble origins by any means possible. The avenue was navigation. At first he wanted to succeed through trade, since sea-trade was the lifeblood of Genova, his birthplace. As a merchant sailor, he went all over the Mediterranean, to the west coast of Africa, and as far north as Ireland. Sometime between 1478 and 1484, the full plan of self-aggrandizement and discovery took shape in his mind. He would win glory, riches and a title by opening a trade-route to the untapped wealth of Asia. No reward could be too great for the man who did that.

This drive is one of the few attributes of Columbus that all the surviving sources agree upon. Even the Spanish crew of the Santa Maria, according to Casas, thought of him as a mad foreigner who would kill them all in the hope of making a great lord of himself. He was entirely, quintessentially self-made. He left home illiterate, and never used Italian again after he arrived in Spain in 1484. He acquired a large library on geography, only four of whose volumes, alas, still survive with his annotations. His idea of the unexplored Atlantic world was formed as much by books as by navigation – writings of the ancients, like Strabo and Pliny and Ptolemy, and the works of medieval cosmographers. These gave him the frame in which he would sell his Enterprise of the Indies to Ferdinand and Isabella. No ship, as yet, had reached the Indies – by which Columbus meant China and what he called "Xipangu", or Japan – by sailing east around the bottom of Africa. But Columbus was convinced that you could reach them faster and easier by going west. His *Empresa de las Indias* had nothing to do with discovering America, or even with any suspicion that America existed. Still less was it an attempt to prove that the world was round – every educated person in Europe knew that already, and all sailors took it for granted. Columbus was looking for China and Japan, and long after reaching the Caribbean he remained certain, against any and all evidence, that he had done so.

Columbus was in fact a very rigid man – the pliable rarely achieve what he did. His inflexibility combined with piety and opportunism to produce behaviour not far from the paranoid. His growing ambition encouraged him to believe, as obsessed loners will, that everyone except God was against him. He was so sure that his voyage was a fulfilment of God's designs that he even greeted the wreck of the Santa Maria as a sign of divine approval. He was by turns petty and apocalyptic. His reports to the Spanish crown were absurdly self-serving: his claims after the First Voyage about "incredible amounts" of gold and spices were a tissue of hustling lies, but they got him the seventeen ships he needed for the next crossing. His fixations often skewed his charting, so that he mistook islands for continental coasts and thus claimed to have found what he had not. As an administrator, he was bad. As a negotiator, arrogant. His efforts to found a permanent colony all failed. And, as we know, the only part of the American continent he actually set foot on was Venezuela.

But lies and self-delusion, inflated reports and greed were the common currency of Renaissance exploration. Columbus' mistakes were no worse than those of explorers a generation later, in the sixteenth century, who blundered out into the Pacific in search of gold and terra Australis, the imagined southern continent of the antipodes. And the fact is that he did discover something – not Asia, but something huge and indistinct – in the West. In doing so, he became the greatest explorer in the history of Europe; his only rival was Captain James Cook, as brave a man but a far more rational and humane one, who added most of the Pacific and Antarctic Oceans to the European horizon, including the real southern continent, my homeland of Australia, nearly 300 years later. Cook is my hero; Columbus is your ex-hero. Cook seems closer to us because he was an Englishman of the Enlightenment. Columbus becomes more remote, because he came from an eschatological culture, that of fifteenth-century Spain, whose attitudes we no longer share and can only understand by an effort of will. In Cook's time there was a difference, which his own achievements express, between discovery and conquest. In the fifteenth century there was none.

The current prejudice against the word "discovery", in the context of Columbus' efforts, is interesting. We have no shortage of claims and hypotheses about other "discoveries" of America. It is probable that the first Europeans to reach the continental mainland of north America, which Columbus didn't, were the Vikings, around the year 1000. And there have been as many other candidates as there are alternative authors of Shakespeare's plays. St Brendan and his Irish monks, blown across in a coracle. Jewish refugees fleeing Roman persecution in the second century AD Japanese fishermen. A fifth-century Chinese monk named Hui-Shen. And for the New Age dingbats, why leave out the extra-terrestrials who landed in Peru to produce the Nazca earth-drawings? All these claims are not only unverifiable, but irrelevant. The people who really found north America were the hunter-gatherers who walked across the archaic land-bridge between Asia and Alaska, whose remnants are the Aleutian Islands, and became the many-times-great-grandparents of the American Indians, the Maya and the Incas. Multiculturalism began with the fall of Man and the expulsion from the garden, which forced us to go wandering – with the result that everyone in this church today, and everyone not in this church too, is originally from somewhere else. The point about "discovery" is not that someone floats ashore somewhere, by accident, leaving no traces. It is inconceivable that over the last few thousand years non-autochthonous people should *not* have fetched up in America before Columbus. But the essence of discovery is that the voyage is repeatable. It entails documentation – logs and records. The discoverer is the person who can get from known A to unknown B, return to A, and show how to get back to B again. Of course, Columbus' claim to be a discoverer is a function of European consciousness. The millions of people and thousands of societies that already existed in North and South America knew perfectly well who and where they were. This is why it makes better sense to talk of "encounter" rather than discovery. But it does not make Columbus' achievement any less real: it was to open a route to a world, new for him, ancient and familiar to its inhabitants, which he and others could take over and over again.

In this sense, he united the Western and Eastern hemispheres of the world across the Atlantic. No man had done so before Columbus, and none can take this away from him. We should not allow our reaction against his nineteenth-century, imperial myth to obscure so immense an achievement. Today we are in some danger of doing so, because, like all generations before us, we are prone to project our own moralities back to where they do not necessarily apply: namely, the past.

The reading of history is never static. Revise we historians must. There is no such thing as the last word. And who could doubt that there is still much to revise in the story of the European conquest of North and South America that we inherited? Its basic scheme was

imperial: the epic advance of Civilization against Barbarism: the con-
quistador brings the Cross and the sword, the red man shrinks back
before the cavalry and the railroad. The notion that all historians
propagated this triumphalist myth uncritically is quite false: you have
only to read Parkman or Prescott to realize that. But after it left the
histories and sank deep into popular culture, it became a potent myth
of justification for the plunder, murder and enslavement of peoples,
and the wreckage of nature, that came with Europe to America.

So now, in reaction to it, comes the manufacture of its opposite
myth. European man, once the hero of the conquest of the Americas,
now becomes its demon; and the victims, who cannot be brought
back to life, are canonized. On either side of the divide between
European and native, historians stand ready with tar-brush and gold
leaf, and instead of the wicked old stereotypes we have a whole new
outfit of equally misleading ones. Our predecessors made a hero,
almost a saint, of Christopher Columbus. To Europeans and North
Americans in 1892, he was Manifest Destiny in tights, surrounded
by deposits of pious folklore, such as Washington Irving's story about
Columbus and the egg or the fiction that Queen Isabella pawned her
jewels, which had actually been hocked long before to pay for cannon,
in order to finance his voyages. Whereas the newer version, inscribed
in politically correct polemics like Kirkpatrick Sale's book *The Conquest of Paradise*, makes him more like Hitler in a caravel, grasping
and genocidal, landing like a virus among the innocent people of the
New World.

This new stereotype, a rebirth of Rousseauist notions about the
Noble Savage, brings a new outfit of double standards into play. Thus
the Taino Indians of Puerto Rico become innocent creatures living
in a state of classless nature, like hippies in Golden Gate Park when
Kirkpatrick Sale and I were young, whereas in fact they liked to be
carried around in litters by their slaves. If only the people of the
Americas, from Patagonia to the Great Lakes, had not been conquered
by the Europeans, would they not still be in bliss? Are we not so
much worse than they?

Well, yes, up to a point. But the speculation is pointless because
America *was* conquered by imperfect and cruel beings who imposed
their own cultures, Spanish and then English and French, over the
existing ones. It is existentially meaningless to talk about what
America might have been like if this hadn't happened, because it did

happen, and it was bound to anyway. If Columbus had not opened the route to the Caribbean, someone else – Spanish, Portuguese, Italian, English – would have done it a few years later, and the results for the societies and ecology of the Americas would have been the same. To expect Mayans, or modern American Indians, to celebrate 1992 is unreasonable; as an Australian Aboriginal remarked to me at the time of our bicentenary in 1988, you might as well ask Jews to celebrate Hitler's centenary, which was due the next year, 1989.

But the historical evidence also shows that the peoples of the Americas had been doing very nicely for centuries, thank you, when it came to murder, torture, materialism, enslavement and sexist hegemony. The civilization of the Maya, the greatest to flourish in Central America before Columbus, reached its peak between AD 250 and 900, at which point a puzzling event called the Mayan Hiatus occurred. It collapsed. Nobody from outside had conquered it. However, recent digs and the slow work of deciphering glyphs, particularly at the site of Dos Pilas in Guatemala, indicate that the classic period of the Maya was ruined by a continuous state of war between local rulers that began around AD 700 and devoured the whole economy and ecology of the Mayan empire by the tenth century. The Mayans fell by self-induced ecological collapse, caused by a devotion to unwinnable wars which was itself sustained by an obsession with ideology – the ideology of the transcendent god-king, viewed by his limestone-toting helots as the embodiment of the whole universe.

Pre-Columbian Meso-America was not the Shangri-La that anti-Columbians would like it to be. You cannot climb the Pyramid of the Sun at Teotihuacan near Mexico City and look down the vast symmetrical perspective of the Avenue of the Dead, abandoned in the eighth century for reasons we know nothing about, without sensing that the society that built them was a theocratic ant-state whose rigidity might have made Albert Speer faint. And try staring at the fangs of the Feathered Serpent and talking about the benign pastoral quality of life before whitey arrived. Aztec culture was messianic and invasive and imperialistic; it had been so ever since the Aztecs came down from the north, under the command of a charismatic ruler whose name translates as Hummingbird-on-the-Left, and slaughtered or enslaved the resident people around what is now Mexico City. But by now, it is as anachronistic to condemn the Aztecs' savagery as it is to condemn, or to find excuses for, the destruction of Aztec society by the Spanish *conquista*. It was an evil fate to be enslaved by sixteenth-century Spanish regidors. But it was no joke to be one of the countless thousands whose hearts were ripped out by the Aztec priests of Tenochtitlan in order that the sun might rise in the morning. The Spanish burned nearly all the written records of Aztec history, except for a few codices. But the Aztecs, when they conquered central Mexico, also destroyed all the records of the previous societies, so that there could be no history before theirs. This is what human beings do to one another, and have done, since time immemorial. And history can only deal with what *was* done. It is the sad art of remembering. To paraphrase Auden: history to the defeated may say alas, but it cannot change the past. And at the very least – though it is no posthumous comfort to the millions of people who were murdered, enslaved, dispossessed, detribalized not by Columbus himself but as a consequence of his voyages – the colossal mechanisms of greed and oppression that unrolled from the conquests of the Caribbean, of South and North America, also contained their own witnesses, men like the priest Bartoleme de las Casas who saw and described very plainly what the sword did in the name of the Cross, and wrote at the end of his life, in 1564, that

> I believe that because of these impious, criminal and ignominious acts, perpetrated unjustly, tyrannously and barbarously upon them, God will visit his wrath and his ire upon Spain for her share, great and small, in the bloodstained riches, obtained by theft and usurpation, accompanied by such slaughter and annihilation of these people – unless she does much penance.

The need for absolute goodies and absolute baddies runs deep in us, but it drags history into propaganda and denies the humanity of the dead: their sins, their virtues, their efforts, their failures. To preserve complexity, and not flatten it under the weight of anachronistic moralizing, is part of the historian's task.

So what are we to feel on Columbus Day? Neither indifference, nor paroxysms of guilt. Neither the old imperialist stereotype of the shining hero nor the new politically correct one of the absolute villain; something else. A broadened sense, I think, of what 1492 meant to all Americans. If 1892 was the year of the Discoverer, 1992 ought in all justice to be that of the Discoverees. At the very least, this 500th anniversary should force a new awareness of the many roles played by Spaniards in early colonial north America, and of all the peoples who up to now, especially on the East Coast where I live, have been shunted out of view behind the screen of Anglo founder-images. But one would like to see something more than that: more public acceptance of the immense social, racial, cultural diversity of American history in general, and a certain humility about the deeds of the forefathers. There is a hideous and destructive separatism at large in this country now; a nativist bigotry of the kind that appears whenever deep change impends. You hear it when Pat Buchanan, the only man that ever made me feel briefly ashamed to be Irish, screws his face into a fist and starts orating about cultural war. For such people, there is no sense of a historical burden. Why should we feel bad about Indian massacres? They happened a century ago, and we ourselves weren't there. Just as, in Australia, it was my convict forebears that slaughtered the Aborigines; I wasn't there. But on those terms you can deny the very concept of original sin; when Adam ate the apple in Eden, none of us were there either – but it doesn't get us off the theological hook. Mind you, I speak as an ex-Catholic, not an Episcopalian. History, like it or not, is partly the record of original sin, and by sweeping it under the psychic carpet we deny some part of ourselves, maybe a part that we don't want to acknowledge, in the act of denying others. On Columbus Day 1992, that is something to think about.

RICHARD FORD

My Mother, in Memory

My mother's name was Edna Akin, and she was born in 1910, in the far northwest corner of the state of Arkansas – Benton County – in a place whose actual location I am not sure of and never have been. Near Decatur or Centerton, or a town no longer a town. Just a rural place. That is near the Oklahoma line there, and in 1910 it was a rough country, with a frontier feel. It had only been ten years since robbers and outlaws were in the landscape. Bat Masterson was still alive and not long gone from Galina.

I remark about this not because of its possible romance, or because I think it qualifies my mother's life in any way I can relate now, but because it seems like such a long time ago and such a far-off and unknowable place. And yet my mother, whom I loved and knew quite well, links me to that foreignness, that other thing that was her life and that I really don't know so much about and never did. This is one quality of our lives with our parents that is often overlooked and so, devalued. Parents link us – closeted as we are in our lives – to a thing we're not but they are; a separateness, perhaps a mystery – so that even together we are alone.

The act and practice of considering my mother's life is, of course, an act of love. And my incomplete memory of it, my inadequate relation to the facts, should not be thought incomplete love. I loved my mother the way a happy child does, thoughtlessly and without doubts. And when I became an adult and we were adults who knew one another, we regarded each other highly; could say "I love you" when it seemed necessary to clarify our dealings, but without passing over it. That seems perfect to me now and did then, too.

My mother's life I am forced to piece together. We were not a family for whom history had much to offer. This fact must have to do with not being rich, or with being rural, or incompletely educated, or just inadequately aware of many things. For my mother there was simply little to history, no heroics or self-dramatizing – just small business, forgettable residues, some of them mean. The Depression had something to do with it, too. My mother and father were people who lived for each other and for the day. In the thirties, after they were married, they lived, in essence, on the road. They drank some. They had a good time. They felt they had little to look back on, and didn't look.

My father's family came from Ireland and were Protestants. This was in the 1870s, and an ocean divided things. But about my mother's early life I don't know much. I don't know where her father came from, or if he too was Irish, or Polish. He was a carter, and my mother spoke affectionately about him, if elliptically and without a sense of responsibility to tell anything at all. "Oh," she would say, "my daddy was a good man." And that was it. He died of cancer in the 1930s, I think, but not before my mother had been left by her mother and had lived with him a time. This was before 1920. My sense is that they lived in the country, back near where she was born – rural again – and that to her it had been a good time. As good as any. I don't know what she was enthusiastic for then, what her thoughts were. I cannot hear her voice from that time long ago, though I would like to be able to.

Of her mother there is much to say – a story of a kind. She was from the country, with brothers and sisters. There was Indian blood on that side of the family, though it was never clear what tribe of Indian. I know nothing about her parents, though I have a picture of my great-grandmother and my grandmother with her new, second husband, sitting in an old cartage wagon, and my mother in the back. My great-grandmother is old then, witchy looking; my grandmother, stern and pretty in a long beaver coat; my mother, young, with piercing dark eyes aimed to the camera.

At some point my grandmother had left her husband and taken up with the younger man in the picture – a boxer and roustabout. A pretty boy. Slim and quick and tricky. "Kid Richard" was his ring name. (I, oddly enough, am *his* namesake.) This was in Fort Smith now. Possibly 1922. My grandmother was older than Kid Richard, whose real name was Bennie Shelley. And to quickly marry him and keep him, she lied about her age, took a smooth eight years off, and began to dislike having her pretty daughter – my mother – around to date her.

And so for a period – everything in her life seemed to happen for a period and never for long – my mother was sent to live at the Convent School of St Ann's, also in Fort Smith. It must've seemed like a good idea to her father up in the country, because he paid her tuition, and she was taught by nuns. I don't exactly know what her mother – whose name was Essie or Lessie or just Les – did during that time, maybe three years. She was married to Bennie Shelley, who was from Fayetteville and had family there. He worked as a waiter, and then in the dining-car service on the Rock Island. This meant living in El Reno and as far out the line as Tucumcari, New Mexico. He quit boxing, and my grandmother ruled him as strictly as she could because she felt she could go a long way with him. He was her last and best choice for something. A ticket out. To where, I'm not sure.

My mother often told me that she'd liked the sisters at St Ann's. They were strict. Imperious. Self-certain. Dedicated. Humorous. It was there, I think, as a boarding student, that my mother earned what education she ever did – the ninth grade, where she was an average good student and was liked, though she smoked cigarettes and was punished for it. I think if she had never told me about the nuns, if that stamp on her life hadn't been made, I might never have ordered even this much of things. St Ann's cast a shadow into later life. In her heart of hearts my mother was a secret Catholic. A forgiver. A respecter of rituals and protocols. Reverent about the trappings of faith; respecter of inner disciplines. All I think about Catholics I think because of her, who was never one at all, but who lived among them at an early age and seemingly liked what she learned and those who taught her. Later in life, when she had married my father and gone to meet his mother, she would always feel she was thought of as a Catholic by them, and that they never truly took her in as they might have another girl.

But when her father, for reasons I know nothing about, stopped her tuition, her mother – now demanding they be known as sisters – took her out of St Ann's. And that was it for school, for ever. She was not a welcome addition to her mother's life, and I have never known why they took her back. It is just one of those inexplicable acts that mean everything.

They moved around. To Kansas City. To El Reno again. To Davenport and Des Moines – wherever the railroad took Ben Shelley, who was going forward in the dining-car service and turning himself into a go-getter. In time, he would leave the railroad and go to work as a caterer at the Arlington Hotel in Hot Springs. And there he put my mother to work in the cigar shop, where a wider world opened an inch. People from far away were here for the baths, Jews from Chicago and New York. Foreigners. Rich people. She met baseball players, became friends with Dizzy Dean and Leo Durocher. And during that time, sometime when she was seventeen, she must've met my father.

I, of course, know nothing about their courtship except that it took place – mostly in Little Rock, probably in 1927. My father was twenty-three. He worked as a produce stocker for a grocery concern there. I have a picture of him with two other young clerks in a grocery store. He is wearing a clean white apron and a tie, and is standing beside a bin of cabbages. I don't even know where this is. Little Rock. Hot Springs – one of these. It is just a glimpse. What brought him down from the country to Little Rock I'll never know, nor what he might've had on his mind then. He died in 1960, when I was only sixteen. And I had not by then thought to ask.

But I have thought of them as a young couple. My mother, black-haired, dark-eyed, curvaceous. My father, blue-eyed like me, big, gullible, honest, gentle. I can think a thought of them together. I can sense what they each must've sensed pretty fast – here was a good person, suddenly. My mother knew things. She had worked in hotels, been to boarding school and out. Lived in cities. Travelled some. But my father was a country boy who quit school in the seventh grade. The baby of three children, all raised by their mother – the sheltered son of a suicide. I can believe my mother wanted a better life than working for her ambitious stepfather and contrary mother, at jobs that went no place; that she may have believed she'd not been treated well, and thought of her life as "rough"; that she was tired of being her mother's sister; that it was a strange life; that she was in danger of losing all expectation; that she was bored. And I can believe my father simply saw my mother and wanted her. Loved her. And that was how that went.

They were married in Morrilton, Arkansas, by a justice of the peace, in 1928, and arrived at my father's home in Atkins the next morning, newlyweds. I have no correct idea what anyone thought or said about any of that. They acted independently, and my mother never felt the need to comment. Though my guess is they heard disapproval.

I think it is safe to say my parents wanted children. How many they wanted or how soon after they were married I do not know. But it was their modest boast that my father had a job throughout the Depression. And I think there was money enough. They lived in Little Rock, and for a while my father worked as a grocer, and then, in 1932, he was fired, and went to work selling starch for a company out of Kansas City. The Faultless Company. Huey Long had worked for them, too. It was a travelling job, and most of the time they just travelled together. New Orleans. Memphis. Texarkana. They lived in hotels, spent their off-hours and off-days back in Little Rock. But mostly they travelled. My father called on groceries, wholesalers, prisons, hospitals, conducted schools for housewives on how to starch clothes without boiling the starch. My mother, typically, never characterized that time together except to say he and she had "fun" together – that was her word for it – and had begun to think they couldn't have a child. No children. This time lasted fifteen years. A loose, pick-up-and-go life. Drinking. Cars. Restaurants. Not paying much attention. There were friends they had in New Orleans, Memphis, in Little Rock, and on the road. They made friends of my grandmother and Bennie, who was not much older than my father – four years, at most. I think they were just caught up in their life, a life in the South, in the thirties, just a kind of swirling thing that didn't really have a place to go. There must've been plenty of lives like that then. It seems a period now to me. A specific time, the Depression. But to them, of course, it was just their life.

Something about that time – to my mother – must've seemed un-narratable. Unworthy of or unnecessary for telling. My father, who was not a teller of stories anyway, never got a chance to recall it. And I, who wasn't trained to want the past filled in – as some boys are – just never asked. It seemed a privacy I shouldn't invade. And I know that my mother's only fleeting references to that time, as if the thirties were just a long weekend – drinking too much, wildness, rootlessness – gave me the impression something possibly untidy had gone on, some recklessness of spirit and attitude, something that a son would be better off not to think about and be worried with. In essence, it had been *their* time, for their purposes and not mine. And it was over.

But looked at from the time of my birth, 1944, all that life lived childless, unexpectant, must've come to seem an odd time to her; a life encapsulatable, possibly even remembered unclearly, pointless, maybe in comparison to the pointedness of a life *with* a child. Still, an intimacy established between the two of them that they brought forward into more consequential life – a life they had all but abandoned any thought of because no children had come.

All first children, and certainly all only children, date the beginning of their lives as extra special events. For my parents my arrival came as a surprise and coincident with the end of World War II – the event that finished the thirties in this country. And it came when my mother had been married to my father fifteen years; when, in essence, their young life was over. He was thirty-nine. She was thirty-three. They, by all accounts, were happy to have me. It may have been an event that made their life together seem conventional for once, that settled them; made them think about matters their friends had thought about years ago. Staying put. The future.

They had never owned a house or a car, although my father's job gave him a company car. They had never had to choose a "home", a place to be in permanently. But now, they did. They moved from Little Rock down to Mississippi, to Jackson, which was the geographic centre of my father's territory and a place he could return most weekends with ease, since my mother wouldn't be going with him now. There was going to be a baby.

They knew no one in Jackson except the jobbers my father had called on and a salesman or two he knew off the road. I'm not sure, but I think it was not an easy transition. They rented and then bought a brick duplex next to a school. They joined a church. Found a grocery. A bus stop – though you could walk to the main street in Jackson from 736 North Congress. Also to the library and the capitol building. They had neighbours – older citizens, established families hanging on to nicer, older, larger houses in a neighbourhood that was itself in transition. This was life now, for them. My father went off to work Monday morning and came back Friday night. He had never exactly done that before, but he liked it, I think. One of my earliest memories is of him moving around the sunny house on Monday mornings, whistling a tune.

And so what my beginning life was was this. A life spent with my mother – a shadow in a picture of myself. Days. Afternoons. Nights. Walks. Meals. Dressing. Sidewalks. The movies. Home. Radio. And on the weekend, my father. A nice, large, sweet man who visited us. Happy to come home. Happy to leave.

I don't think my mother longed for a fulfilling career or a more active public life. I don't think my father had other women on the road. I don't think the intrusion of me into their lives was anything they didn't think of as normal and all right. I know from practice that it is my habit to seek the normal in life, to look for reasons to believe this or that is fine. In part, that is because my parents raised me that way and lived lives that portrayed a world, a private existence, that *could be* that way. I do not think even now, in the midst of my own life's concerns, that it is a bad way to see things.

So then, the part of my life that has to do with my mother.

The first eleven years – the Korean War years, Truman and Eisenhower, television, bicycles, one big snowstorm in 1949 – we lived on North Congress Street, down a hill from the state capitol and across from the house where Eudora Welty had been a young girl thirty-five years before. Next door to Jefferson Davis School. I remember a neighbour stopping me on the sidewalk and asking me who I was; this was a thing that could happen to you. Maybe I was nine or seven then. But when I said my name – Richard Ford – she said, "Oh, yes. Your mother is the cute little black-headed woman up the street." And that affected me and still does. I think this was my first conception of my mother as someone else, as someone whom other people saw and considered: a cute woman, which she was not. Black-haired, which she was. She was, I know, five feet five inches tall. But I never have known if that is tall or short. I think I must have always believed it was normal. I remember this, though, as a signal moment in my life. Small but important. It alerted me to my mother's – what? – public side. To the side that other people saw and dealt with and that was there. I do not think I ever thought of her in any other way after that. As Edna Ford, a person who was my mother and also who was someone else. I do not think

I ever addressed her after that except with such a knowledge – the way I would anyone I knew.

It is a good lesson to learn. And we risk never knowing our parents if we ignore it. Cute, black-headed, five-five. Some part of her was that, and it didn't harm me to know it. It may have helped, since one of the premier challenges for us all is to know our parents, assuming they survive long enough, are worth knowing, and it is physically possible. This is a part of normal life. And the more we see them fully, as the world sees them, the better all our chances are.

About my mother I do not remember more than pieces up until the time I was sixteen: 1960, a galvanizing year for us both – the year my father woke up gasping on a Saturday morning and died before he could get out of bed; me up on the bed with him, busy trying to find something to help. Shake him. Yell in his sleeping face. Breathe in his soft mouth. Turn him over onto his belly, for some reason. Feeling terror and chill. All this while she stood in the doorway to his bedroom in our new house in the suburbs of Jackson, pushing her knuckles into her temples, becoming hysterical. Eventually she just lost her control for a while.

But before that. Those pieces. They must make a difference or I wouldn't remember them so clearly. A flat tyre we all three had, half-way across the Mississippi bridge at Greenville. High, up there, over the river. We stayed in the car while my father fixed it, and my mother held me so tightly to her I could barely breathe. I was six. She always said, "I smothered you when you were little. You were all we had. I'm sorry." And then she'd tell me this story. But I wasn't sorry. It seemed fine then, since we were up there. "Smothering" meant "Here is danger", "Love protects you". They are still lessons I respect. I am not comfortable on bridges now, but my guess is I never would've been.

I remember my mother having a hysterectomy and my grandfather, Ben Shelley, joking about it – to her – about what good "barbers" the nuns at St Dominic's had been. That made her cry.

I remember once in the front yard on Congress Street something happened, something I said or did – I don't know what – but my mother began running out across the schoolyard next door. Just running away. I remember that scared me and I yelled at her, "No," and halfway across she stopped and came back. I've never known how serious she was about that, but I have understood from it that there might be reasons to run off. Alone, with a small child, knowing no one. That's enough.

There were two fights they had that I was present for. One on St Louis Street, in the French Quarter in New Orleans. It was in front of Antoine's Restaurant, and I now think they were both drunk, though I didn't know it, or even know what drunk was. One wanted to go in the restaurant and eat. The other didn't and wanted to go back to the hotel around the corner. This was in 1955. I think we had tickets to the Sugar Bowl – Navy vs. Ole Miss. They yelled at each other, and I think my father yanked her arm, and they walked back separately. Later we all got in bed together in the Monteleone and no one stayed mad. In our family no one ever nagged or held grudges or stayed mad, though we could all get mad.

The other fight was worse. I believe it was the same year. They were drinking. My father invited friends over and my mother·didn't like it. All the lights were on in the house. She swore. I remember the guests standing in the doorway outside the screen, still on the porch looking in. I remember their white faces and my mother shouting at them to get the hell out, which they did. And then my father held my mother's shoulders up against the wall by the bathroom and yelled at her while she struggled to get free. I remember how harsh the lights were. No one got hit. No one ever did except me when I was whipped. They just yelled and struggled. Fought that way. And then after a while, I remember, we were all in bed again, with me in the middle, and my father cried. "Boo hoo hoo. Boo hoo hoo." Those were the sounds he made, as if he'd read somewhere how to cry.

A long time has passed since then, and I have remembered more than I do now. I have tried to put things into novels. I have written things down and forgotten them. I have told stories. And there was more, a life's more. My mother and I rode with my father summers and sat in his hot cars in the states of Louisiana and Arkansas and Texas and waited while he worked, made his calls. We went to the coast – to Biloxi and Pensacola. To Memphis. To Little Rock almost every holiday. We *went*. That was the motif of things. We lived in Jackson, but he travelled. And every time we could we went with him. Just to be going. The staying part was never stabilized. Only being with them, and mostly being with her. My mother.

And then my father died, which changed everything – many things, it's odd to say, for the better where I was concerned. But not for my mother. Where she was concerned, nothing after that would ever be quite good again. A major part of life ended for her 20 February 1960. He had been everything to her, and all that was naturally implicit became suddenly explicit in her life, and she was neither good at that nor interested in it. And in a way I see now and saw almost as clearly then, she gave up.

Not that she gave up where I was concerned. I was sixteen and had lately been in some law scrapes, and she became, I'd say, very aware of the formal features of her life. She was a widow. She was fifty. She had a son who seemed all right, but who could veer off into trouble if she didn't pay attention. And so, in her way, she paid attention.

Not long after the funeral, when I was back in school and the neighbours had stopped calling and bringing over dishes of food – when both grief and real mourning had set in, in other words – she sat me down and told me we were now going to have to be more independent. She would not be able to look after me as she had done. We agreed that I had a future, but I would have to look after me. And as we could, we would do well to look after each other. We were partners now, is what I remember thinking. My father had really never been around that much, and so his actual absence was, for me (though not for her), not felt so strongly. And a partnership seemed like a good arrangement. I was to stay out of jail because she didn't want to get me out. *Wouldn't get me out*. I was to find friends I could rely on instead. I could have a car of my own. I could go away in the summers to find a job in Little Rock with my grandparents. This, it was understood but never exactly stated (we were trying not to state too much then; we didn't want *everything* to have to be explicit, since so much was now and so little ever had been), *this* would give her time to adjust. To think about things. To become whatever she would have to become to get along from there on out.

I don't exactly remember the time scheme to things. This was 1960, '61, '62. I was a tenth-grader and on. But I did not get put in jail. I did live summers with my grandparents, who by now ran a large hotel in Little Rock. I got a black '57 Ford, which got stolen. I got beaten up and then got new friends. I did what I was told, in other words. I started to grow up in a hurry.

I think of that time – the time between my father's death and the time I left for Michigan to go to college – as a time when I didn't see my mother much. Though that is not precisely how it was. She was there. I was there. But I cannot discount my own adjustments to my father's death and absence, to my independence. I think I may have been more dazed than grieved, and it is true my new friends took me up. My mother went to work. She got a job doing something at a company that made school pictures. It required training and she did it. And it was only then, late in 1960, when she was fifty, that she first felt the effects of having quit school in 1924. But she got along, came home tired. I do not think she had trouble. And then she left that. She became a rental agent for a new apartment house, tried afterwards to get the job as manager but didn't get it – who knows why? She took another job as night cashier in a hotel, the Robert E. Lee. This job she kept maybe a year. And after that she was the admitting clerk in the emergency room at the University of Mississippi Hospital, a job she liked very much.

And there was at least one boyfriend in all that time. A married man, from Tupelo, named Matt, who lived in the apartment building she worked at. He was a big, bluff man, in the furniture business, who drove a Lincoln and carried a gun strapped to the steering column. I liked him. And I liked it that my mother liked him. It didn't matter that he was married – not to me, and I guess not to my mother. I really have no idea about what was between them, what they did alone. And I don't care about that, either. He took her on drives. Flew her to Memphis in his aeroplane. Acted respectfully to both of us. She may have told me she was just passing time, getting her mind off her worries, letting someone be nice to her. But I didn't care. And we both knew that nothing she told me about him either did or didn't have to match the truth. I would sometimes think I wished she would marry Matt. And at other times I would be content to have them be lovers, if that's what they were. He had boys near my age, and later I would even meet them and like them. But this was after he and my mother were finished.

What finished them was brought on by me but was not really my doing, I think now. Matt had faded for a time. His business brought him in to Jackson, then out for months. She had quit talking about him, and life had receded to almost a normal level. I was having a hard time in school – getting a D in algebra (I'd already failed once) and having no ideas for how I could improve. My mother was cashiering nights at the Robert E. Lee and coming home by eleven.

But one night for some reason she simply didn't come home. I had a test the next day. Algebra. And I must've been in an agitated state of mind. I called the hotel to hear she had left on time. And for some reason this scared me. I got in my car and drove down to the neighbourhood by the hotel, a fringe neighbourhood near a black section of town. I rode the streets and found her car, a grey and pink '58 Oldsmobile that had been my father's pride and joy. It was parked under some sycamore trees, across from the apartments where she had worked as a rental agent and where Matt lived. And for some reason I think I panicked. It was not a time to panic but I did anyway. I'm not sure what I thought, but thinking of it now I seem to believe I wanted to ask Matt – if he was there – if he knew where my mother was. This may be right, though it's possible, too, I knew she was there and just wanted to make her leave.

I went in the building – it must've been midnight – and up the elevator and down the hall to his door. I banged on it. Hit it hard with my fists. And then I waited.

Matt himself opened the door, but my mother was there in the room behind him. She had a drink in her hand. The lights were on, and she was standing in the room behind him. It was a nice apartment, and both of them were shocked by me. I don't blame them. I didn't blame them then and was ashamed to be there. But I was, I think, terrified. Not that she was there. Or that I was alone. But just that I didn't know what in the hell. Where was she? What else was I going to have to lose?

I remember being out of breath. I was seventeen years old. And I really can't remember what anybody said or did except me, briefly. "Where have you been?" I said to her. "I didn't know where you were. That's all."

And that *was* all. All of that. Matt said very little. My mother got her coat and we went home in two cars. She acted vaguely annoyed at me, and I *was* mad at her. We talked that night. Eventually she said she was sorry, and I told her I didn't care if she saw Matt only that she tell me when she would be home late. And to my knowledge she never saw Matt Matthews, or any other man, again as a lover as long as she lived.

Later, years later, when she was dying, I tried to explain it all to her again – my part, what I thought, *had* thought – as if we could still open it and repair that night. All she needed to do was call me or, even years later, say she would've called me. But that was not, of course, what she did or how she saw it. She just looked a little disgusted and shook her head. "Oh, that," she said. "My God. That was just silliness. You had no business coming up there. You were out of your mind. Though I just saw I couldn't be doing things like that. I had a son to raise." And here again she looked disgusted, and at everything, I think. All the cards the fates had dealt her – a no-good childhood, my father's death, me, her own inability to vault over all of this to a better life. It was another proof of something bad, the likes of which she felt, I believe, she'd had plenty.

There are only these – snapshot instances of a time lived indistinctly, a time that whirled by for us but were the last times we would ever really live together as mother and son. We did not fight. We accommodated each other almost as adults would. We grew wry and humorous with each other. Cast glances, gave each other looks. Were never ironic or indirect or crafty with anger. We knew how we were supposed to act and took pleasure in acting that way.

She sold the new house my father had bought, and we moved into a high-rise. Magnolia Towers. I did better in school. She was switching jobs. I really didn't register these changes, though based on what I know now about such things they could not have been easy.

I did not and actually do not know about the money, how it was, then. My father had a little insurance. Maybe some was saved in a bank. My grandparents stepped forward with offers. They had made money. But there was no pension from his job; it was not that kind of company. I know the government paid money for me, a dependent child. But I only mean to say I don't know how much she needed to work; how much money needed to come through; if we had debts, creditors. It may have been we didn't, and that she went to work to thrust herself in the direction life seemed to be taking her – independence. Solitariness. All that that means.

There were memorable moments. When my girlfriend and I had been experimenting in one kind of sexual pleasure and another, quite suddenly my girlfriend – a Texas girl – sensed somehow that she was definitely pregnant and that her life and mine were ruined. Mine, I know certainly, felt ruined. And there was evidence aplenty around of kids marrying at fourteen, having babies, being divorced. This was the South, after all.

But I once again found myself in terror, and on a Sunday afternoon I just unburdened myself to my mother; told her *all* we'd done, all we hadn't. Spoke specifically and methodically in terms of parts and positions, extents and degrees. All I wanted from her was to know if Louise *could* be pregnant, based upon what she knew about those things (how much could that really have been?). These were all matters a boy should take up with his father, of course. Though, really, who-ever would? I know I wouldn't have. Such a conversation would've confused and embarrassed my poor father and me. We did not know each other that well at our closest moments. And in any case, he was gone.

But my mother I knew very well. At least I acted that way and she did, too. She was fifty-two. I was eighteen. She was practised with me, knew the kind of boy I was. We were partners in my messes and hers. I sat on the couch and carefully told her what scared me, told her what I couldn't get worked out right in my thinking, went through it all; used the words *it, hers, in.* And she, stifling her dread, very carefully assured me that everything was going to be fine. Nobody got pregnant doing what we were doing, and I should forget about it. It was all a young girl's scare fantasies. Not to worry. And so I didn't.

Of course, she was wrong. Couldn't possibly have been wronger. My girlfriend didn't get pregnant, but only because a kind fate inter-vened. Thousands of people get pregnant doing what we were doing. Thousands more get pregnant doing much less. I guess my mother just didn't know that much, or else understood much more: that what was done was done now, and all the worry and explaining and getting-straight wouldn't matter. I should be more careful in the future if I was to have one. And that was about it. If Louise was pregnant, what anybody thought wouldn't matter. Best just not to worry.

And there is, of course, a lesson in that – one I like and have tried ever since and unsuccessfully to have direct me. Though I have never looked at the world through eyes like hers were then. Not yet. I have never exactly felt how little all you can do can really matter. Full understanding will come to me, and undoubtedly to us all. But my mother showed that to me first, and best, and I think I may have begun to understand it even then.

In the sixties after that I went away to college, in Michigan. It was a choice of mine and no one else's, and my mother neither encouraged nor discouraged me. Going to college in Mississippi didn't enter my mind. I wanted, I thought, to be a hotel manager like my grandfather, who had done well at it. I do not, in fact, remember my mother and me ever talking about college. She hadn't been and didn't know much about it. But the assumption was that I was simply going, and it would be my lookout. She was interested, but in a way that was not vital or supervisory. I don't think she thought that I would go away for good, even when it happened that Michigan State took me and I said I was going. I don't know what she thought exactly. She had other things on her mind then. Maybe she thought Michigan wasn't so far from Mississippi, which is true and not true, or that I wouldn't stay and would come home soon. Maybe she thought I would never go. Or maybe she thought nothing, or nothing that was clear; just noticed that I was doing this and that, sending and getting letters, setting dates, and decided she would cross that bridge when the time came.

And it did come.

In September 1962, she and I got on the Illinois Central in Jackson and rode it to Chicago (our first such trip together). We transferred crosstown to the old La Salle Street Station and the Grand Trunk Western, and rode up to Lansing. She wanted to go with me. I think she wanted just to see all that. Michigan. Illinois. Cornfields. White barns. The Middle West. Wanted to see from a train window what went on there, how that was. What it all looked like, possibly to detect how I was going to fit myself among those people, live in their buildings, eat their food, learn their lingo. Her son. This was how she saw her duty unfolding.

And, too, the ordinary may have been just what she wanted: accompanying her son to college, a send-off; to see herself and me, for a moment in time, fitted into the pattern of what other people were up to, what people in general did. If it could happen to her, to us, that way, then maybe some normal life had reconvened, since she could not have thought of her life as normal then.

So, at the end of that week, late September 1962, when I had enrolled, invaded my room, met my roomies, and she and I had spent days touring and roaming, eating motel dinners together until nothing was left to say, I stood up on a bus-stop bench beside the train tracks, at the old GTW station in Lansing, and held up my arms in the cool, snapping air for her to see me as she pulled away back towards Chicago. And I saw her, her white face recessed behind the tinted window, one palm flat to the glass for me to see. And she was crying. Good-bye, she was saying. And I waved one arm in that cool air and said, "Good-bye. I love you," and watched the train go out of sight through the warp of that bricky old factory town. And at that moment I suppose you could say I started my own life in earnest, and whatever there was left of my childhood ended.

After that the life that would take us to the end began. A fragmented, truncated life of visits long and short. Letters. Phone calls. Telegrams. Meetings in cities away from home. Conversations in cars, in airports, train stations. Efforts to see each other. Leaving dominating everything – my growing older, and hers, observed from varying distances.

She held out alone in Mississippi for a year, moved back into the house on Congress Street. She rented out the other side, worked at the hospital, where for a time, I think, the whole new life she'd been handed worked out, came together. I am speculating, as you can believe, because I was gone. But at least she said she liked her job, liked the young interns at the hospital, liked the drama of the ER, liked working even. It may have started to seem satisfactory enough that I was away. It may have seemed to her that there was a life to lead. That under the circumstances she had done reasonably well with things; could ease up, let events happen without fearing the worst. One bad thing did finally turn into something less bad.

This, at least, is what *I* wanted to think. How a son feels about his widowed mother when he is far away becomes an involved business. But it is not oversimplifying to say that he wants good to come to her. In all these years, the years of fragmented life with my mother, I was aware (as I have said) that things would never be completely all right with her again. Partly it was a matter of choosing; partly it was a matter just of her own character – of just how she could see her life without my father, with him gone and so much life left to be lived in a not ideal way. Always she was resigned somewhere down deep. I could never plumb her without coming to that stop point – a point where expectation simply ceased. This is not to say she was unhappy after enough time had passed. Or that she never laughed. Or that she didn't see life as life, didn't regain and rejoin herself. All those she did. Only, not utterly, not in a way a mother, any mother, could disguise to her only son who loved her. I always saw that. Always felt it. Always felt her – what? – discomfort at life? Her resisting it? Always wished she could relent more than she apparently could; since in most ways my own life seemed to spirit ahead, and I did not like it that hers didn't. From almost the first I felt that my father's death surrendered to me at least as much as it took away. It gave me my life to live by my own designs, gave me my own decisions. A boy could do worse than to lose his father – a good father, at that – just when the world begins to display itself all around him.

But that is not the way it was with her, even as I can't exactly say how it *was*. I can say that in all the years after my father died, twenty-one years, her life never seemed quite fully engaged. She took trips – to Mexico, to New York, to California, to Banff, to islands. She had friends who loved her and whom she spoke well of. She had an increasingly easy life as her own parents died. She had us – my wife and me – who certainly loved her and included her in all we could. But when I would say to her – and I did say this – "Mother, are you enjoying your life? Are things all right?" she would just look at me impatiently and roll her eyes. "Richard," she'd say. "I'm never going to be ecstatic. It's not in my nature. You concentrate on your life. Leave mine alone. I'll take care of me."

And that, I think, is mostly what she did after his death and my departure, when she was on her own: she maintained herself, made a goal of that. She became brisk, businesslike, more self-insistent. Her deep voice became even deeper, assumed a kind of gravity. She drank in the evenings to get a little drunk, and took up an attitude (particularly towards men, whom she began to see as liabilities). She made her situation be the custom and cornerstone of her character. Would not be taken advantage of by people, though I suspect no one wanted to. A widow had to look out, had to pay attention to all details. No one could help you. A life lived efficiently wouldn't save you, no; but it would prepare you for what you couldn't really be saved from.

Along the way she also maintained me and my wife, at a distance and as we needed it. She maintained her mother, who finally grew ill, then crippled, but never appreciative. She maintained her stepfather – moved, in fact, back to Little Rock. She sold her house, hers and my father's first house, and lived with my grandparents in the hotel, and later – after Ben died – in apartments here and there in the town. She became a daughter again at fifty-five, one who looked after her elderly mother. They had money enough. A good car. A set of friends who were widowed, too – people in their stratum. They accompanied each other. Went to eat in small groups, played canasta afternoons, spoke on the phone, watched TV, planned arguments; grew bored, impatient, furious. Had cocktails. Laughed about men. Stared. Lived a nice and comfortable life of waiting.

Our life during this time – my mother's and mine – consisted of my knowledge of what her life was like. And visits. We lived far away from each other. She in Little Rock. I, and then I and Kristina, in New York, California, Mexico, Chicago, Michigan again, New Jersey, Vermont. To us she arrived on trains and planes and in cars, ready to loan us money and to take us to dinner. To buy us this and that we needed. To have a room painted. To worry about me. To be there for a little while wherever we were and then to go home again.

It must be a feature of anyone's life to believe that particular circumstances such as these are not exactly typical of what the mass of other lives are like. Not better. Not worse. Only peculiar in some way. Our life, my mother's and mine, seemed peculiar. Or possibly it is just imperfect that it seemed. Being away. Her being alone. Our visits and departings. All this consumed twenty years of both our lives – her last twenty, my second, when whatever my life was to be was beginning. It never felt exactly right to me that during all these years I could not see my mother more, that we did not have a day-to-day life. That the repairs we made to things after my father's death could not be shared entirely. I suppose that nowhere in time was there a moment when life for us rejoined itself as it had been before he died. This imperfection underlay everything. And when she left again and again and again, she would cry. And that is what she cried about. That we would never rejoin, that that was gone. This was all there was. Not quite enough. Not a full enough repaying of all that time together lost. She told me once that in an elevator a woman had asked her,

"Mrs Ford, do you have any children?" And she had said, "No." And then thought to herself, "Well, yes, I do. There's Richard."

Our conversations over these years had much to do with television, with movies we had seen and hadn't, with books she was reading, with baseball. The subject of Johnny Bench came up often, for some reason. My wife and I took her to the World Series, where she rooted for the team we didn't like and complained about the seats we'd moved mountains to get – for her, we thought. We took her on the Universal Tour. We took her back to Antoine's. We drove her to California and to Montreal. To Maine. To Vermont. To northern Michigan. To wherever we went that we could take her. We, she and I, observed each other. She observed my wife and my marriage and liked them both. She observed my efforts to be a writer and did not fully understand them. "But when are you going to get a job and get started?" she asked me once. She observed the fact that we had no children and offered no opinion. She observed her life and ours and possibly did not completely see how one gave rise to the other.

I observed that she grew older; saw that life was not entirely to her liking and that she made the most of its surfaces – taking a job once in a while, then finally retiring. I observed that she loved me; would sometimes take me aside early on a morning when we could be alone together as two adults and say: "Richard, are *you* happy?" And when I told her I was, she would warn, "You must be happy. That's so important."

And that is the way life went on. Not quite pointlessly. But not pointedly, either. Maybe this is typical of all our lives with our parents – a feeling that some goal should be reached, then a recognition of what that goal inevitably is, and then returning attention to what's here and present today. To what's only here.

Something, some essence of life, is not coming clear through these words. There are not words enough. There are not events enough. There is not memory enough to give a life back and have it be right, exact. In one way, over these years apart, my mother and I lived towards one another the way people do who like each other and want to see each other more. Like friends. I have not even said about her that she didn't interfere. That she agreed my life with Kristina had retired a part of her motherhood. That she didn't cultivate random judgments. That she saw her visits as welcome, which they were. Indeed, she saw that what we'd made of things – she and I – was the natural result of prior events that were themselves natural. She was now, as before, not a psychologist. Not a quizzer. She played the cards she was dealt. By some strange understanding, we knew that this was life. This is what we would have. We were fatalists, mother and son. And we made the most of it.

In 1973, my mother discovered she had breast cancer. It must've been the way with such things, and with people of her background. A time of being aware that something was there. A time of worry and growing certainty. A mention to a friend, who did nothing. Finally a casual mention to me, who saw to it immediately that she visit a doctor, who advised tests and did not seem hopeful.

What I remember of that brief period, which took place in Little Rock, is that following the first doctor visit, when all the tests and contingencies were stated and planned, she and I and my wife took the weekend together. She would "go in" on Monday. But Saturday we drove up to the country, visited my father's family, his cousins whom she liked, his grave. She stated that she was "going in for tests", and they – who were all older than she was – put a good face on it. We drove around in her Buick and just spent the time together. It was, we knew somehow, the last of the old time, the last of the period when we were just ourselves, just the selves we had made up and perfected, given all that had gone before. Something in those tests was about to change everything, and we wanted to act out our conviction that, yes, this has been a life, this adroit coming and going, this health, this humour, this affection expressed in fits and starts. This has been a thing. Nothing would change that. We could look back, and it would seem like we were alive enough.

Death starts a long time before it ever ends. And in it, in its very self, there is life that has to be lived out efficiently. There were seven years to go, but we didn't know it. And so we carried on. We went back to being away. To visiting. To insisting on life's being life, in the conviction that it could easily be less. And to me it seems like the time that had gone on before. Not exactly. But mostly. Talking on the phone. Visits, trips, friends, occasions. A more pointed need to know about "how things were", and a will to have them be all right for now.

48   RICHARD FORD

My mother, I think, made the very best of her bad problems. She had a breast removed. She had some radiation. She had to face going back to her solitary life. And all this she did with a minimum of apparent fear and a great deal of dignity and resignation. It seemed as if her later years had been a training for bad news. For facing down disasters. And I think she appreciated this and was sharply aware of how she was dealing with things.

This was the first time I ever thought seriously that my mother might come to live with me, which was a well-discussed subject all our life, there having been precedent for it and plenty of opportunity to take up a point of view. My mother's attitude was very clear. She was against it. It ruined lives, spoiled things, she thought, and said no in advance. She had lived with her mother, and that had eventuated in years of dry unhappiness. Bickering. Impossibilities. Her mother had resented her, she said, hated being looked after. Turned meaner. Vicious. It was a no-win, and she herself expected nothing like that, wanted me to swear off the idea. Which I did. We laughed about how high and dry I would leave her. How she would be in the poor-house, and I'd be someplace living it up.

But she was practical. She made arrangements. Someplace called Presbyterian Village, in Little Rock, would be her home when she was ready, she said. She'd paid money. They'd promised to do their duty. And that was that. "I don't want to have to be at anybody's mercy," she said, and meant it. And my wife and I thought that was a good arrangement all the way around.

So then it was back to regular life, or life as regular as could be. We had moved to New Jersey by then. We had a house. And there were plenty of visits, with my mother doing most of the visiting – walking out in our shady yard, afternoons, talking to our neighbours as if she knew them, digging in the flower beds. She seemed healthy. In high spirits. Illness and the possibility of illness had made her seize her life harder. She wanted to do more, it seemed. Take cruises. Visit Hawaii. Go. She had new friends, younger than she was. Loud, personable Southerners. We heard about them by name. Blanche. Herschel. Mignon. People we never met, who drank and laughed and liked her and were liked by her. I had pictures in my mind.

The year was counted from medical exam to medical exam, always these in the late winter, not long after my birthday. But every year there was good news after worrying. And every year there was a time to celebrate and feel relief. A reprieve.

I do not mean to say that any of our lives then were lived outside the expectation and prism of death. No one, I think, can lose his parent and not live out his life waiting for the other one to drop dead or begin to die. The joy of surviving is tainted by squeamish certainty that you can't survive. And I read my mother's death in almost all of her life during those days. I looked for illness. Listened to her complaints too carefully. Planned her death obscurely, along with my own abhorrence of it — treated myself to it early so that when the time came I would not, myself, go down completely.

At first there were backaches. It is hard to remember exactly when. The spring, 1981 — six years since her first operation. She came to New Jersey to visit, and something had gone wrong. She was seventy, but pain had come into her life. She looked worn down, invaded by hurting. She'd seen doctors in Little Rock, but none of this had to do with her cancer, she said they said. It was back trouble. Parts were just wearing out. She went home, but in the summer she hurt more. I would call her and the phone would ring a long time, and then her answering voice would be weak, even barely audible. "I hurt, Richard," she'd tell me, wherever I was. "The doctor is giving me pills. But they don't always work." I'll come down there, I'd say. "No. I'll be fine," she'd say. "Do what you have to do." And the summer managed past that way, and the fall began.

I started a job in Massachusetts, and then one morning the phone rang. It was just at light. I don't know why anyone would call anyone at that hour unless a death was involved; but this wasn't the case. My mother had come to the hospital the night before, in an ambulance. She was in pain. And when she got there her heart had paused, briefly, though it had started again. She was better, a nurse said over the phone from Little Rock. I said I'd come that day, from Massachusetts; find people to teach my classes, drive to the airport in Albany. And that's how I did it.

In Little Rock it was still summer. A friend of my mother's, a man named Ed, met me and drove me in. We went by old buildings, over railroad tracks and across the Arkansas River. He was in a mood to comfort me: this would not turn out well, he said. My mother had been sicker than I knew; had spent days in her apartment without coming out. She had been in bed all summer. It was something I needed to prepare myself for. Her death.

But really it was more than her death. Singular life itself – hers in particular, ours – was moving into a new class of events now. These things could be understood, is what he meant to say to me. And to hold out against them was hopeless and also maybe perverse. This all was becoming a kind of thing that happens. It was inevitable, after all. And it was best to see it that way.

Which, I suppose, is what I then began to do. That ride in the car, across town, to the hospital, was the demarking line for me. A man I hardly knew suggested to me how I should look at things; how I should consider my own mother, my own life. Suggested, in essence, I begin to see *myself* in all this. Stand back. Be him or like him. It was better. And that is what I did.

My mother, it turned out, was feeling better. But something very unusual had happened to her. Her heart had stopped. There had been congestion in the lungs, the doctor told me and her. He had already performed some more tests, and the results weren't good. He was a small, curly-headed, bright-eyed young man. He was soft-spoken, and he liked my mother, remembered how she'd looked when she first came to see him. "Healthy," he said, and he was confused now by the course of a disease he supposedly knew about. I do not remember his name now. But he came into her room, sat down in the chair with some papers, and told us bad news. Just the usual bad news. The back pain was cancer, after all. She was going to die, but he didn't know when she would. Sometime in the next year, he imagined. There didn't seem to be any thought of recovering. And I know he was sorry to know it and to say it, and in a way his job may even have been harder than ours was then.

I do not really remember what we said to him. I'm sure we asked very good questions, since we were both good when the chips were down. I do not remember my mother crying. I know I did not cry. We knew, both of us, what class of events *this* was, this message. This was the message that ended one long kind of uncertainty. And I cannot believe we both, in our own ways, did not feel some relief, as if a curiosity had been satisfied and other matters begun. The real question – how serious is this? – can be answered and over with in a hurry. It is actually an odd thing. I wonder if doctors know how odd it is.

But still, in a way, it did not change things. The persuasive powers of normal life are strong, after all. To accept less than life when it is not absolutely necessary is stupid.

I think we had talks. She was getting out of the hospital again, and at least in my memory I stayed around and got out with her before I had to go back to my job. We made plans for a visit. More going. She would come to Massachusetts when she was strong enough. We could still imagine a future, and that was exactly all we asked for.

I went back to teaching, and talked to her most days, though the thought that she was getting worse, that bad things were going on there and I couldn't stop them, made me miss some days. It became an awful time, then, when life felt ruined, futureless, edging toward disappointments.

She stayed out of the hospital during that time, took blood trans-fusions, which seemed to make her feel better, though they were ominous. I think she went out with her friends. Had company. Lived as if life could go on. And then in early October she came north. I drove down to New York, picked her up and drove us back to my rented house in Vermont. It was misty, and most of the leaves were down. And in the house it was cold and bleak, and I took her out to dinner in Bennington just to get warm. She said she had had another transfusion for the trip and would stay with me until its benefits wore off and she was weak again.

And that was how we did that. Just another kind of regular life between us. I went to school, did my work, came home nights. She stayed in the big house with my dog. Read. Cooked lunches for herself. Watched the World Series. Watched Sadat be assassinated. Looked out the window. At night we talked. I did my school work, went out not very much. With my wife, who was working in New York and commuting up on weekends, we went on country drives, invited visitors, paid visits, lived together as we had in places far and wide all those years. I don't know what else we were supposed to do, how else that time was meant to pass.

On a sunny day in early November, when she had been with me three weeks and we were, in fact, out of things to do and talk about, she sat down beside me on the couch and said, "Richard, I'm not sure how much longer I can look out after myself. I'm sorry. But it's just the truth."

"Does that worry you?" I said.

"Well," my mother said, "yes. I'm not scheduled to go into Presbyterian Village until way next year. And I'm not quite sure what I'm going to be able to do until then."

"What would you like to do?" I said.

"I don't exactly know," she said. And she looked worried then, looked away out the window, down the hill, where the trees were bare and it was foggy.

"Maybe you'll start to feel better," I said.

"Well, yes. I could. I suppose that's not impossible," she said.

"I think it's possible," I said. "I do."

"Well. OK," my mother said.

"If you don't," I said, "if by Christmas you don't feel you can do everything for yourself, you can move in with us. We're moving back to Princeton. You can live there."

And I saw in my mother's eyes, then, a light. A *kind* of light, anyway. Recognition. Relief. Concession. Willingness.

"Are you sure about that?" she said and looked at me. My mother's eyes were very brown, I remember.

"Yes, I'm sure," I said. "You're my mother. I love you."

"Well," she said and nodded. No tears. "I'll begin to think towards that, then. I'll make some plans about my furniture."

"Well, wait," I said. And this is a sentence I wish, above all sentences in my life, I had never said. Words I wish I'd never heard. "Don't make your plans yet," I said. "You might feel better by then. It might not be necessary to come out to Princeton."

"Oh," my mother said. And whatever had suddenly put a light in her eyes suddenly went away then. And her worries resumed. Whatever lay between then and later rose again. "I see," she said. "All right."

I could've not said that. I could've said, "Yes, make the plans. In whatever way all this works out, it'll be just fine. I'll see to that." But that is what I didn't say. I deferred instead to something else, to some other future, and at least in retrospect I know what that future was. And, I think, so did she. Perhaps you could say that in that moment I witnessed her facing death, saw it take her out beyond her limits, and feared it myself, feared all that I knew; and that I clung to life, to the possibility of life and change. Perhaps I feared something more tangible. But the truth is, anything we ever could've done for each other after that passed by then and was gone. And even together we were alone.

What remains can be told quickly. In a day or two I drove her to Albany. She was cold, she said, in my house, and couldn't get warm, and would be better at home. That was our story, though there was not heat enough anywhere to get her warm. She looked pale. And when I left her at the airport gate she cried again, stood and watched me go back down the long corridor, waved a hand. I waved. It was the last time I would see her that way. On her feet. In the world. We didn't know that, of course. But we knew something was coming.

And in six weeks she was dead. There is nothing exceptional about that to tell. She never got to Princeton. Whatever was wrong with her just took her over. "My body has betrayed me" is one thing I remember her saying. Another was, "My chances now are slim and none." And that was true. I never saw her dead, didn't care to, simply took the hospital's word about it when they called. Though I saw her face death that month, over and over, and I believe because of it that seeing death faced with dignity and courage does not confer either of those, but only pity and helplessness and fear.

All the rest is just private – moments and messages the world would not be better off to know. She knew I loved her because I told her so enough. I knew she loved me. That is all that matters to me now, all that should ever matter.

And so to end.

Does one ever have a "relationship" with one's mother? No. I think not. The typical only exists in the minds of unwise people. We – my mother and I – were never bound together by guilt or embarrassment, or even by duty. Love sheltered everything. We expected it to be reliable, and it was. We were always careful to say it – "I love you" – as if a time might come, unexpectedly, when she would want to hear that, or I would, or that each of us would want to hear ourselves say it to the other, only for some reason it wouldn't be possible, and our loss would be great – confusion. Not knowing. Life lessened.

My mother and I look alike. Full, high forehead. The same chin, nose. There are pictures to show that. In myself I see her, even hear her laugh. In her life there was no particular brilliance, no celebrity.

No heroics. No one crowning achievement to swell the heart. There were bad ones enough: a childhood that did not bear strict remembering; a husband she loved forever and lost; a life to follow that did not require comment. But somehow she made possible for me my truest affections, as an act of great literature would bestow upon its devoted reader. And I have known that moment with her we would all like to know, the moment of saying, "Yes. This is what it is." An act of knowing that certifies love. I have known that. I have known any number of such moments with her, known them even at the instant they occurred. And now. And, I assume, I will know them forever.

LYDIA CHUKOVSKAYA

Anna Akhmatova

Lydia Korneevna Chukovskaya, daughter of Korney Chukovsky, was born in St Petersburg in 1907. She worked in the Leningrad office of the State Publishing House for Children's Literature under Samuil Marshak until its entire editorial staff was purged in 1937. In 1938 her husband was arrested and she went to seek Akhmatova's advice on how to get him released – Akhmatova having (if only temporarily) effected the release of her son by writing direct to Stalin himself. Almost immediately, the young Lydia Chukovskaya found herself becoming the poet's confidante and amanuensis, memorizing the poems that Akhmatova did not at that time dare to commit to paper. The Akhmatova Journals *are the record of this friendship and a monument to the power and importance of memory in a totalitarian regime.*

In these extracts from The Akhmatova Journals 1938–41 *(vol. 1), the story of the bizarre competition between two publishing houses, Goslitizdat (the State Publishing House) and the Writers' Publishing House, for the right to publish Anna Akhmatova's first collection since 1922 is told. Akhmatova's fortunes rise from those of a non-person in December 1939 to partially rehabilitated literary celebrity in just six months. This brief, wartime window was firmly closed again in 1946 with the poet's expulsion from the Writers' Union.*[*]

---

[*] Numbers in superior script refer to notes at the end of these extracts (see pp. 80–2). Certain poems referred to by number in bold type in the footnotes are reproduced on pp. 76–9 and on p. 149.

15 December '39

Today, as I was about to go to the library, the doorbell rang all of a sudden – it was Anna Andreevna.

"I was in the neighbourhood to collect my pension, so I wandered over," she explained.

"I at last got hold of the house-manager today. I held out my pension book to him and asked him to witness my signature but he said: 'Please sign on a separate piece of paper first.' Why? What for? Does he think my signature in the book is forged? I was furious. In general I have a positive attitude towards people but in this case I was very offended. I wrote out my name on a piece of paper and said to him: 'You obviously want to sell my autograph to the Literary Museum? You are right: they'll give you 15 roubles for it.' That embarrassed him, he tore up the piece of paper. Then he asked: 'You were a writer once, weren't you?'" [...]

13 January '40

Today, just now, I was at Anna Andreevna's for the first time since my return from Detskoe.* Rumours of her being honoured reached my ears even there.†

"So, what did you hear about me?" was her first question.

She said she didn't feel well, even worse than before: insomnia, and at night either her feet go numb or her head does. In my view, though, she looks a bit better. She sat on the divan, in a coat, with her hair done and in it, her famous comb.

All the rumours proved justified. Indeed, she had already been sent a lump sum of 3,000 roubles from Moscow and her pension had been raised to 750 roubles a month. Zoschenko has been going around Leningrad City Council with a petition sent from Moscow and already signed by some people (Lebedev-Kumach, Aseev), to get her a flat. She was admitted to the Writers' Union with great ceremony.‡ A

---

* I had been to Detskoe [formerly Tsarskoe Tselo], to the House of Creativity, to write *Sofia Petrovna*.

† After some phone call "from above".

‡ This was on 5 January 1940.

secretary and a member of the board – Lozinsky – had fetched her. The proceedings were presided over by Slonimsky.

"I still call him Misha by force of habit. Somehow he stayed a little boy for a long time . . . Misha said that I was among those present and suggested welcoming me. Everyone applauded. I stood up and bowed. Then Mikhail Leonidovich spoke. He said some awful things. Just imagine: You have been friends with someone for thirty years and suddenly he stands up and says that your poems will live for as long as the Russian language exists and that every last grain of them will be garnered like lines by Catullus. Come now, really, how could he! There were many people there, and all strangers. Then Brykin reported on the small series of the Library of Poets. And also mentioned another edition of my work."

I brought up the subject of the flat. I so want her to have a decent place to live in! Without those footsteps and records playing from behind the wall, without continual humilations! But she, it turned out, seems to feel quite differently: she wants to remain here, wants the Smirnovs to move to a new room and give her theirs. She wants to live here, but in two rooms.

"I truly think a communal flat, you know, is better than an unknown one. I'm used to things here. Furthermore, when Lyova* returns – he will have a room. For he will come back someday . . ."

This hope gladdened me.

She poured us some so-called tea which was really no more than hot water, and pulled the cranberry jam over.

"I ran out of tea about three weeks ago," she explained.

Then she told me about Shakilik.† He has suddenly started to speak and he can say anything. Yesterday, when the light went out, he cried out: "I'm scared, where's my mama?"

"And he already calls me 'Andreevna'. Whereas before he used to call me 'T'anna'. You understand? The direction, where to: 'To Anna'. To him, this was my name. Now he has a cold, sits in bed and tugs at the pages of Krylov's *Fables*. That's his favourite book. I'm reading it to him. He understands – and yet he's only eighteen months old. And now I'm expecting some people from *Leningrad*. I prepared 'To

* Lyova – son of Anna Akhmatova and Nikolay Stepanovich Gumilyov [who had been arrested for a second time in 1938].

† Akhmatova's next-door neighbour's son.

the artist' and 'That city, loved by me since childhood . . .' for them.*
Every day they keep on coming round, from all the editorial offices.
Yesterday Druzin came with his secretary and some military person.
I had Shakalik in my arms at that moment. I handed him to Tanya
and jokingly told her in a whisper: '. . . .'† she believed me. It really
did seem like it . . . That's just my wickedness, though. Druzin was
all magnanimity and encouragement. It turns out he once suffered on
account of Acmeism. Didn't you know? Neither did I. He added that
the Acmeists had merit: they depicted Russian nature admirably. How
kind, don't you think?"[1]

Her story was interrupted by the arrival of a young lady from the
magazine *Leningrad*. The young lady oozed honey and treacle from
every pore. Anna Andreevna handed her the prepared poems. And
when she'd left she suddenly fell silent and put on her glasses:

O Stars of heaven.

I couldn't bear to watch. Like being an accomplice in a murder.‡

When I had pulled myself together we moaned a bit about the
impending confiscation of all electrical appliances.

"And just when I got a new one," said Anna Andreevna, "a cigarette
lighter-cum-ashtray. Vladimir Georgievich gave it to me. And this
too, look, what a lovely little box. Made of Lapis Lazuli. It's a

---

* A.A. gave the journal *Leningrad* not two but six poems. In issue no. 2 for 1940
the following were published: "Some gaze into affectionate eyes . . .", "From you I
hid my heart . . .", "To the artist", "Voronezh" and "Here Pushkin's banishment
began . . ." (FT, *The Reed*). The poem "That city, loved by me since childhood . . ."
(FT, *The Reed*) was not included in that issue. [FT: Anna Akhmatova, *The Flight of
Time (Beg vremeni)*. Moscow and Leningrad: Sovetsky Pisatel, 1965. BBP: Anna
Akhmatova, *Stikhot voreniya: poemy*. Leningrad: Sovetsky Pisatel, B-ka poeta Bolshaya
scriya, 1976.]

† "They've come for me." In the original entry there was a blank space: I didn't
dare write down these words.

‡ A.A. wrote the poem "To the New Year! To New Grief! . . ." on a piece of
paper, gave it to me to read and then, as was her habit, burned it over an ashtray;
no. 9.

May I remind the reader that the war with Finland had started on 30 November
1939. The poem was published abroad thirty-five years later in the collection *Pamyati
Anny Akhmatovov*, Paris: YMCA-Press, 1974. [. . .] It was first published in the
USSR in the magazine *Daugava*, 1987, no. 9. Published by R. D. Timenchik. (*Note
added in 1987.*)

powdercase. I like the fact that they are new, modern objects. Because, otherwise, we live surrounded by things from bygone eras."

I told her that she should go to the House of Creativity, in Detskoe, for a rest.

"No, I wouldn't get any rest there. Tsarskoe is such a source of tears for me . . ."

17 January '40

The moon.

Because of it the city and its sorrow are still more terrifying.

But I'm grateful to the moon.

Today Anna Andreevna phoned me and asked me to go round. To tell the truth, this request was rather merciless, for it was −35°C outside. However, I pulled on my felt boots, wrapped myself in a shawl and set off. And the moon guided me safely to her through the darkness.*

I brought her half a packet of tea. She was delighted and immediately put the kettle on. She is deeply worried that Goslitizdat sent her a contract for four thousand lines at exactly the moment when the Writers' Publishing House had accepted a volume of her poems.

She started to look everywhere for the contract: on top of the armchair and underneath among some papers.

"I had a visit from Kr., the director of Goslitizdat. I think she's a bitch."

I burst out laughing. I love it so much when I hear such words from her lips.

"Yes, yes, don't laugh, a bitch. I tell her: 'My poems have already been given to the Writers' Publishing House.' And she says: 'That's no problem, as long as the material is different.' *Material*, for God's sake!" "Judging by this remark, she's rather a fool," I said. "The phone rings for days on end," continued Anna Andreevna. "They are ringing from every magazine. One person called, gave his name, but I didn't catch who he was and where from. Asking for poems. I reply: 'I have already given everything out.' Silence. And then: 'You know what? Search *there*!'"

---

* The city was blacked out because of the war with Finland.

I advised her to discuss the matter of the Writers' Publishing House and Goslit with Yury Nikolaevich Tynyanov.*

Suddenly the contract turned up. I had a look: absolutely standard [. . .]

She was anxious about whom they would ask to write the foreword of the Writers' Publishing House book. She was afraid it might be Volkov, some specialist on the Acmeists.

"He was always railing against us. I will tell him to his face: one should only write about what one loves."[2]

"Cup of sorrow."[†]

23 January '40

Vladimir Georgievich called me yesterday saying that Anna Andreevna had completely gone to pieces, she wouldn't eat, wouldn't drink, that in a few days the publishers would be sending someone for the manuscript but the manuscript wasn't ready. I arranged to have the rest typed up urgently. That evening I went to see her. This time the moon didn't fulfil its duty and I hurt my head badly in the Entertaining entrance: there wasn't a single light bulb.

Anna Andrevna looked in bad shape, yellow, greyish. She smiled for a second when I handed her a small packet of sugar: "Now there's sugar – but the tea's run out.

"I don't sleep at all. And all night long I write. Everything is dying off – I can't walk, can't sleep, can't eat, but this for some reason remains."

And she recited: about a willow tree, about poetry, about a portrait, about emeralds.[‡]

* [Yury Nikolaevich Tynyanov (1896–1943) – university professor, leading journalist, critic and historical novelist.]

† A title thought up by Anna Andreevna for one of her cycles of poems. Which one, I do not recall.

‡ I think this list of poems can be deciphered as follows: "The Willow"; "I have no need for a host of odes . . ."; "When a Man is Dying" – that is: *FT, The Reed*; *FT, Seventh Book*; *FT, The Reed* and BBP, p. 196. As to how A.A. and I later reconstructed "The Cellar of Memory" [**No. 24**, reproduced here on p. 77] together, see volume two of my *Journals*.

When I first heard the poem "I have no need for a host of odes . . .", A.A. recited the last line as: To your joy and my *torment*.

She recited calmly, in her even, deep voice, breathing easily.

I was totally lost for words. Anna Andreevna had probably never had such a muddle-headed listener. The ones about poetry were miraculous.

"I've been trying to steal up to this for a long time," said Anna Andreevna, "but somehow I couldn't quite get to it."

I tried to talk Anna Andreevna into giving me these poems for retyping too, so that they could be included in her book.

She agreed to three.*

Someone knocked at the door.

"That's Aleksandr Nikolaevich," said Anna Andreevna. "Let's put the shade on the lamp. I don't look my best today."

A tall young man entered. Anna Andreevna sat him down next to her on the divan. They discussed some things concerning the Hermitage. I broke into their conversation and asked Anna Andreevna to set me up for copying in the meantime. She searched for her notebook a long time, on the armchair and under it, then she looked for paper. She pointed out the pages in her notebook containing new poems and asked me, while I was at it, to copy out a few of her old, previous ones "which once could not exist": "Little Song", "I both wept and I was penitent . . .", "Not for your love do I ask . . .", "White is the sky with frightening whiteness . . .".†

"But please put the punctuation in yourself, I don't know how to . . . Dates? Please don't ask about dates. People always talk to me about dates as if I were a dangerously ill person who can't be told frankly about her illness."

I finished copying and said goodbye. She announced that she wanted to get out of her den and tomorrow, when the typist had copied everything for me, she would come to my place for the poems.

Today, after I'd got everything from the typist and proofread it, I phoned Anna Andreevna at two and at three o'clock – she was asleep. At five o'clock Lyusha and I took the poems round to her place ourselves and handed them over to Vladimir Georgievich in the

* She did not agree to offer "The Cellar of Memory" to the publishers.

† "Little Song" ("From Morning I Would Hold My Peace") – FT, *Anno Domini*; "I both wept and I was penitent . . ." – BBP, p. 53; "Not for your love do I ask . . ." – FT, *Rosary*, "White is the sky with frightening whiteness . . ." ("The White Night") – BBP, p. 281.

kitchen: he said that Anna Andreevna was unwell and had only just fallen asleep.

"What's wrong with her?"

"She's utterly incapable of fighting her neurasthenia. She has turned night into day, and of course this is bad for her. On top of that, she doesn't eat a thing. And besides, nothing is organized. Maybe I'll manage to talk the Smirnovs into giving her lunch."

(It's all true; but, one might ask: why, if a person does the most necessary and most difficult task in the world – and afterwards naturally feels battered and worn out – should this state be described as: "incapable of fighting her neurasthenia".)

6 May '40

Yesterday I got very tired and on my return from the Library I lay down. The phone rang. It was Vladimir Georgievich: "Anna Andreevna is unwell and *begs* you to come."

I rested for a bit and went. I went, even though I realized that nothing had happened, that she simply couldn't sleep, was depressed and wanted someone to sit beside her.

Indeed she "simply couldn't sleep" – but I did the right thing in going.

Again the dressing gown, the divan, the crumpled blanket, unkempt hair, dishevelled. It's hard to believe that just two days earlier she had looked so youthful, so well dressed, so triumphant. Now this sallow, pinched, old face. She complains of a pain in her leg.

The proofs will be ready on the 7th. From Goslitizdat? From the Writers' Publishing House? I don't remember, I've got confused. At any rate – the proofs will be ready. Anna Andreevna wants to give me the task of reading them and, most importantly, of making sure that everything – including the punctuation – is consistent with the proofs which Lozinsky has just read.

I promised.

"Bear in mind that there are eleven printer's sheets to be done," said Anna Andreevna.

"I'm not afraid," I replied.

"In the Goslit edition there are 150 fewer lines than in the Writers' Publishing House edition. In the Writers' Publishing House edition, apart from what was agreed, only one poem, 'The Last Toast', has been removed so far.* I ordered 10 copies at the reduced price for myself; I will give my friends the Writers' Publishing House book, but I won't give anyone the Goslitizdat."

She fell silent. She performed the ritual.

"Nor the agitated linden shadows . . ."†

And I immediately understood everything: her sallowness, her dishevelled hair, her sleeplessness.

"Did you do that last night?"

"No, yesterday. Between continuous phone calls from the publishers."

She put on her glasses and began to leaf through her notebook. I saw that the notebook was filled to the very last page. She snapped it shut, without having read anything to me.

"You'll have to get a new one," I said.

"I've got two new ones! Just look at them."

She pulled two albums out of her chest of drawers, one was antique, wonderful, with thick paper.

"Nikolay Ivanovich gave it to me. From Pushkin's time, see?"

She sat on the divan, feet tucked beneath her, and took a cigarette. She was very agitated – why? – probably because of the imminent publication of her book, although she was hiding it. She showed me her portrait by Tyrsa, which was going to be included in the Writers' Publishing House volume. I didn't like the portrait – too superficial. She liked it, though. (From the end of the '20s.)

Lighting a cigarette, she said: "And all this for nothing: the portrait, the proofs . . . There won't be enough paper, or something else will be in short supply. We'll see. You know I've at last understood why I can't stand my early poems. Now I see them all perfectly for what they are. I hadn't seen them for a long time but when I was looking at the proofs with Lozinsky I realized exactly what they're like: unkind

* **No. 28** [reproduced here on p. 78].

† A.A. wrote down, gave me to read and burned over the ashtray: "Already madness with its wing . . .", a poem about a visit to her son in prison: **No. 29** [reproduced here on p. 79].

It was first published with many censorial distortions and under the heading "To a friend" in the collection: *Anna Akhmatova. Izbrannoe*. Tashkent Sov. Pisatel 1943. Then in 1974, with censorial distortions and with misprints in the collection: *Anna Akhmatova. Izbrannoe*. M. : Khudozh. lit. For the most authentic text see: *Neva*, 1987, no. 6 ("Requiem").

in their attitude to the lyric heroine, unwise, naïve and shameless. I assure you, that's precisely what they're like. And I just can't understand why people like them so much."

I said that I could perhaps agree on only one point: unkindness towards the lyric heroine.

"No, no, it's exactly as I say . . . Art is a dangerous thing. You don't realize this when you're young. What a terrible fate, with traps, snares. I now understand parents who try to shield their children from poetry, from the theatre . . . Just think, what terrible fates . . . You don't see it when you're young, and even if you see it, you don't give a damn . . ."

She was agitated and focused. She obviously wanted to talk.

"You do know Lotta, don't you? The sharpest of women. Razor-sharp. She's charming. A few days ago I told her: 'I would like to recite to you, Lotta, I've written a poem . . .' And she said to me: 'Who? You?' Charming, isn't it? It's very funny: 'Who? You?' "[3]

We started talking about Dostoevsky.

"I've recently reread Dostoevsky's *The Idiot*, *A Raw Youth* and *The Insulted and Injured*. Yes, you are right, *The Idiot* is the best. An astounding novel. And you know what I've noticed? Have you ever thought about the little old men in Dostoevsky? Those perfumed, courteous, naïve old men, who flutter around, clicking their heels, trying to be French, always falling in love? I've understood that they are all people from Pushkin's day – that's what Prince Vyazemsky, for instance, was like for them."

I began to question her about Moscow, about Boris Leonidovich.*

"He is slowly dying at home . . . He's not writing his own poetry any more, because he's translating other people's – nothing destroys your own poetry more than translating other people's. Take Lozinsky, he started translating and stopped writing . . . But in Boris Leonidovich's case the main problem is something else: it's his home life. I feel infinitely sorry for him . . . Zina† loses herself in card-playing for days on end; Lyonechka‡ is neglected. He himself says: Lyonechka goes around in rags, and when you try to explain to her – she starts screeching. From the very start everybody around could see that she

---

* Pasternak.
† Pasternak's second wife.
‡ Pasternak's son by his second wife.

was a course and vulgar woman, but he didn't see it, he was blindly in love. Since there was absolutely nothing to be enraptured by, he admired the fact that she washed the floors herself . . . And now he sees everything, understands everything clearly and says terrible things about her . . . Had he said them to me in private, of course I wouldn't have repeated them to anyone, but he spoke about Zina in front of Nina Antonovna whom he hardly knows. Nina and I couldn't bring ourselves to look at each other, that's how embarrassed we felt.[4] 'She's a storm on a parquet floor, who has been to the beauty salon and acquired a veneer of bad taste.' Accurate isn't it? Then: 'If she was at least extreme in some respect, you know, like a hovel which you can point out to foreigners and say, "look at this terrible hovel of ours!"' – like the one I had (she pointed her finger at the wall, behind which lived Nikolay Nikolaevich) – 'but she is merely common as muck.' He understands everything, but he won't leave, of course. Because of Lyonechka. And, besides, he belongs to the breed of conscientious men who cannot get divorced twice. But is it possible to work in such conditions? Side by side with vulgarity? Poverty has never hampered anybody. Neither has grief. Rembrandt painted all his best works in the last two years of his life, after having lost everybody around him: his wife, son, mother . . . No, grief doesn't interfere with work. But a Zina like that can ruin everything . . ."

"But if she is like that," I said, "I don't understand why she needs Boris Leonidovich. It's not only that he needs a different wife, she too needs a different husband. He can't be any good for her either."

"You see, their romance began at the height of his prosperity. He was proclaimed the best poet, there was plenty of money, they could go off to Tbilisi in a sleeping car. Oh, if only one could find her a nice prosperous book-keeper. But, I fear, it won't happen." [. . .]

10 May '40

Three days ago, Anna Andreevna rang me in the morning and asked me to come over. Goslit were sending the proofs over to her at once. I went. We sat around for a long time, drinking tea, watching the clock, waiting. Anna Andreevna complained that Goslit's selection is

much worse than that of the Writers' Publishing House: it is one
hundred and fifty lines shorter, has no epigraphs and all in all is
*Akhmatova pour les pauvres.**

A book in colour. Its table of contents.†

The proofs were delivered at last. They really did look pitiful,
shoddy. Anna Andreevna absolutely insisted that the new poems in
it should be checked against the Writers' Publishing House proofs,
against the ones Mikhail Leonidovich had checked. I rang our dear
Tanya[5] at the publishers, but she said that the proofs had already gone
to the printers and nothing could be done about it. Anna Andreevna
got angry and made me phone back several times: "Tell her that the
dotty old lady doesn't understand a thing and keeps insisting." But I
did understand and I felt very embarrassed at doing this to Tanechka
who, even without my phone calls, would have been prepared to do
anything for Anna Andreevna. Within the hour Tanya herself phoned
and suggested the following – Anna Andreevna, using the author's
prerogative, should keep the Goslit proofs for four days, as she was
legally entitled to do, by which time the proofs would be back from
the printers. But Anna Andreevna said: "I don't have the strength to
squabble with them, Goslit are pressurizing me."

Sweeping up the proofs, I set off for Tusya's.‡ She would do everything perfectly, no worse than Lozinsky. We worked avidly, hardly
stopping, from four o'clock in the afternoon until 1 a.m. When we
had finished I phoned Anna Andreevna. She asked me to bring the
proofs over, not in the morning, but at once.

I did.

Last night she came round to my place with a briefcase. It was the
first time I had seen her carrying a briefcase! She was listless, irritable
– obviously the fuss over the book had exhausted her, and then there
had also been news from Moscow about B.'s fruitless effort.§

She unfolded her list of corrections – some amendments, some new
punctuation and some misprints. One misprint which infuriated her
was "needle" [*igloi*] instead of "arrow" [*streloi*] in the lines:

---

  * *Pour les pauvres* (Fr.): for the poor.
  † I am unable to decipher this line. Evidently, it concerned some planned, but
unrealized book.
  ‡ Tusya: Tamara Grigorevna Gabbe's. See note [6] (p. 81).
  § Some failure concerning efforts on Lyova's behalf.

And on the tower clock the large hand
Does not seem to me a deadly needle

– "How absurd! You have arrows of death, not needles. How care-
lessly people read poetry. They all read it, they all like it, they all write
letters – and they don't notice that it's utter nonsense."[*]
    Then she showed me the new punctuation at the end of the poem
"Like a white stone in the depths of a well . . .": the line "That my
wonderful sorrows should live for ever . . ." should be separated from
the following line "You have become a memory of mine . . ." by a
punctuation mark; it doesn't relate to it.[†]
    Then I began putting questions to her from a list of queries Tusya
and I had prepared. I suggested some changes in the punctuation.
She responded and agreed willingly. Just once, when I suggested
putting an elipsis, did she reply: "Don't . . . I don't like it." Sometimes
she couldn't answer the question – this or that punctuation mark?
Then I would ask her to read out two or three lines, putting in the
punctuation marks myself according to her intonation.
    She dictated to me a stanza from the poem "Boris Pasternak" which
had been included in the Writers' Publishing House book but had
for some reason been omitted from the Goslit edition. And she
restored several epithets.[‡]
    Tanechka had sent her the set of proofs which Yury Nikolaevich
had brought back from Detskoe for her – the very one, with Anna
Andreevna's and Mikhail Leonidovich's corrections. I took a look: it
really did have a totally different appearance. Yu. N. and Tanya had
fought hard to obtain an old-fashioned type face.
    I checked all the new poems in the Goslit proofs line by line against
the Writers' Publishing House text. Anna Andreevna wasn't a help to

---

[*] The misprint "needle" [*igloi*] instead of "arrow"[*streloi*] in the poem "Weak is
my voice, but my will does not weaken . . ." appeared in the collection *White Flock*
(1917); and, to my amazement, in spite of Anna Andreevna's correction, that very
same misprint was repeated in the collection *From Six Books* [1940], on p. 122. In
all subsequent editions, including *The Flight of Time* it says "arrow" (p. 93).

[†] However, in both collections – in *From Six Books* and in *FT* the punctuation
does not correspond to my notes.

[‡] Which stanza – I do not remember; one of three: IV, V or VI; I think the
epithets were "deadly" [*smertelny*] and "graveyard" [*kladbishchensky*]. [The poem is
reproduced here on p. 149.]

me, and even distracted me by talking, but she looked at the proof-readers' marks with reverence and took a humorous delight in my ability to put them in.

I finished.

"Do you really think all the poems are bad?" I asked, remembering our recent conversation.

"All, or almost all of them . . . I assure you: the poems are bad, the book's bad . . . But this "The heavy amber day drags on for ever . . ." – this I do like."

I said that the poem "Tall woman, where is your little gypsy boy . . ." always nearly moved me to tears.

"That's history", Anna Andreevna replied cryptically. And, without any explanation, she dictated some minor corrections to the poem "We shall not drink from the same glass . . ." to me.

"Mikhail Leonidvoich was offended to see that I had changed it, made it different from the way it had been in our youth. And so, I'm restoring it to how it was," she explained.

"What? That means, it was to him!" I thought, but didn't say.

Ida served us lunch. Anna Andreevna tried to be friendly and gracious but was cold and distracted. Although she did speak very nicely of our Daniil Ivanovich; she had met him a few days ago and had liked him.

"He told me he believes that a genius must possess three qualities: perspicacity, authority and intelligibility. Khlebnikov possessed perspicacity but did not posses intelligibility and authority. I recited 'The Way of All the Earth' to him. He said: 'Yes, you do seem to have authority, but not much intelligibility.'"[7]

She was in a hurry to get home: Vladimir Georgievich was supposed to bring some doctor back with him by six o'clock.

She left. And Goslit sent someone to my place for the proofs. I wrote out instructions for the technical editors and the proofreaders: I also enclosed a photograph which Anna Andreevna had brought (1936, "a good photograph, here I wasn't trying to make myself look younger any more").

That evening, when she got home from the publishing house, Tanya phoned me. It turns out that there is a big intrigue surrounding Anna Andreevna's books – and she was right not to want to sign contracts with two publishers at once. Goslit had tricked her with the assurance that they had some special authorization. They did not and could not have any: on the contrary, the publication of two identical books at the same time in two different places is categorically prohibited. And now both publishers are rushing to get the book out first, in order to jeopardize the other.

And caught up in all this is a person who so earnestly does not want, so passionately does not want to be put in a false, unworthy position . . .

I'm not going to tell her. It would make her ill. Anyway, nothing can be done about it now. And what if "Akhmatova pour les pauvres" comes out first? And the Writers' edition doesn't come out at all?*

8 June '40

Yesterday morning, I called Anna Andreevna and invited her to come with me for a few days to join the girls at the dacha. I would squeeze in with Lyusha and Tanya and would give her my room. She replied: "I can't today. Come round quickly."

I arrived about two. She looked very bad, tired eyes, her face drawn and blurred, as if the features had lost the clarity of their outlines.

"What's the matter with you? Have you been ill these last few days?"

"No."

And she told me her latest Dostoevskian episode, truly both horrifying and tiresome. What an imbroglio – those children she looks after, and this Court of Wonders.†

She was getting ready to go to the Rybakov's for lunch, but would not let me go, and we talked for a long time. I admitted that I was very hungry, and Anna Andreevna, to my surprise, very deftly warmed up a rissole and potatoes for me on the electric hotplate.

"So, you really are perfectly able to rustle up a meal," I said.

---

* The reverse happened: *From Six Books*, the Writers' Publishing House collection was published: the Goslit collection was killed off. I do not know exactly when it was killed off or under what circumstances.

† A.A. suspected that Tanya Smirnova, her neighbour, Valya's and Vova's mother, had been assigned to keep watch on her, to spy on her, and she even detected some signs of this surveillance. "It always turns out," she told me, "that I end up paying my own informers."

A.A. called the watch kept on her and her manuscripts, which she felt constantly, the activity of the Court of Wonders.

"I can do everything. And if I don't do it, it's just out of spite," replied Anna Andreevna.

I said that today I'd been at Tusya's since early morning, and, instead of doing our work, we had discussed Anna Andreevna's poetry, and Tusya had expressed her own theory on that score.

"Please tell me, she's a clever woman, and I'm interested," asked Anna Andreevna.

Immediately, I regretted having let it slip. Tusya has a remarkable gift for words, which I lack. She herself would have developed her idea much more forcefully and profoundly, whereas I could only get the outline across.

When you first apprehend it, Akhmatova's poetry does not strike you by the novelty of its form as does, say, the poetry of Mayakovsky. You can hear Baratynsky and Tyutchev and Pushkin – sometimes, more rarely, Blok – in the movement of the poem, in its rhythms, in the fullness of the line, in the precision of the rhymes. At first it seems like a narrow path, going alongside the wide road of Russian classical poetry. Mayakovsky is deafeningly novel, but at the same time he is unfruitful, barren: he brought Russian poetry to the edge of an abyss, one step further – and it would have disintegrated. One should not follow him or one comes to the abyss, to the total disintegration of poetry. Akhmatova's little path turns out to be a wide road in fact; her traditional style is purely external; she is daring and innovative and, while maintaining the appearance of classical verse, she brings about earthquakes and upheavals. And, in contrast to Mayakovsky's poetry, one can follow Akhmatova's – without repeating and without imitating it, but continuing, carrying on the tradition of great Russian poetry.

Anna Andreevna listened attentively and, it seemed, sympathetically, but did not respond to me.

I asked if she had written anything in the last few days.

"Very little, I'm finishing 'Dusk falls and in the dark blue sky . . .', I'm working on the end."

She told me that some lover of books, catching sight of a pile of copies of her volume on a chair at her flat, had suggested: "Give me five of them, I'll bring you 500 roubles tomorrow."

"That means that speculation has already started. How disgusting . . . And just think: it turns out that the writers are already signing a list at the Writers' Bookshop for the next one, the Goslit edition.

What do they want it for? How outrageous. Again, nobody, except them, will get the book."

She sat on the divan, legs tucked under, and smoked one cigarette after another. I asked her something about her previous readings, she told me about one – and moved from that to Sologub. She told me that over twenty years ago, once, at Sologub's – or organized by Sologub? – there had been a party for the benefit of exiled Bolsheviks where tickets were being sold for 100 roubles.

"I took part too. I wore a white dress with big flounces, with a wide, high collar and had awful tuberculosis . . . For several years Sologub was extremely celebrated, the most celebrated of poets. Nastya loved lavishness but had no taste whatsoever, so the luxury of the house was heavy, vulgar.* They needed a lot of money, so Sologub published lousy little stories in insignificant little magazines, and they lived lavishly. Nastya was plain but had a lively, intelligent, attractive face. I was friends with her through Olya, rather not with her, but with her sister. [. . .]

"I know what destroyed Nastya. Nobody really knows why, but I know how and why it all happened. She became mentally ill as a result of unhappy love. She was about forty-two at the time, she fell in love with a cold and indifferent man. At first he was surprised at receiving frequent invitations to the Sologubs'. Later, when he found out about Anastasya Nikolaevna's feelings for him, he stopped going there. She would take me to her room and talk and talk about him endlessly, for hours. Sometimes she would put on a white dress and go to him to declare her love . . . In general she did frightful things which no woman should ever do. The last time I saw her was a few days before she died: I was going to meet Volodya at the Marble Palace and she walked with me. The whole way, she talked about her love – she was no longer able to talk about anything else. When she threw herself into the Neva, she was on the way to her sister's. It was established precisely that she had set off from home in order to go and see her sister, but two doors from her sister's house she threw herself into the Neva . . . Fyodor Kuzmich later moved in with Nastya's sister and lived there, not knowing that Nastya had drowned beneath his window.

"Somewhere, I still have the newspaper in which he put a notice

* *Nastya* – Anastasiya Nikolaevna Chebotaryevskaya (1876 – 1921): writer, translator, wife of the poet Fyodor Kuzmich Sologub.

searching for her. I got it by chance. A stranger sent me flowers – it does happen to me sometimes – and the bouquet was wrapped in the newspaper carrying this notice." [. . .]

12 June '40

Yesterday I called Anna Andreevna to make more specific arrangements for today: she had promised to come. She said: "Come over to my place now, and we'll go to yours together . . ." It was already late, but, as ever, I obeyed.

She opened the door to me herself. She greeted me with the words: "I tricked you: I'm not going to your place today. I'm tired. You stay with me for a while."

She told me the bad news. First of all, according to Nadya R., F. had been summoned to see the Director in connection with the book. This displeased me greatly.[*]

"Boris Mikhaylovich[†] says," continued Anna Andreevna very seriously, "that the book is a major one, an important one."

(As if we wouldn't have known that without Boris Mikhaylovich!)

"Letters have already started pouring in. Today I received two: one a typical gushing woman's letter, the other – very nice – from Kruchyonykh. Read it."

I read it. To me the letter seemed not a bit nice, but very stupid and not interesting in any way.

Kruchyonykh writes that the poems "burnt through" him, and as proof he encloses "endings" to some of the poems which he had thought up himself – to "When a Man Is Dying" for example – the endings were extremely empty and flat. Could it be a joke? If it is a joke, it's not funny. His own poem dedicated to Anna Andreevna is also included: now she is no longer a "Lady of the Evening" but something else.

Seeing that this letter did not amuse or please me, Anna Andreevna

---

[*] Who F. is, and why "F.'s being summoned" was a bad omen for Akhmatova's book, I do not recall.

Nadya R. – Nadezhda Yanuarevna Rykova (b. 1901): literary critic, translator, specialist in French and English literature, at the time she was working as an editor at Goslitizdat.

[†] Boris Mikhaylovich – Eikhenbaum.

put it away in her handbag. And she recited to me the end of a poem: "Dusk falls and in the dark blue sky . . ."

"Now it is no longer a fragment, but a finished work, wouldn't you agree?" she asked. And we started to discuss whether it would be possible to include it in the Goslit edition, which had been delayed for so long. It depends on the proofs – if there is room on the same page. But above all – on the editor's wishes.

We started talking about *Anna Karenina* at the Moscow Art Theatre. Criticizing this play, I said that what appeals most to the public is the chance of seeing "the opulent life of high society".

"Historically, it's quite untrue," said Anna Andreevna. "The supposed opulence of high society never existed. High society people dressed very modestly: black gloves, a black collar buttoned to the throat . . . They never dressed according to fashion: a gap of at least five years was obligatory for them. If everybody wore enormous hats, then high society ladies would wear small, modest ones. I saw many of them at Tsarskoe: a luxurous landau with a coat of arms, the coachman in furs – and on the seat a lady, all in black, in mittens, with a sour expression on her face . . . Now that was an aristocratic lady . . . But the ones who dressed luxuriously according to the latest fashion, and walked around in gold shoes were the wives of famous lawyers, or else actresses or courtesans. Upper-class people behaved very calmly, freely, simply in society . . . But it is not the theatre which is at fault here: it is impossible to convey modesty and a kind of old-fashioned style on stage . . ."

Then she started talking about not liking *Anna Karenina* at all.

"Haven't I told you why? I don't like repeating myself."

I lied, saying no – and I don't regret it. This time Anna Andreevna explained her dislike in more detail, more fully and differently.

"The entire novel is based on a false physiological and psychological premise. While Anna lives with a middle-aged husband whom she does not love and whom she finds repulsive, she doesn't flirt with anyone, behaves modestly and morally. Whereas when she lives with a young, handsome one whom she loves – she flirts with every man around, holds his hands in a certain way, walks around almost naked . . . Tolstoy wanted to prove that a woman who leaves her lawful husband inevitably becomes a prostitute. And his attitude towards her is vile . . . Even after her death he describes her 'shamelessly naked' body – he has created some kind of morgue by the railway. And she loves Seryozha, but not the girl, because Seryozha is legitimate but the girl is not . . . I assure you . . . That is the point of view of the people around him: his aunt's and Sofya Andreevna's. And can you please tell me, why did she imagine that Vronsky had stopped loving her? Eventually he dies for her . . ."

"Eventually," I said. "Yes, eventually he does."

This time, I couldn't contain myself and started to argue with her. Vronsky really doesn't love her as before. I reminded Anna Andreevna of their meeting on the carriage platform: "Why are you going?" Anna asks Vronsky, who has suddenly appeared beside her. "To be where you are," replies Vronsky. And later, when she has already left her husband and son, and they are together, he is bored with her, seeks ways to amuse himself, and once stays out late at his club. Anna asks: "Why did you stay?" – "I wanted to stay so I stayed," replies Vronsky.

"You must agree," I said, "that between the first and the second dialogue something has changed in Vronsky's feelings, and fundamentally so. Love is always dependence ('I am going in order to be where you are'), but when it starts being a question of asserting your independence ('I wanted to stay so I stayed') – that's the end of love. And as for his dying later, that's because his conscience troubles him: it's no joke having driven the woman you loved under a train."

Anna Andreevna did not agree with me on anything.

"Rubbish," she said. "She did not have any grounds for thinking that he had stopped loving her. Or for doubting him. Love always manifests itself a hundred times a day. And this excessive suspicion of hers is not without purpose for Tolstoy: Anna thinks that Vronsky cannot love her because she herself knows in her heart that she is a prostitute . . . And please don't try to defend that rubbishy old man!"*

---

* In those years when A.A. and I spoke about *Anna Karenina* her point of view seemed interesting to me, but incorrect, invented . . . About two years later by chance I picked up one of the old Tolstoy volumes of *Literaturnoe nasledstvo*: a chapter was published there which Tolstoy subsequently removed from the final text. During one of Vronsky's absences, Anna, bored and angry, asks a Guards officer, who she knows is in love with her, to escort her to a flower show; in the semi-darkness of the carriage she behaves so provocatively that when they reach their destination and he opens the door for her – that gesture contains more contempt than courtesy.

Having read this chapter, I understood that in spite of Tolstoy's having deleted this page, A.A. had profoundly understood his intention.

I will return to this attitude of Akhmatova's to Tolstoy more than once in volume two of my *Journals* ("a demigod" is how she used to refer to him sometimes . . .).

Our conversation turned to Freud. I said that I didn't like and didn't believe him; the only thing that appeals to me in his teachings is the idea that early childhood plays a huge part in every person's life. The longer you live, the more clearly you see that.

"Yes, maybe so," Anna Andreevna agreed without enthusiasm. "But as far as the rest goes . . . all you see in these arguments and myths is the reflection of the stagnant, stale, provincial milieu in which he lived . . .

"I read a book by that banal Zweig about Leonardo da Vinci. In it he quotes Freud: 'Leonardo, of course, had an Oedipus complex and if he loved birds, that's because babies are brought by storks . . .' Just imagine, what nonsense: why does he assume that the custom of lying to children about storks existed even in those days?"

We agreed that she would come round tomorrow at four, and I left.

Translated from the Russian by Milena Michalski and Sylva Rubashova
Poetry translated by Peter Norman

The jokey nickname "a rubbishy old man" came about like this: soon after Tolstoy's death, B.V. Tomashevsky visited Yasnaya Polyana and tried to question the local peasants about him. In reply to all the questions about Lev Nikolaevich they persistently talked about Sofya Andreevna. When B.V. Tomashevsky still tried to steer the conversation on to Tolstoy, one of the peasants replied: "What is there to remember about him! He was a rubbishy old man."

9

To the New Year! To New Grief!
Here he dances, mischief-maker
Above the smoky Baltic Sea,
Bandy-legged, bent and wild.
And what fate has he in store
For those who have eluded torment?
They've gone to the fields to die.
O stars of heaven, shine on them!
Earthly bread they will not see
Nor the eyes of those they love.

JANUARY 1940

24

The Cellar of Memory

But it's arrant nonsense that I live in sadness
And that remembrance nags at me.
Not often am I guest of memory,
And it always leaves me confused.
When I go down with a lantern to the cellar,
It seems to me once more a landslip
Thunders down the narrow stairway after me.
The lantern smokes, I cannot now return,
But I know I go there to the enemy.
And I pray as if for mercy . . . But there
It's dark and quiet. My feast day has come to an end!
Thirty years have gone since bidding the ladies farewell,
That joker is dead from old age . . .
I have come too late. As if it matters!
I may not show myself anywhere,
But on the walls I touch the paintings
And by the fire I warm myself. Is that not a miracle?
Through this mould, these fumes, this dust
Two sparkling emeralds flashed,
And a cat mewed. Well, let's go home!

But where is my home and where my reason?

1940

28

The Last Toast

I drink to my ruined home,
To my cruel life I drink,
To the loneliness we shared
And to you I drink -
To the lie on the lips which betrayed me,
To the deathly cold of your eyes,
To the cruelty and crudeness on earth,
To the God who forsook me.

1934

29

Already madness with its wing
Has spread itself over half my soul
And gives me fiery wine to drink
And lures me into the black valley.

And I understood that I have
To cede victory to it, whilst
Hearkening to my own delirium
As if someone else were raving.

And it will not permit me
To take anything away of mine
(However much I may ask;
However much I do entreat it) –

Neither the petrified eyes of my son –
Which have turned to stone from suffering,
Nor the day, when the storm arose,
Nor the hour of prison meeting,

Nor the dear, cool touch of hands,
Nor the agitated linden shadows,
Nor the distant gentle murmur –
The final words of consolation.

4 MAY 1940
FONTANNY HOUSE

NOTES

1. *It turns out . . . the Acmeists had merit: . . . How kind, don't you think?*: Coming from the mouth of the critic Valery Pavlovich Druzin (1930–80), a member of LAPP, this review of the Acmeists really did sound tolerant, even courteous. In 1929, in the book *Stil sovremennoy literatury*, Druzin wrote: "inimical to the revolution [Acmeism] was devoid of alimentary juices". In 1936, in the newspaper *Literaturny Leningrad* he wrote: "The greatest masters of Soviet poetry . . . each one in his own way in his creative growth, in his struggle for realism had to *rid himself of the legacy of Acmeism and Futurism* . . . The Symbolist tradition of disdain for the authentic depiction of reality and the traditions of *Acmeist props*, each in their different ways *prevents one from seeing* the world . . . *How poor* Balmont's or *Akhmatova's* landscape is beside the richness of colour of Pushkin's and Nekrasov's (italics all mine. – *L. Ch.*).

Akhmatova's world appeared poor to Druzin: but, then again, later he would express a high regard for the richness of the visual world not only in Pushkin's and Nekrasov's works, but also in Vs. Kochetov's (1955, 1961, 1962), Firsov's (1966, 1972) and Gribachyov's (1971).

Druzin was always vilifying those whom, at that given moment, the authorities wanted vilified: it was no accident that after the 1946 Resolution, Druzin was the one appointed to "reinforce" the editorial staff of the journal *Zvezda* after the rout. During the anti-semitic campaign of 1948–53 Druzin published articles under such expressive titles as: "Expose the Remnants of Bourgeois Cosmopolitism and Aestheticism" (*Zvezda*, 1948, no. 2) and "Hangers-On of an Anti-Patriotic Group . . ." (*Sov. iskusstvo*, 12 February 1949).

Of course, in 1940 Akhmatova didn't yet know Druzin's article of the late '40s and all the subsequent ones, but his anti-literary and, in particular, his anti-Acmeist activities were already well known to her.

2. *Anatoly Andreevich Volkov* (1909–81): critic, literary historian, about whom the *Short Literary Encyclopaedia* [KLE] says that his works "are primarily of a compilatory nature". However, Volkov's works on the Acmeists could more accurately be described as pogrom-like. Here is the title of a 1933 article: "Acmeism and the Imperialist War" (*Znamya*, no. 7): the title of a 1935 book: *Poeziya russkogo imperializma.* [The Poetry of Russian Imperialism.]

I will cite a few lines from these works: ". . . Acmeism is not merely chronologically linked with the Imperialist war, but, in the full sense of the word, is its true ideological offspring. [. . .] The Stolypinist bloc, which consisted of Black-Hundred landlords and the bourgeoisie, strengthened the police-bureaucratic regime, set the conditions for the aggression of Russian Imperialism. it is in Gumilyov's works that the aggressive intentions of this bloc found their fullest expression [. . .] Akhmatova felt and expressed fully in her poetry the ideological 'creak' which accompanied the Stolypinist-bourgeois break-up of the gentry's feudal estates."

Inspired by the 1946 Resolution, A.Volkov published an article on "the theory and poetry of Acmeism" entitled "The Flag-Bearers of an Ideological Vacuum" (*Zvezda*, 1947, no.

1) and in the '50s in *Istoriya russkoy literatury* he called Akhmatova a petit-bourgeois poetess.

("Volkov, in a rather gentler way," wrote Akhmatova, "in some or other fourth edition, continues to rant on about a link between the Acmeists and the bourgeoisie ..." (See: "Anna Akhmatova. Autobiographical prose." *Literaturnoe obozrenie*, 1989, no. 5, p. 7. See *Journals*, vol. 2).

3. *Lotta* – Rakhil Moiseevna Khay (1906–49): specialist on seventeenth-century Dutch painting, who worked for the West European art section of the Hermitage. During the war R. M. Khay was the executive curator of the Hermitage collection which had been evacuated to Sverdlovsk. Her scholarly works were published mainly in *Trudy Otdela Zapadnoebvropeyskogo iskusstva* for 1940, 1941 and 1949.

4. *Nina* – Nina Antonovna Olshevskaya (1908–91): actress, director, close friend of Anna Andreevna's, wife of the writer V. E. Ardov. Olshevskaya and Akhmatova met in 1934 in Moscow at the Mandelstams'. For more on N. A. Olshevskaya see also *Journals*, vol. 2.

When she came to Moscow, more often than not, A. A. would stay – sometimes for weeks, sometimes even for months – "at the Ardovs' on Ordynka" (Ordynka, 17, flat 13), that is with Nina Antonovna's family.

5. ... *our dear Tanya*: that is Tatyana Yevseevna Gurevich (c. 1905–41), who, for several years, worked on the editorial staff of the journals *Chizh* and *Yozh*. During the rout of the Leningrad editorial staff she proclaimed at a meeting that she did not believe that the editors who had been arrested were saboteurs, and for that she was dismissed. Tatyana Yevseevna struggled a long time without any work: then the Writers' Publishing House gave her a job. She was killed in Autumn 1941: as a result of a direct hit by a high-explosive bomb on Gostinyy Dvor, where the publishing house was then situated.

6. *Tusya* – Tamara Grigorevna Gabbe (1903–60): member of the "Marshak editorial staff" which was routed in 1937: playwright and folklorist. Her children's plays, published as individual little books, brought her the highest acclaim: they were staged repeatedly in Moscow and other theatres across the country with great success: *Gorod masterov, ili Skazka o dvukh gorbunakh: Khrustalnyy bashmachok: Avdotya Ryazanochka.*

The most significant of her works on folklore – the book *Bly i nebyl. Sbornik russkikh skazòk, legend i pritch* – was published posthumously (1967): before that, but also posthumously, an anthology was published *Po dorogam skazki* (coauthored by A. Lyubarskaya, 1962): in Tamara Grigorevna's lifetime a number of translations and adaptations by her, of French popular tales, Perrault's fairy tales, Andersen's fairy tales, the Brothers Grimm and others, were published.

All her life, even after leaving the State Publishing House, she remained an editor; a mentor to writers. My book *Vlaboratorii redaktora* is dedicated to her with good reason.

Her main literary talent remained undisclosed: she was one of the most sensitive specialists on Russian poetry I ever met in my entire life.

For more about T. G. Gabbe see also *Journals* vol. 2.

7. The discussion concerns *Daniil Kharms* (1905–42): poet and prose writer who belonged to the *Oberiu* group. I call him "ours" because in the late '20s S. Ya. Marshak involved the *Oberiuty*, Kharms in particular, in writing books for children. In a few years Kharms had become one of the

most significant children's poets: in
spite of continual attacks by bureau-
cratic pedagogical critics, the
Leningrad branch of Gosizdat managed to publish a considerable number
of poems and stories by Kharms: *How
Papa Shot me a Pole-cat*; *Ivan Ivanych
Samovar*; *The Game*; *How Kolka Pan-
kin Flew to Brazil* . . . and others. He
was also permanently employed by the
journals *Yozh* and *Chizh*.

Kharms survived the rout of the
Leningrad editorial staff in 1937–38.
But during the war, in besieged
Leningrad, they "got" him all the
same, and he died in prison. After his
rehabilitation the Moscow publishing
house Detskiy Mir commissioned me
to compile a collection of his poems:
the collection was published in 1962
under the title *The Game*. My name
should have appeared on the title page
as compiler, but, due to carelessness,
the publishers omitted it.

ALEKSANDR KUSHNER

Lidiya Ginzburg

Speaking Directly About Life

In this essay, which will appear as the introduction to Lidiya Ginzburg's Behind the Lines: Notes, Memoirs, Narratives 1920–90, *Aleksandr Kushner describes the importance of Ginzburg to Russian literature and sets her work in the context of world literature.*

Lidiya Ginzburg (1902–90) the celebrated literary scholar and author of *The Lyric, Psychological Prose, The Literary Hero*, as well as a whole series of learned articles on Russian literature, kept a diary and wrote essays all her life. This material, however, perhaps the most significant part of her literary output, remained unknown to the reader for many years. Someone once said that in Russia you need to live long, in the sense that only longevity will enable you to see any change for the better in that country, and your most important works published. And in actual fact, it is only now, at the end of the eighties, that her essays have at length appeared, initially in journals, then in book form. *Behind the Lines* contains notes, memoirs and narratives.

Lidiya Ginzburg was born in Odessa, on the Black Sea littoral, in an averagely well-off intellectual family; as a young woman, she moved to post-revolutionary Petrograd/Petersburg and entered the History of Arts Institute. Her teachers were gifted philologists and men of letters like Yu. Tynyanov, V. Shklovsky, B. Eikhenbaum and other representatives of the celebrated formalist school of Russian criticism, who had, in 1916, founded OPOYAZ – the Society for the Study of Poetic Language. This movement, as distinct from academic eclecticism, sought to apply a new critical method, concentrating on the study of form as the primary feature of a literary work. It came under fierce critical attack, and at the beginning of the thirties was crushed by official Soviet literary theory – at the behest and with the direct intervention of the party.

Thus Lidiya Ginzburg and several of her friends and contemporaries, who made up the younger generation of the formalist school, found themselves victimized and persecuted at the very outset of their creative lives: talent turned out to be superfluous; their hopes of serious work in scholarship and literature collapsed. They were compelled to make do with chance earnings and move onto the margins of literary life; indeed, their own lives hung by a thread: the first two-week arrest came in 1933. There is a very brief note of the occurrence in the diary: "In February of 1933, Mandelstam came to Leningrad; there was an evening of his poems taking place. Anna Andr. invited Borya and myself to her place 'to Mandelstam'. As it happened, we both got arrested (soon to be released). A.A. said to Mandelstam: 'Here's the cheese, here's the sausage, but I'm sorry, the guests are in jail.'"

The fear of arrest remained with her for the rest of her life, especially in 1937. At the end of 1952, the threat of death in one of Beria's torture chambers came close: it was at this time that, parallel with the "doctors' plot", a case was being prepared against "Jewish sabotage in literary studies". Only the death of the leader prevented bloody violence from being done.

Over and above all this was the war of 1941–45, the siege of Leningrad, covered by the "Blockade Diary" in this volume, the struggle against cosmopolitanism, unleashed by the Stalin regime in 1947 to crush freedom of thought in the country once and for all . . .

It was only after 1956, the time of the Khrushchev "thaw", that literature began to return to a more or less normal existence, and Lidiya Ginzburg's critical articles and books started to appear. Finally, as the curtain came down on her life, the splendid essays, which she had written "for the desk-drawer" all her life, without hope of publication, also saw the light of day. She enjoyed a belated glory – a glory by now incapable of really warming her old age: "Besides, delayed success is always joyless," she states, "It's always too little. Because every rung is one which should have been left behind long ago." Her success was no doubt joyless for another reason: those whose opinion the author esteemed, or to whom she wanted to prove

something, those whose regard would have been flattering, had
died. Her teachers were no more: Tynyanov, Eikhenbaum, Shklovsky,
Zhirmunsky; nor were her old friends and acquaintances, her
great contemporaries: Akhmatova, Mayakovsky, Mandelstam,
Kuzmin, Pasternak; nor indeed those splendid writers of her own
age: Zabolotsky, Oleinikov, Shvarts among others.

I have listed many names which the reader will encounter in these
pages. Others which might have been mentioned include Korney
Chukovsky, Nadezhda Mandelstam, Osip and Lily Brik, Gukovsky,
Gofman, Punin . . . I cite this glittering array here so as to recall the
great flowering of Russian culture in the twentieth century, without
which our judgment on this century would be one-sided, incomplete,
lacking even a glimmer of hope.

Life was indeed terrible, but terror was not its sum totality; the
reader will be convinced of that from the very first pages of this book:
it was extraordinarily intense, filled to the brim with love, scholarly
and literary interests, encounters and friendships with gifted people,
a keen appraisal of current events coupled with a sedulous concern
with the achievements of western thought (the Russian intelligentsia
never lost touch with western culture and regarded themselves as a
constituent part of it).

It is the done thing nowadays to damn and revile the revolution
which turned the life of the country upside down. And indeed it was
a fateful and disastrous moment in Russian history; but at the same
time, its ideals and the hopes it inspired in succeeding generations of
the Russian intelligentsia tend to be lost sight of. In her essay "Generation at the Turning Point", Lidiya Ginzburg speaks of the great illu-
sions of the Russian intelligentsia, its readiness for self-sacrifice in the
name of justice and the happiness of the people: "A willingness to
sacrifice is a special emotion, like love, because it can only be directed
outwards."

Of her own generation, the author writes that they "were brought
up to feel shame for their advantages", and therefore "the young
people of 1917 barely noticed the transition from prosperity to absolute poverty . . . and paid it no attention. Our minds were occupied
with quite other matters. I don't even remember any conversations
among my elders about it either . . . who was going to complain
about history when it had put an end to evil?" Evil was understood
to mean the inequitable social structure, the poverty of the people,

their lack of rights, the illiteracy which cut them off from any kind of political, cultural or scientific knowledge and ideas.

The everlasting curse of Russia is impatience, the desire to cover in one leap the distance which it has taken western civilization several centuries to cover. The result was failure and collapse, an almost fatal trauma. But during the years of preparation, the moment of achievement and the first decade of inertial velocity, the revolutionary afflatus gave a colossal acceleration to Russian culture. This explains the abundance of remarkable names and achievements in painting, the theatrical arts, music, philosophy, science, and above all in literature.

This is why, encountering things in the book which are utterly inconceivable to the normal person (and really, how can a sentence like: "Not long ago, he had a book suppressed" be translated into English, or words like "purge" or "directive": how do we understand Akhmatova's calm story about writing *Anno Domini*, a book of exquisite lyrical poems "in a sanatorium, where we were five to a room"?), all the same, the English reader should not imagine that he has landed up among savages or on some alien planet. No, this land gave the world Pushkin, Tolstoy, Dostoevsky, Chekhov; and if Mandelstam, Pasternak, Akhmatova and Shostakovich were able to exist in such frightful conditions, then the reader should be tough enough mentally to overcome his incomprehension or even revulsion, and try to understand what he is being told. This book is not for the nervous. The English reader has travelled with Gulliver, he has experience of residence in upside-down worlds of fantasy.

Nor should it be thought that the tragic Russian experience has no relevance to the Westerner. It has. Because everything that is done on earth relates to each one of us, however distant we may be from the epicentre of historical disasters and suffering. Nor is it a matter of praise or blame whether we are born healthy or ailing, in the West or the East, in a prosperous country or a wretched one.

Sometimes it occurs to me to wonder how one or another of Tolstoy's characters would have behaved under Soviet circumstances: the frivolous and feeble Stiva Oblonsky, bon vivant and sybarite, would doubtless have been broken: the police investigators would easily have made informers – "knockers" – out of the likes of him; Konstantin Levin would in all probability have landed up in the MVD torture-chambers, or been shot or done to death in Stalin's camps.

The reader, wherever he is, can picture himself in our place, and ponder what might have happened to him here.

Life is tragic by definition. Man is doomed to illness and suffering even in the most propitious of epochs or the most prosperous of countries. Pushkin's fairy tale of the fisherman and the little fish ends up with the poverty-stricken peasant woman, who, with the aid of the little fish, had become a gentlewoman, even a queen, finds herself once more back where she started, standing by her broken trough. "Every life ends up by the broken trough," says Lidiya Ginzburg. Even the great Goethe was embittered at the close of his life by the rejection of his colour theories, the duke's neglect, the younger generation's interest in Schiller. This applies even more so to the ordinary individual. Everyone in old age finds themselves in the position of one sentenced to death, waiting in the condemned cell for the summons to execution.

The only difference in the case of someone living in twentieth-century Russia is that this expectation of death was all too familiar even in the days of his youth; it became an everyday matter, as it were.

What does "siege man" recall in the beleaguered city under bombardment? He recalls that in peacetime he used to listen to the sound of the ascending lift with a sinking heart; usually they came to arrest an individual at night. The bombardment was like waiting to be arrested. There are many such fearful similes in the book. The starvation from which hundreds of thousands of people perished in blockaded Leningrad also had its "masks", its "psychological disguises". In a dystrophic daze, a man asks himself the question: "And what was it so nauseously like? Something from the previous life?" And perceives that it resembles both an unhappy love affair and the endless humiliations to which Soviet existence has subjected him – one such humiliation being the vain hope of realizing one's potential in a totalitarian state. "That night, the instinct for trying to understand something and putting it into words held me back from despair. Thus does man utilize his hurts, griefs, even his emptiness, converting them into grist for the mill," notes the author in 1931 in connection with the latest failure in her literary career, poisoned and defiled by the party's interference in literature.

Ten years later, amid the ice and starvation of the blockade, the individual is saved from despair by that same creative effort.

What new thing did man learn about life, what was the value of this experience, the point of this unprecedented abasement and suffering? Or was what took place in Russia merely a play of chance, the mockery of history, a pointless absurdity?

Lidiya Ginzburg responds: "Talk of life being an empty and stupid joke is very much out of place, since contemporary life offers too many means for the ending of life, both personal and in the mass. For one thing let us recall the lives of our friends. Every one of them has had so many more opportunities of not existing than the opposite, that he cannot now speculate on the vanity of existence."

In the twentieth century, she considers, "the age-old argument about the vanity of life came to an end, to be replaced by another on how to survive and how to endure without losing one's human image."

The realization of human solidarity, "the sense of the human nexus" – that is the countervailing force against individualism and helps man to preserve his humanity in the cruellest of circumstances.

This is what makes art contemporary, art which rejects the classical antinomies of individualism. "What is productive is art that explains why a man lives (not from cowardice alone is it?), demonstrates or strives to demonstrate the ethical potential of life, even in the catastrophic circumstances of the twentieth century."

The intellectual heroes of the old literature have become obsolete, since "the new themes do not work with them". While they are busy resolving the "eternal" question of whether life is worth living – and then go on living, while denying life's meaning, the man who has passed through the tragic school of the twentieth century has other concerns – the daily struggle for his own personal dignity and the right to live. "One possible way out . . . lies in giving the floor to the intellectual author to speak directly about life."

That is precisely what takes place in Lidiya Ginzburg's books, in their rejection of conventional literary characters and the invented subjects of traditional prose. She does have precursors in world literature, above all the French seventeenth-century thinkers, Pascal, La Rochefoucauld and before them, Montaigne.

Any individual who has passed through the tragic experience of

Russia – well of course not everyone, but the thinking person, a great rarity in any society – knows the value of simple human pleasures: bread and the light-web of sunbeams, ice-floes "rustling under bridges", "grainy granite", a child's sledge stuck in a snowdrift, a Rembrandt canvas, "seaweed's false hair", "narrow, cunning wasps", a lake "standing sheer", "a black-voiced violin bow", French honey-suckle, a Chaplin film, "niggardly roses", an earthenware jug, a Grecian flute . . . He knows the value of these pleasures because he can picture only too well how speedily they can be taken from him for ever. Only those who have not had to pay a high price for "the gentle joy of living and breathing", as Mandelstam puts it in one of his poems, can allow themselves feelings of melancholy denial and lofty contempt. It was from his poems, written in the disastrous year of 1937, in anticipation of looming catastrophe, that I have borrowed this list of objects and phenomena. The more arbitrary the list, the more convincing it is, I do believe.

"Modern art," says Lidiya Ginzburg, "should speak of happiness and beauty. Because those two things are the reality of our experience and it is only this experience which gives a value to suffering and a dialectical meaning to negation . . . Misfortune feeding on itself will never show a tragic flame."

The value of the tragic experience described by the author of *Behind the Lines* lies precisely in this awareness of everyday existence, in the affirmation of the possibility of happiness. That is our answer to God, if he exists, our "prayer of gratitude". In this way, an unbeliever turns out to be religious in his attitude to life, his perception of its mysterious meaning – despite all the misfortunes that fall to his lot. People of a genuinely religious sensibility are distinguished by an inner spiritual gaiety, a joyous disposition in relation to other people and new experiences, a confidence in life. Such were, no doubt, the Russian "elders" from the Optina Pustyn, such was Francis of Assisi.

It is wonderful that even a non-religious person, believing in history "because I know how it can remake minds", and in the mighty power of social mechanisms, which are capable of making "the supreme act of selflessness (the redemptive sacrifice of Christ is its symbol) into a paragraph of military regulations, intended for general use", can, as a result of comprehending the tragic experience of life, take on the same chaste and joyous attitude. "It would be absurd to declare that one should avoid unhappy people, but one should certainly steer clear of people who are unhappy on principle . . . It means more to me to talk with a happy man than someone important . . . It's terrible how easy it is to be unhappy; happiness, on the other hand, like anything fine, is only attained with difficulty." I love those words of hers.

I made Lidiya Yakovlevna's acquaintance in 1959. I was still quite young then and what struck me as so attractive was not just her analytical mind and tenacious memory, but the ability of a person of her age to react so ardently to poetry, to respond so gratefully to the rustling and seething of the foliage outside the window, the scents of spring, the glimmering white night of Leningrad. And also of course, her wit (the notebooks are sprinkled with it), her trenchant views, her keen attention to psychological detail and minutiae. How could she, and those with whom she began her literary career, retain their interest in life to the very end? She could do it because life is not just a chronicle of suffering, but also a system of distractions from that, because it contains love, poetry, the beauties of nature and, incidentally, humour. Lidiya Yakovlevna knew what she was doing when she noted in her diary something which is not only very sad, but also very funny: "Akhmatova told Mandelstam once: 'Nobody complains, only you and Ovid complain.'"

I should not like the unknown reader of this book, gripped as he may be by the author's intellectual power, to picture her in his imagination as unsociable, or an ascetic recluse. Lidiya Ginzburg was surrounded by people till the very last day; she loved friendly talk around the table, where, towards supper time, a decanter of vodka would invariably make its appearance. Thus it was that she invited me and my wife to visit her on the evening of 9 July 1990. That day, several hours before we were due to arrive, she suffered a stroke.

It was wonderful, all the same, that she witnessed the downfall of the system, lived long enough to see the dizzying changes, receive the enthusiastic plaudits of new generations and read her published works (though there were one or two things she didn't release to the press while she lived: mistrust and fear fostered by the long years of enforced silence still held sway). *Behind the Lines*, like others of her works, tells more of the experience of life in twentieth-century Russia, than many multi-volume novels and poems. If one does live in Russia, truly one needs to live long.

Translated from the Russian by Alan Myers

YULIA PYATNITSKAYA

The Diary of a Bolshevik's Wife

Solzhenitsyn, Mandelstam, Ginzburg, Chukovskaya – the Russian dissidents who have testified against the monstrous evil of Stalin's dictatorship are numbered among the nation's great writers. But with Yulia Pyatnitskaya we have a new voice and a new perspective: she was a dedicated Communist and the wife of a high official, Osip Pyatnitsky, a member of the Central Committee. For Yulia, the State could do no wrong, and when her husband was arrested as "an enemy of the people" in July 1937 – he had criticized Stalin – she had initially to conclude that he must have been guilty of some treachery. The diary she kept from the time of her husband's arrest (which was soon followed by that of her elder son) is a document remarkable not only for its account of the material difficulties encountered by a woman who overnight has become a "non-person" in the community, but also for the constant self-questioning of a loyal Communist who remains convinced of the enduring wisdom of the State. The whole text of the diary has been published in France under the title Chronique d'une déraison— Moscow 1937–8.

21 March 1938

What has Pyatnitsa become, or rather, how do they regard him in the NKVD and the Party? Has he been ruined physically or has he suffered a more severe punishment? "He is alive and has not been destroyed – like an honest man, a Leninist revolutionary." What more frightful could they think up for him? Yagoda* and the other swine

---

* Chief of Secret Police, dismissed in 1937, arrested in 1938 and condemned to death in Moscow.

received much gentler treatment. My very best son* is being tormented in prison, and I have no idea what the future holds for him. Complete material ruin, as though we had been living at someone else's expense – it was probably the modest style of our life (we had a puritanical regime) . . . Pyatnitsky did not understand it, because he ate in the hospital . . . but I know it . . . That also probably was not to his advantage. I hardly touched the money he received as royalties. Only when I needed to buy some things for the children or myself. In recent years he had had it on his mind that he was getting older and would not have time to bring the children up to be adults. So I thought the royalties would be for the children if the worst came to the worst. When Mitskevich† died, for example, he left three children, but his wife remained a Party official and an operator (she could turn everything to account), but I don't have such talents. And in case Pyatnitsky were to die it would be . . . the same as it is now – that is, complete loneliness and the loss of the people whom Pyatnitsky cared for. If only we had a flat and they didn't make us suffer such indignities. The children would study like real Soviet children and I would be working like a real Soviet citizen, not one who had been rejected. No, of course I'm talking rubbish: in the event of the death of Pyatnitsky, Comrade Pyatnitsky – it would be hard for me to lose him (you see, I am very lonely), but it would be impossible to compare with the present situation. Sometimes it seems to me that it would have been easier to go through all this under Hitler – the execution of my husband, the imprisonment of my son, the ransacking of my flat (if it were possible to imagine a ransacking of such a kind and degree anywhere else), and finally my unemployment. There I could have been treated to all this by the enemy, while here . . . I am firmly convinced that every one of the members of the Pyatnitsky family, beginning with Pyatnitsky himself and ending with Vova,‡ would without hesitation give his life for the Soviet regime yet, because of some circumstances or somebody's will, we have been driven off into the herd of stupid, loathsome enemies. Well, how is one to take it, how can one reconcile oneself to it, how can one extract

* Igor, her eldest.
† Member of executive committee of Komintern. Died in 1935 and posthumously accused of being a Trotskyite. His wife was arrested.
‡ Volodya, her younger son, still at school.

oneself from this situation honourably? I honestly beg the NKVD
for sympathy and help; I ask for a hard life for myself, but it would
be at least a life, but instead of that I have been thrown, like a kitten
no one wants, into a raging, angry river . . . Let her swim for it. But
I cannot accept such a struggle for existence, a monstrous struggle
for a Soviet person, because it is not a matter of indifference to me
who I am in society – I am not trusted, no one expects anything good
from me. And I can't live like that, that is what I feel every day. There
is no answer and I must perish . . . But my reason tells me that this
is an unworthy decision for a person. So I go on, running round in
circles with all these gloomy thoughts. I've gone on until I have again
ruined my eyes.

So the whole of my physical surroundings contributes to my present
situation: the table at which I am writing is covered with oil-cloth
and ink-stains, a French dictionary that I've just bought for Vova, his
exercise books, a few other books, not one of which I need or care
about; a darning machine, an old lamp (mine was taken), and on the
lamp, in the absence of a shade, hangs my favourite blue scarf with
snowflakes on it. It was thrown aside and wearing out. Not once have
I wanted to mend it, and now it's in rags. All that is on the table . . .
There are a lot of moths around that are seriously damaging our
last things; mothballs don't have any effect; the moths have already
managed to get at my costume, which I haven't worn once since the
spring – I go around all the time in the old tattered working clothes
that I was going to throw out but that now suit me very well. I wear
my only sand-coloured warm overcoat, and my hair no longer wants
to adorn my head – it prefers to end its days in the rubbish bin: every
morning a whole comb-full falls out, and my comb has broken in half
though it was always so white and strong as if made from ivory. And
the heels of my shoes are worn down, and the wardrobe with the
door hanging loose (the workmen who moved our things would not
have it otherwise), and in the wardrobe with its broken locks that
won't shut, and in the suitcases, old linen in need of repair. The new
things were in Pyatnitsky's study (in his wardrobe) and they were
confiscated. And the clothes-line strung from the window to Lyuba's
wall. In the evening I hang a blanket on it to prevent the light shining
in our eyes (which makes it difficult to sleep) . . . The mice scratch
around in the kitchen – at night nobody disturbs them, and even the
door squeaks, because it doesn't close properly and the wind rattles

it because it is placed immediately opposite the front door. Every time one of the steam hammers, or even several hammers, strikes a blow it seems to sigh (the Palace of the Soviets building site), but that no longer affects my room. Then there's the door at the entrance to No. 1, which keeps banging whenever one of the watchmen enters; our room is immediately above it – third floor, and because of that banging it is often impossible not only to sleep but even to lie down in peace.

They have built the new bridge and opened it, and I have taken no part at all in it – I have been unemployed now for nine months.

22 March 1938

I spent four hours waiting at room No. 1. The Military Prosecutor was a new man, not dark and severe but a cheerful fair-haired man, quite attentive. It seemed to me as though he had something unpleasant to tell me about Igor. I will know this on 27 March. Apart from my enquiry about Igor, I told him about my mood and my thoughts because of which I ought to be isolated from society. I told him that I had isolated myself all that time – nine months already – but that it would be expedient to remove me quite officially. He heard me out and gave me an appointment for 27 March. While I was telling him my story, with his permission or at his request, a woman entered the room. He said: "She's in charge of the queue" when I showed my surprise. She stood behind me sideways to the desk. Perhaps she wasn't in charge of the queue but just an employee or a secretary. She was among the public. But I have no intention whatsoever of concealing anything from the NKVD.

At half-past eleven at night I walked round the Kremlin and derived pleasure from the walk, as I always do at the sight of the towers, the walls, the square and the walls near the Mausoleum. I watched the changing of the guard at Lenin's tomb. What a remarkable ritual it is, and how wonderful are the Red Army men. Vova is always saying: "The moral strength of our Red Army . . ." Everything is on the whole so familiar and so beloved, but I am alien and unwanted. But today I don't have to suffer for ever. That's the way it's got to be: no point in being cowardly, I shall die and that will be that. Vova was not well today and didn't eat his supper. But I did nothing in the home.

26 March 1938

I spent three and a half hours in the library. Looked through *Engineering* for March. Every day I live through makes me more out of date. New machines are being produced: new lathes, agricultural machines, machines for the construction of the Moscow underground railway, bridge-building machines, and so forth. Production has been reorganized at . . . Workers are inventing things: Comrade Dorofeyev at the ball-bearing plant received a bonus for a device to attach to a lathe to avoid accidents. Engineers are approaching questions of organization and of the technology of instrumentation in a new way. In general life is certainly moving ahead in spite of some "spokes in the wheel". There's a marvellous palace of culture for the ZIS factory. I was really envious – why am I not working in their collective? After all, I had every chance of working there, and I love the car and have already studied it in detail. Everything is so interesting, but they threw me out. Tomorrow I shall learn Igor's fate. I still don't know whether I shall remain alive. The floods have already begun. But how stupid to die when your mind can still work, when there are still people close to your heart, and when you want to know how our affairs turn out later. Perhaps they have already succeeded in postponing war; anyway, they are afraid of us; but the English have already come to terms with Hitler. I can understand that. I didn't read the newspaper yesterday.

Translated from the Russian by David Floyd

GEORGE MacDONALD FRASER

Battle: Recollections of the Burma Campaign

In the spring of 1945 the British and Indian XIVth Army launched the last major campaign of the Second World War against the Japanese armies occupying Burma. A vital stroke in the campaign was the capture by General Cowan's 17th Indian Division of the town of Meiktila, a strongpoint behind the enemy lines, and its subsequent defence against the surrounding Japanese forces. Among the outnumbered garrison was Nine Section, a typical group of ten British infantrymen of whom the author was the youngest, a nineteen-year-old Scot among Cumbrian veterans. His first experience of combat came when his battalion, patrolling to a village south of the town, fought a night action against an enemy column, and obtained intelligence of an impending Japanese counter-attack on Meiktila itself. This extract from his account of the campaign, Quartered Safe out Here, *describes what followed.*

A few miles south of Meiktila there was, and probably still is, a wood containing a little temple. The trees were very tall and close together on its outskirts, forming a thick protective screen, but within the wood they were more widely spaced, with dim clearings under the high spreading branches. How wide the wood was I never discovered, but it can't have been more than fifty or sixty yards in depth, and beyond there was open ground stretching to another belt of trees. It must have been quite a pretty place, with those shaded clearings and the tall trunks reaching up to the high foliage through which the light filtered. I sometimes wonder what it looks like now.

That wood and a nearby village were among the places used by the

Japanese as concentration points for their counter-attack on Meiktila, and I believe our intelligence pin-pointed it as a result of a chance discovery made following the night action I've just described. Among the Japanese killed by our dawn patrols outside the wire was an officer – I heard he had taken cover in a culvert – and on his body were found plans listing the Jap concentration points: one of them was the temple wood, and our divisional command marked it for urgent attention.

Nine Section, of course, was not aware of this. Following the night action the whole battalion withdrew to Meiktila, after an excursion which had lasted several days, accounted for more than a hundred Japanese, and more importantly had helped to embarrass his build-up. Similar actions had been fought all round Meiktila at this time – the official history likens Cowan to a boxer using straight lefts to prevent his opponent getting close in, and it's a good simile: Jap was never given time to settle for a major assault.

Nine Section's impression – and it is still mine – is that Jap had taken far worse than he gave, and I am surprised by the official history's statement that our battalion took 141 casualties in two days during our foray from Meiktila. The regimental histories don't confirm the figure, and I wonder if the official version isn't referring to a longer period. But not for me to argue; I can only say that if the battalion did take that kind of punishment, we weren't aware of it.

We came back to Meiktila and spent the next week or so in our pits, watching the wire, brewing up, and waiting, and in that time other units of 17th Div threw two of Cowan's straight lefts at the little temple wood and its adjacent village. According to the official history the first attack ended in failure, with three tanks brewed up, and Jap following our withdrawal uncomfortably closely; the second attempt was also repulsed, and two more tanks were lost. Then it was our turn.

We rode out on the Shermans of Probyn's Horse on a fine sunny morning, knowing that something was in the wind, for three men had been added to the section. One was a lance-corporal (for some reason we had been short of a section second-in-command until now), another a rotund South Cumbrian called Wattie, and the third was reputed to be a recaptured deserter, and looked it. So Corporal Little had been told, anyway; he and I were riding on the front of the tank, either side of the gun with our backs to the turret, flanked by Forster and the Duke, and with Grandarse, who needed room, reclining on the sloping front at our feet and delivering judgement:

"Ah doan't see the point o' desertion, mesel'. Not oot 'ere, anyways. Ah mean, in Blighty a feller can stay on the roon, livin' in the railway Naafis an' Toc H canteens, but w'eer the 'ell ye gan to ga in India – unless yer Jock theer, an' look like a bloody wog–"

"Much obliged."

"No offence, lad, but ye doan't 'alf ga broon. Admit it, noo. Put a *dhoti* on ye, an' ye could git a job dishin' oot egg banjoes at Wazir Ali's.* Any roads, w'at Ah'm sayin' is that if ye desert oot 'ere – Ah mean, in India; ye'd 'ev to be doolally† to booger off in Boorma – the ridcaps is bound to cotch thee, an' court-martial gi'es thee the choice o' five years in Trimulghari or Paint Joongle, or coomin' oop t'road to get tha bollicks shot off. It's a moog's game."

"You don't have to be a deserter to be sent up the road and have your bollocks shot off," said the Duke. "Or hadn't you noticed?"

"Mind you," continued Grandarse, "there's this to be said for bein' a deserter – they say that if ye ask t'ga oop the road, an' ye gits kilt or wounded, the Army reckons ye've made amends, like, an' scroobs yer record. Ah doan't think that's bloody fair – they gid me sivven days in close tack for ga'in' absent in Blighty once, an' if Ah git kilt, it'll still be on me crime-sheet."

"That's 'cos ye didn't try 'ard enoof," said Little. "Ye've got to commit a big crime to git a big remission."

"Why did you go absent, Grandarse?" I asked.

"Aw, there was this tart in Silloth. An' Ah was yoong an' daft." He sighed. "She wasn't woorth it. Ah was grossly deceived. Aye, thing's 'as coom tae siccan a pass, thoo can't tell mistress f'ae servant lass. She wore troosers, an' a'. Bloody foony. Ah fancied 'er in troosers."

"Yer a bloody pervert, you are," said Forster.

"Oh, aye, lissen to Dr Freud!"

"Oo's Doctor Freud?"

"A fookin' professor."

"I don't suppose that's what they called him in Vienna," said the Duke, "but it's a not inaccurate description."

---

* The military canteens run by the contractor Wazir Ali were famous throughout India; probably the best-remembered was at Deolali. An egg banjo is a fried egg between two slices of bread.
† mad

"Anyways," said Grandarse with finality, "if Ah was ivver daft enoof to desert, an' got done for it, Ah'd sooner tek the chance of a bullet in me bum than spend five year fillin' an' emptyin' wells in't glass'oose! So theer!"

Someone said unkindly that anybody shooting Grandarse could hardly fail to hit him in the bum, and Grandarse retorted that at least he wadn't git 'is brains blew oot if they did, not like soom clivver boogers; they were having to shout to make themselves heard above the rattle of the tracks as the Shermans rumbled over the sunlit paddy, and the swirling dust was becoming a nuisance, so I withdrew from the conversation to read for the third or fourth time the letter that had arrived from home last night.

My parents knew I was in Burma, and that (with the possible exception of air crew) it was generally believed to be the worst ticket you could draw in the lottery of active service. Those months must have been the longest of their lives; whatever anxieties the soldier may experience in the field can be nothing to the torment of those at home. I don't know how parents and wives stand it. Perhaps family experience is a help: every generation of my people, as far back as we knew, had sent somebody to war, and my grandmother's comment on Chamberlain's speech on September 3, 1939, had been simply: "Well, the men will be going away again." Her uncle had served in the Crimea, her brother had died in the Second Afghan, two of my aunts had lost sweethearts in the Great War, my father had been wounded in East Africa, and two uncles had been in the trenches; probably it was a not untypical record for a British family over a century, but whether it made my absence easier or harder to bear, who knows?

One thing was certain: they were not going to distress me by letting a hint of worry show in their letters, which were full of news and trivia and comedy. (I hope mine were, too; I was guiltily aware of being a poor correspondent who wrote briefly and usually when I wanted something; my last had contained a request for cigarettes.) My father wrote that they were on their way, and described how my aunts, those genteel maiden ladies, had exclaimed in dismay on learning that I had started *smoking,* at which my grandmother, a lively nonagenarian, had demanded to know if they would deny the solace of tobacco to a man who was standing at Armageddon; she had added mischievously that there were worse temptations than cigarettes for a young soldier in the Orient, and she didn't mean drink, either. This had opened up such visions of their nephew's possible depravity that they couldn't sleep, and in the waking small hours my elder aunt had been sure she'd heard the rattles which meant that the German bombers were dropping poison gas; she had ventured out, in dressing-gown, slippers, and gas-mask, with her handkerchief steeped in eau-de-cologne, and the A.R.P. wardens had found her shining her torch on the local pillar-box to see if it had changed colour.* And so on . . . my grandmother had taken to referring to two of the Nazi leaders as "Ribbonstrip" and "Gorbals"; my father had been to see *A Night at the Opera* and wished that *he* could swing on trapezes like the Marx Brothers; there had been unpleasant scenes, with allegations of fixing and corruption, at the church jumble sale, because the minister's daughter had won the prize doll by correctly guessing its name ("Wellwoodina"!); my father and mother, respectively Liberal and Conservative, were thinking of voting Labour at the forthcoming election because the candidate was one of my father's patients and an old friend – it was a picture of that happy, funny, eccentric family of mine and their little world, so far and yet so near.

Corporal Little asked me what I was grinning about, and Forster opined that it was a loov-letter frae soom bint, an' yer wastin' yer time, Jock, she'll be gittin' shagged by soom Yank pilot, and Grandarse said, leave the lad alone, he'll larn for hissel'. Oh, yes, you got the cream of intellectual discourse in Nine Section.

The tanks rumbled to a halt not far from a low bund,† and about fifty yards beyond it lay the temple wood, dense and silent in the sunlight. We debussed, and Long John and Gale and Sergeant Hutton passed among us, checking that all was as it should be. There were three companies of the battalion spread across the paddy facing the wood, with the Shermans at intervals, but we were aware only of the sections immediately on either side. And there we waited, the section in a rough line, settling our equipment, taking a last swig from the chaggles,‡ charging our magazines, and finally, at a word from Little, fixing bayonets.

---

* The tops of pillar-boxes were treated with a special paint which reacted in the presence of poison gas.
† embankment
‡ canvas water-bags

So it was going to be a pukka attack – until that moment I, for one, had not been sure what the object of the operation was; the strength of our force, the presence of the tanks, had suggested something big, and now it was confirmed. The screen of trees beyond the little bund looked peaceful enough, but Jap would be there, well dug in; he would be watching us at this moment.

There are few sounds as menacing as a bayonet being fixed. Mine was the old sword type with the locking ring clicking into place with the smoothness of good Edwardian machinery; Grandarse, on my immediate right, was nipping his fingers with one of the new pig-stickers, and cursing, his face crimson in the heat; on my left Parker was drawing his kukri and re-sheathing it, and automatically I reached back to make sure mine was loose in its sheath, and that my knife-hilt was handy in my small pack. Suddenly it seemed very hot indeed, with hardly a breath of wind; just behind us the Sherman's engine coughed and roared; a bearded and turbanned head peered out of the turret and shouted in Hindustani to someone inside and the roaring died to a murmur.

Little came towards me, two grenades in his hands. "Gi'es yer Bren magazines, Jock, an' tek these; they're Stan's." Stanley was number two to Steele, the Bren gunner, and Little was seeing to it that he had plenty of spares.

"Are we going in, corp?"

"Aye, in a bit. When the Yanks 'ev doon their stoof."

He nodded past me, and as I tested the grenade pins and put them in my pouch I turned to look; I had been aware of a far-off murmur, growing louder; from behind us three distant dots in the sky were coming closer – Tomahawk fighters in camouflage paint which covered the famous shark's jaws with which the Flying Tigers decorated their engine cowlings. They came roaring in at tree-top level over us and zoomed up in a climb as they passed above the wood, banking as they soared up into the blue.

"Advance to the bund!" shouted Hutton. "Take cover – an' keep yer 'eids doon!"

We moved forward and lay against the low bank, and from overhead came the thundering whine as the first Tomahawk hurtled down in a steep dive; while it was still behind us two small dark objects detached from it, falling at a steep angle to land on the edge of the wood with a crashing double explosion and sheets of orange flame.

Smoke and dust billowed up, obscuring the trees, and then the second Tomahawk came, repeating the performance, with the third on its heels. The ground shook as they pounded the wood, which was now entirely hidden by a great cloud; in came the Tomahawks again, unloading their bombs, and this time three of them failed to explode. The aircraft banked away in a great arc, and soon the whine of their engines died away; that was the air strike over, and now it was the Shermans' turn.

As the engines roared, Grandarse, lying on the bank two yards away, looked along at me.

"Loocky boogers, them Yank pilots. They'll be sittin' in the Casanova in Cal the neet, suppin' cocktails. Warra life, eh?"

Parker must have heard him, for he laughed on my other side and turned on his back, looking up at the sky, and hummed:

I'd like to be a wop a.g.*
I'd fly all over Germanee
And blow the Huns to buggeree
It's foolish but it's fun!

"Aw reet, pipe doon!" said Hutton, but he was grinning; it must have been a new one to him. But now the Sherman was clanking forward, through a gap in the bund; the great mass of dust-coloured steel rolled on a few yards, and stopped. Its hatch was closed, but the big gun was traversing from side to side, and lowering to the point-blank position. Suddenly it crashed, the tank shook, and the shell burst with an almighty roar in the depths of the wood. Up and down the line the other tanks began blazing away, and then the machine-guns started chattering, and the whole screen of trees was shaking as though in a gale; through the slowly-dispersing haze left by the Tomahawks' bombs we could see the foliage being ripped to shreds. All along the bank men were craning as they watched; I stole a glance behind and saw Hutton was on his feet; farther along Long John was checking his watch; Gale, rifle in hand, his bush-hat at a rakish angle, was talking to his runner. Abruptly the firing stopped.

"On yer feet!" roared Hutton, and as we stood up: "Wait for it!"

This was it, then, the moment you read about in books and see in

---

* wireless operator/air gunner

films – and by God it was happening to me. Ahead the wood still seemed to be sending back the echo of the cannonade, but now the foliage was steady again, and the dust had settled. There was a long moment's stillness, broken only by the growl of the Sherman, holding its ground twenty yards ahead, not more than thirty from the edge of the wood. A branch, hanging by a thread after the bullet-hail, suddenly fell, sending up a little swirl of dust. I glanced right: Grandarse had one foot on the bank, leaning forward; beyond him were two of the new men, the lance-jack and the reputed deserter. Parker, on my left, had his rifle at the port, and beyond him Steele was adjusting his Bren sling, the big l.m.g. resting on his hip; Stanley was removing his hat and replacing it firmly. I found I was hissing through my teeth, and recognised it as "Bonnie Dundee", but I hadn't time to digest this peculiar reaction when Little was walking forward between Parker and Steele, crossing the bank, and Hutton was shouting again:

"Ad-vance! Keep yer distance, noo! Advance!"

Up the bank and over, the shuffle of boots in the morning quiet, the slight creak and rustle of equipment, the dark green figures on either side moving in a slow, steady advance; the stationary tank, its tracks clogged with earth and coarse grass, ten yards to my right front, the slight figure of Little, rifle at the trail, his head obscured by the tilted bush-hat, to my left and out in front – and there was a faint crack, like a cap-pistol, from the wood, and Little gave a sharp cough, spun half-round, and went down like an empty sack.

Hitting the deck, face down on the scrubby earth, automatically whipping rifle to shoulder in the lying position, puffs of dust leaping from the ground to my left, Parker rolling over, yelling, the left breast of his bush-shirt blood-stained; a scream from the right, a blinding cloud of dust and gravel striking me in the face, the rattle of machine-gun fire from the wood and the irregular cracks of rifle-fire. Someone was bawling "Covering fire!", and I was shooting obediently into the wood at ground level, aware that on my right Grandarse was doing the same, and that Parker was crawling rapidly back to the bank – one glance I took, and he was dripping blood as he scrambled to the bank and over. Caught in the bloody open, flat-footed – Jesus! beyond Grandarse the lance-jack was trying to pull himself clear, with his leg trailing, and the deserter was absolutely sitting up! (I still don't know why.) I pumped off another couple of shots, realised the futility of it, looked left, and Steele had the Bren at his shoulder, left hand on the stock, right hand reaching forward for the magazine. There was a sharp clang, a silver streak appeared on the side of the magazine, and Steele reared back, his face contorted, scrambling up on to his knees. Blood was streaming down his arm – the bullet had gone through hand and shoulder. He yelled something and – this I shall never forget – actually shook his uninjured fist at the wood before turning to run for the shelter of the bund.

And there was the Bren gun, the section's most precious possession, lying unattended.

I've asked myself a thousand times: did I hesitate? God only knows, and perhaps some day He'll tell me, for I genuinely am not sure. Probably I wanted to, and this is what has made me wonder; that, and the knowledge that with four men hit all around me in as many seconds, and the shots kicking up the dirt in what seemed to be your proverbial hail of lead, that Bren was about as untempting an article as I've ever seen. And then I was starting to crawl towards it, and Hutton, flat on the ground behind me, was yelling and signalling to Stanley, the Bren's number two, and Stanley, who had been face down just beyond it all the time, was grabbing its handle and hauling it away.

"Jock!" It was Hutton. "Coover 'im!"

For what it was worth I started to fire into the wood, and Stanley and Bren rolled over the bank and out of sight. Behind me Hutton spoke, more quietly now.

"Awreet, haud tha fire! Heid doon!"

I put my head flat on the butt, reaching behind me for another clip from my bandolier, moving cautiously in the belief that any obvious movement was liable to attract those goddamned Jap snipers. To my right Grandarse was lying as close to Mother Earth as his great belly would let him; he looked towards me and blew out his cheeks. There was no one on my left, just two patches of blood where Steele and Parker had been hit. Christ, I thought, are Grandarse and I the only ones left? Intermittent cracks were sounding in the wood, but they didn't seem to be coming this way; the Sherman's l.m.g. was rattling away, and in behind it an Indian soldier (don't ask me where he had come from) was leaning against the metal, clutching his thigh; his trouser leg was sodden with blood.

"Grandarse!" Hutton again. "When Ah say *jao*,* git oot of it! Jock
– five roonds rapid, fire!"

I blasted away, and through the din heard Hutton's "*Jao!*" and the
sound of a great body taking flight. "Reet, Jock–*jao!*" Grandarse was
still short of the bank when I went over it like a bird.

The first thing I saw was Steele, a yard away. He was white as
paint, his eyes shut, but his jaw was working up and down. An orderly
had torn away his shirt, and his shoulder and chest were a mass of
blood; the orderly was padding the shoulder wound while another
wrapped a gauze dressing round his hand. Beyond him Parker was
propped up against the bank, stripped to the waist, holding a field
dressing to his shoulder; Gale was bending over him, then turning
away to shout. A jeep came bouncing up to the bank, and Gale helped
Parker to climb in; the orderlies were lifting Steele on to a stretcher,
preparing to load him in also. I didn't see them, but the lance-corporal
and the alleged deserter had both been hit. Farther along the bank
rifles and Brens were firing, the Sherman guns were crashing again.
I realised that I was sitting idle, breathing hard, and that one knee
was painful where I had grazed it in hitting the deck. I would guess
that perhaps three minutes had passed since we started to advance. I
jerked open my bolt, ejecting a spent case, and saw that my magazine
was empty. While I was charging it, a tall lance-corporal whose face,
in my memory, is that of the late Lyndon Johnson, came running in
a crouch to confer with Hutton. They peered over the bank, and
Hutton signalled to me.

"When Kang ga's ower the top, you give 'im cooverin' fire as 'ard
as ye can! Stanley, you give automatic fire! Reet, Jack – on ye go,
son!"

Kang took a run at the bank and went over, dodging from side to
side as he ran towards the still, green figure of Corporal Little, face-
down on the earth. Kang dived down beside him, and even as I was
firing I could see that he was speaking; I reloaded, and began firing
again as he came ziz-zagging back towards us. Halfway he stumbled,
Hutton swore, and then Kang came tumbling over the bank in a
shower of dust, gasping and clutching his forearm; blood was running
between his fingers. He shook his head.

* go!

"*Bus,*"* was all he said, and Hutton groaned deep in his throat.

Two more jeeps were pulling up, scattering the earth, and the wounded were being helped into them. The one carrying Parker and Steele was reversing with a rasp of tyres, and Parker, his dressing in place, actually grinned and waved with his sound arm. All along the bank men were lying, waiting; I think I remember Long John on one knee, talking to Gale, and pointing off to the left. The firing along our front had died away to an occasional shot or Bren burst; the tank firing had stopped, and the wood itself was silent. They had stopped us almost before we had started, and now they would be reloading in their pits and bunkers, waiting for us to try again.

I remembered the wounded Indian, and took a cautious look over the bank. He was standing up now, talking to the bearded Indian, who was presumably the tank commander, and was looking out of his hatch – something which, in his position, I'd not have done for a pension. I had the impression, from their gestures, that the wounded man wanted to get into the tank, and was being denied. Grandarse rolled up beside me.

"Tich 'as 'ed it! Fook me!" His face was purple, running sweat. "That shows ye w'at air strikes an' tanks is woorth! Fookin' 'ell!"

"Will we go in again?"

"We'll fookin' 'ev to! Not by the front fookin' door, tho'! 'Ey, w'at the 'ell's ga'n on? That booger's 'ed it, an' a'!"

He was peering over the bank at the Sherman. The hatch was down again, and the wounded sepoy was dragging himself in behind the tank, feebly, a foot at a time. He rolled over on his back, his whole trouser leg was black with blood to the thigh, and then he was dead – you could tell from the way the body seemed to subside, as though something had been let out of it.

"Awoy!" said Grandarse, and scrambled to his feet. Hutton was waving to us, and we doubled towards him, crouching to keep under cover of the bank. The rest of the section, what was left of it, was there: Stanley with the Bren, Nixon, Wedge, the Duke, and other men whom I didn't know – this presumably was Nine Section reconstituted; in less than a minute we'd lost over a third of our original number.

* finished

Then Gale was leading the way to the left, along the bank which must have curved in towards the wood, for presently we were on the edge of the trees, taking up firing positions. I have to say that I am not sure how we got there; it is another of those hiatuses in memory when nothing much happened to compare with the minute of frenzied violence which had followed our advance over the bank, or with what was to follow when we got into the wood. That day's battle, for me, was in two distinct parts, both of them vivid in my mind, but the connecting period is hazy. No doubt my mind was too full of what had happened to notice; I don't know how long a time elapsed in making that leftward movement, or how far we came from our original position on the bank, or what units of the company were on either side, or behind. Fighting was going on elsewhere – a young corporal was winning the M.M. clearing bunkers single-handed at about this time – and the interval may have been five minutes or thirty. Battle concentrates your attention on your own immediate front, and all I was aware of, now, was the fringe of trees in which we lay, and the shadowy interior beyond. The snipers who had cut down Parker and Steele and Little and the others must be in the wood ahead and to the right.

Stanley, lying next to me, touched me on the shoulder. Beyond him Gale was on his feet, motioning the section forward and stepping ahead into the wood; someone muttered something about bunkers. Stanley and I looked at each other; what he saw, God knows, but what I saw was his sweating face with the lips drawn back from the teeth. He adjusted the Bren sling; I waited until he was ready and we rose together and moved warily through the fringe of trees. There was undergrowth to our front, so I moved to the right with Stanley at my left elbow.

It was dim after the glare of the open country, but through the trees immediately to our right front I could make out a clearing. What I couldn't see was any sign of a bunker, but they must be in there somewhere, so I took a nervous glance to see that Stanley was still there, and moved on slowly through the trees, safety catch off, finger just touching the trigger. There was no one to my right, and the section was now out of eyeshot to my left; for a moment Stanley and I might have been alone in the wood, but I knew bloody well we weren't; the one comfort was that its other inhabitants hadn't seen us yet. I nerved myself to go on walking, as softly as could be, scanning the clump of bushes ahead, the tree trunks on either side, and the clearing beyond. There wasn't a sound, or a sign of a Jap, and if firing was taking place farther off, I wasn't aware of it. A few more steps brought me to the bushes, and I knelt down, listening.

The simple truth about war is that if you are on the attack, you can't do a damned thing until you find your enemy, and the only way to do that is to push on, at whatever speed seems prudent, until you see or hear him, or he makes his presence known by letting fly at you – as witness our first advance over the bank. Now it was the same thing over again, the difference being that the left flanking movement had brought us inside his position, and it was a question of who saw whom first and shot the straighter.

Life closes in; I had no idea of what was happening elsewhere, no thought or use of the senses to spare for anything but what I saw as I knelt behind the bushes – across the clearing, maybe ten yards away, was the bunker. It was a big one, three-man at least, a mound of hard red earth about four feet high, and probably the same depth underneath. There was a wide firing-slit at ground level, but what lay behind the slit was darkness. No movement, and nothing in the trees beyond the bunker.

I looked at Stanley, a yard behind me, his Bren at the ready, and then I was going like a bat out of hell for a palm on the other side of the clearing. There was a crack from the firing-slit, but it was threepence (or three yen) wasted, and as I fetched up at the tree, its trunk between me and the bunker, Stanley ran forward, firing from the hip at the firing-slit. Dust flew from the bunker as the Bren burst hit it – and then the bloody gun jammed, Stanley yelled and tugged at the magazine, I thought I saw movement inside the firing slit, and as Stanley jumped aside I found myself running forward, firing into the slit – three shots, I think, and I believe there was a return shot, and then I was diving down beside the bunker wall, about a yard to the side of the firing-slit, fumbling for a grenade.

I was facing back the way we'd come, and there were dark bush-hatted figures running through the trees, and the wood was suddenly alive with small-arms fire, rifle and automatic. I yanked out the grenade pin, let the plunger go, forced myself to count one-thousand-two-thousand and stretched sideways, back flat on the bunker, to whip the bomb through the firing-slit. One thousand-two-thousand-three – an ear-ringing crump, and I was snatching for a second grenade when

Gale came running past, gesturing, and I followed him round the
bunker side. There was the bunker entrance, a low narrow doorway,
and Gale had a green 77 phosphorus grenade in his hand.

He threw aside the black safety cap as he reached the doorway, and
was in the act of tossing the grenade inside when he suddenly stood
straight up, his bush-hat fell off, and the side of his face was covered
with blood. He fell full length, landing almost at my feet, and someone
grabbed him and pulled him away. I was at one side of the doorway,
and a small sharp-faced sergeant whom I didn't know was at the
other, with a tommy-gun. Gale's phosphorus bomb hadn't exploded
– they're dicey things with a tape which unwinds in flight and a ball
and spring mechanism – but I had my second 36 grenade in one hand
and my rifle in the other. The little sergeant also had a 36; he nodded,
we pulled our pins together, he waited *three* seconds that seemed like
hours, and we tossed them in, flattening against the bunker. On the
heels of the double explosion he darted in, Thompson stuttering; two
quick bursts and he was out again.

"Three on 'em!" he shouted, and his jaw dropped as he stared past
me. I turned to see a Jap racing across in front of the bunker, a sword
flourished above his head. He was going like Jesse Owens, screaming
his head off, right across my front; I just had sense enough to take a
split second, traversing my aim with him before I fired; he gave a
convulsive leap, and I felt that jolt of delight – I'd hit the bastard! –
and as he fell on all fours the Highland officer with whom I'd played
football dived on him from behind, slashing at his head with a kukri.
Someone rounded the bunker, almost barging into me; it was Stanley,
shouting: "Where? Where?" – in that kind of mad scramble all that
matters is seeing the enemy. He had a Bren magazine in one hand,
and was trying to change it for the one on the gun; I grabbed the
barrel to steady it, burned myself, yelped, and seized the folded legs
while he pushed the full magazine home – one of his puttees was
coming loose, a yard away Gale was lying dead with two men bending
over him, the whole wood was echoing with shots and explosions
and yelling voices. Stanley ran past me, dropping the empty magazine
– and as some Presbyterian devil made me pick it up I noticed Gale's
hat lying in the bunker doorway, and the little sergeant was shouting
and running towards a second bunker.

The sixty seconds I have just described, being among the most
eventful of my life, I have been able to relate almost step by step;

after that it was more disconnected. There were half a dozen men at the second bunker, feeding in grenades and firing through the slit, a Jap was shot and bayonetted in the entrance, and then we were past it, making for the far verge of the wood. Shots came from an earthwork to our left, a man had his bush-hat shot from his head – usually when a hat is hit it stays in place, but this one spun off like a plate, landing several feet away – and a Jap appeared between the trees and I shot him and he fell against a trunk, and the little sergeant dropped his tommy-gun and swore and picked it up again – the sequence of these things I can't be certain of because it all happened so quickly – or seemed to. I've spoken at the start of this paragraph of "sixty seconds" because I can't believe it took any longer, and probably the rush from the first bunker to the second and on to the wood's edge took about the same – but if that little sergeant were to appear and tell me it took twenty minutes, I couldn't contradict him. We were in that wood four hours, according to the regimental history, killed 136 Japanese, and lost seven dead and 43 wounded ourselves in the whole operation, but I wasn't conscious of time, only of the highlights of action. The fight at the first bunker is crystal clear, but the rest is a series of unrelated incidents.

It was a hectic murderous confusion: the whole section was in the wood, but Stanley is the only one I remember – indeed, Gale is the only other I can positively identify from the entire platoon. The little sergeant was there most of the time – when we were lying on the edge of the wood, covering the open ground beyond, I heard him asking for a field dressing – but which platoon he belonged to I never knew. When we opened fire at Japs moving on the open ground, the men on either side of me were strangers; one of them kept seeing Japs in the trees beyond the open space, and blazed away, cursing, but I believe it was wishful thinking.

Then we were withdrawing. Behind us the company were leaving the wood by the way we'd come in, and when we on the far side were ordered to fall back we went quite slowly, with the little sergeant shouting hoarsely to take our time. He knew his business, that one, for as we retreated past the cleared bunkers to the front of the wood he kept up an incessant patter of orders and encouragement (I have an idea he was a Welshman) keeping us in a rough line, well spaced out, firing as we went, for Japs were filtering into the trees we had just left. He was next to me, firing short bursts; I had a shot at one running figure among the trees, and he went down, but I think it was a dive for cover.

There was a film called *Honky Tonk*, in which Clark Gable had to back out of a saloon, covering the occupants with his gun and remarking: "This reminds me of the days when we used to do all our walking backwards." The words came back to me in the temple wood, as such things will, and at some point the man on my left dropped to his knees shouting: "Look what I've got!" I didn't identify the object, but what he did get a second later was a bullet in the leg from an unseen Jap, and he rolled over shouting: "They got me! The dirty rats, they got me!" It wasn't a bad wound, a furrow just above the knee, and he hobbled out of the wood under his own steam, blaspheming painfully.

That was the battle in the temple wood, an insignificant moment in the war; its importance is personal! It was typical of the kind of action that was going on all around Meiktila, and if figures mean anything, we won it, although I am still puzzled about its conclusion. Japs were re-entering the wood as we left it, but they cannot have reoccupied it, for the battalion history's tally of Japanese killed is exact, not an estimate, and must have been made on the ground afterwards, with ourselves in possession. So I conclude that the withdrawal in which I took part was not the end of the action, as I thought at the time.

This is the trouble with eye-witness: it sees only part of the whole, and is incomplete. If mine is patchy, I can only excuse it on the ground that I had never been in a fight to the death before, with the enemy at close quarters, which is, to say the least, confusing. I have tried to describe in plain terms what I saw, and can be sure of; what I thought at the time is less clear, but some strong impressions remain.

At the moment of fixing bayonets I had that hollow feeling which most writers locate in the stomach but in my case manifests itself in the throat; after we were fired on I didn't notice it. To say I was shocked at seeing Parker and Steele hit is correct in the sense that one is shocked by running into a brick wall; astonishment and fascination came into it, too. You read of such things, now you see the reality, and think: "So *that's* what it looks like!" The thought of being hit myself occurred only in the moment before I started crawling towards the Bren, to be submerged in relief when Stanley took possession. Going into the wood I was scared stiff but not witless; given Aladdin's lamp I would have been in Bermuda. No, that's not true; if it were, I'd have kept out of the Army in the first place. Being there, with the choice made, you go ahead – and if anyone says you could always change your mind, and run away, he's wrong; you can't. It sounds pompous to say it's a matter of honour, but that's what it comes down to, and Falstaff knew it. He was quite right, though, that honour hath no skill in surgery – which is why you are perfectly entitled to be scared.

There is the consolation that once the shooting starts, the higher thought takes a back seat. Putting a grenade into a bunker had the satisfaction of doing grievous bodily harm to an enemy for whom I felt real hatred, and still do. Seeing Gale killed shocked me as our first casualties had done, and I think enraged me. I wanted a Jap then, mostly for my own animal pride, no doubt, but seeing Gale go down sparked something which I felt in the instant when I hung on my aim at the Jap with the sword, because I wanted to be sure. The joy of hitting him was the strongest emotion I felt that day; I notice I've mentioned it twice.*

Perhaps I'm too self-analytical, but I'm trying to be honest. It's hard to say where fear and excitement meet, or which predominates. The best way I can sum up my emotions in that wood is to say that a continuous nervous excitement was shot through with occasional flashes of rage, terror, elation, relief, and amazement. So far as I have seen, most men are like that, by and large, although there are exceptions. A few really enjoy it; I've seen them (and I won't say they're deranged, because even the most balanced man has moments of satisfaction in battle which are indistinguishable from enjoyment, short-lived though they may be). Some are blessed with the quick reflexes which, combined with experience, enable them to keep cool, like the little sergeant. Others seem to be on a "high", like the man who cried "Look what I've got!"

I was glad to come out of it, but even then I felt what I feel now, and what every old soldier feels: a gratitude for having been there, and an abiding admiration amounting to awe for the sheer ability of

---

* Strictly speaking I should probably have held my fire, since the Jap was between me and comrades who were advancing into the wood, but I have since learned that I was not alone in letting fly at him and breaching what battle school instructors call "fire discipline". I can only plead the heat of the moment and say that it seemed a good idea at the time.

my comrades. Nowadays the highest praise a soldier can get is the word "professional". Fourteenth Army weren't professionals. They were experts.

The aftermath was as interesting as the battle. Fiction and the cinema have led us to expect certain reactions from men in war, and the conventions of both demand displays of emotion, or a restraint which is itself highly emotional. I don't know what Nine Section felt, but whatever it was didn't show. They expressed no grief, or anger, or obvious relief, or indeed any emotion at all; they betrayed no symptoms of shock or disturbance, nor were they nervous or short-tempered. If they were quieter than usual that evening, well, they were dog-tired. Discussion of the day's events was limited to a brief reference to Gale's death, and to the prospects of the wounded: Steel had been flown out on a "flying taxi", one of the tiny fragile mono-planes to which stretchers were strapped; it was thought his wound was serious.* Parker was said to be in dock in Meiktila (and a few weeks later there were to be ironic congratulations when he returned to the section with a romantic star-shaped scar high on his chest; penicillin was a new marvel then).

Not a word was said about Tich Little, but a most remarkable thing happened (and I saw it repeated later in the campaign) which I have never heard of elsewhere, in fact or fiction, although I suspect it is as old as war.

Tich's military effects and equipment – not, or course, his private possessions, or any of his clothing – were placed on a groundsheet, and it was understood that anyone in the section could take what he wished. Grandarse took one of his mess-tins; Forster, his housewife, making sure it contained only Army issue and nothing personal; Nixon, after long deliberation, took his rifle, an old Lee Enfield shod in very pale wood (which surprised me, for it seemed it might make its bearer uncomfortably conspicuous); I took his pialla,† which was of superior enamel, unlike the usual chipped mugs. Each article was substituted on the groundsheet with our own possessions – my old pialla, Forster's housewife, and so on – and it was bundled up for

---

* It was. I visited him after the war, when he had had to give up his job as a builder because his right arm could not be fully lifted, and he could not mount scaffolding in safety.
  † drinking-mug

delivery to the quartermaster. I think everyone from the original section took something.

It was done without formality, and at first I was rather shocked, supposing that it was a coldly practical, almost ghoulish proceeding – people exchanging an inferior article for a better one, nothing more, and indeed that was the pretext. Nick worked the bolt, squinted along the sights, hefted the rifle, and even looked in its butt-trap before nodding approval; Grandarse tossed his old mess-tin on to the groundsheet with a mutter about the booger's 'andle being loose. But of course it had another purpose: without a word said, everyone was taking a memento of Tich.

An outsider might have thought, mistakenly, that the section was unmoved by the deaths of Gale and Little. There was no outward show of sorrow, no reminiscences or eulogies, no Hollywood heart-searchings or phony philosophy. Forster asked "W'ee's on foorst stag?";* Grandarse said "Not me, any roads; Ah's aboot knackered", and rolled up in his blanket; Nick cleaned Tich's rifle; I washed and dried his pialla; the new section commander – that young corporal who earlier in the day had earned the Military Medal – told off the stag roster; we went to sleep. And that was that. It was not callousness or indifference or lack of feeling for two comrades who had been alive that morning and were now names for the war memorial; it was just that there was nothing to be said.

It was part of war; men died, more would die, that was past, and what mattered now was the business in hand; those who lived would get on with it. Whatever sorrow was felt, there was no point in talking or brooding about it, much less in making, for form's sake, a parade of it. Better and healthier to forget it, and look to tomorrow.

The celebrated British stiff upper lip, the resolve to conceal emotion which is not only embarrassing and useless, but harmful, is just plain common sense.

But that was half a century ago. Things are different now, when the media seem to feel they have a duty to dwell on emotion, the more harrowing the better, and to encourage its indulgence. The cameras close on stricken families at funerals, interviewers probe relentlessly to uncover grief, pain, fear, and shock, know no reticence or even decency in their eagerness to make the viewers' flesh creep,

* sentry-go

and wallow in the sentimental cliché (victims are always "innocent", relatives must be "loved ones"). And the obscene intrusion is justified as "caring" and "compassionate" when it is the exact opposite.

The pity is that the public shapes its behaviour to the media's demands. The bereaved feel obliged to weep and lament for the cameras (and feel a flattering importance at their attention). Even young soldiers, on the eve of action in the Gulf, confessed, under a nauseating inquisition designed to uncover their fears, to being frightened – of course they were frightened, just as we were, but no interviewer in our time was so shameless, cruel, or unpatriotic as to badger us into admitting our human weakness for public consumption, and thereby undermining public morale, and our own. In such a climate, it is not to be wondered at that a general should agonise publicly about the fears and soul-searchings of command – Slim and Montgomery and MacArthur had them, too, but they would rather have been shot than admit it. They knew the value of the stiff upper lip.

The damage that fashionable attitudes, reflected (and created) by television, have done to the public spirit, is incalculable. It has been weakened to the point where it is taken for granted that anyone who has suffered loss and hardship must be in need of "counselling"; that soldiers will suffer from "post-battle traumatic stress" and need psychiatric help. One wonders how Londoners survived the Blitz without the interference of unqualified, jargon-mumbling "counsellors", or how an overwhelming number of 1940s servicemen returned successfully to civilian life without benefit of brain-washing. Certainly, a small minority needed help; war can leave terrible mental scars – but the numbers will increase, and the scars enlarge, in proportion to society's insistence on raising spectres which would be better left alone. Tell people they should feel something, and they'll not only feel it, they'll regard themselves as entitled and obliged to feel it.

It is a long way from the temple wood to Sheffield – and not only in miles. I knew a young Liverpudlian who, following the Hillsborough disaster, stayed away from work because, he said, of the grief he felt for those supporters of his team who had died on the terraces. He didn't know them, he hadn't been there, but he was too distressed to work. (Suppose Grandarse or the Battle of Britain pilots, with infinitely greater cause, had been too distressed to fight?) One shouldn't be too hard on the young man; he had been conditioned to believe that it was right, even proper, to indulge his emotions; he probably felt virtuous for having done so.

Fortunately for the world, my generation didn't suffer from spiritual hypochondria – but then, we couldn't afford it. By modern standards, I'm sure we, like the whole population who endured the war, were ripe for counselling, but we were lucky; there were no counsellors. I can regret, though, that there were no modern television "journalists", transported back in time, to ask Grandarse: "How did you *feel* when you saw Corporal Little shot dead?" I would have liked to hear the reply.

ANDREI BITOV

Passions of a City Planner

From *A Captive of the Caucasus*, Journeys in
Armenia and Georgia

THEN AND NOW

The more natural and profound my experience of Armenia became,
the hazier and more distant was my specific purpose in being here.
As long as I was adjusting and acclimatizing, as long as I wasn't
myself, that purpose survived, perfectly in accord with the general
awkwardness of the situation. But the moment I began to *live*, then
immediately – as though some dark supreme force, which found my
non-life quite convenient, had been vigilantly observing my every step
– immediately, retribution poked its head up out of the past and
shook its finger at me: Don't live.

The time allotted for my trip was running out, just as inexorably
as the per diem runs out when you're still on the road. The day of
reckoning was imminent; the pure and honest image of my editor's
chief bookkeeper harassed and confounded me.

"Then and Now" – that was my assignment. An impassioned, lyrical
report on modern city planning.

Only now was I beginning to perceive the full extent of the frivolity
that allows people to move from place to place at their own whim.
Temptation is the hope that we won't have to pay. In life, we pay at
the exit, not the entrance. And I would have to exit this situation,
which I had entered more or less lightly . . . Such were my dwindling
thoughts as I gradually brought myself back to the level of journalism.

First, the "Then". I didn't know what the city used to be like.
Someone had suggested that I read an essay by M. Koltsov to find
out. But even the essay remained unread.

Second, the "Now". It required an unconditionally enthusiastic attitude. This followed from the assignment, it was clear by the nature of the assignment. There had been more than enough enthusiasms, yet they all seemed irrelevant. Well, just as in school – anything but the lessons . . . If only I could paint the fence for Tom Sawyer.

Schoolboy thoughts before the exam.

I walked around Erevan, looking at its modern architectural complexes. They were as well executed as if even your enthusiasm had been allowed for by the architect and channelled in the right direction. They were constructed in such a way that you couldn't help noticing them, you were duty-bound to be overcome with enthusiasm.

Here a dim idea occurs to me. Which is better: a totally *bad* bad thing, or a slightly better bad thing? A thing that is almost good? A thing that incriminates itself right away, or is gradually eliminated by time, or remains useful to this day? Imagining the era when Lenin Square was built, for example, we can easily grant that it was an almost impossible extreme of naturalness, taste, and integrated design, for its own era; to bring this concept to realization required an almost audacious boldness and talent. Its contemporaries felt the breeze of progress on their faces. But something has happened over these years – and although their time has departed, the buildings remain. They stand in another time.

Drawing the boundary between "then" and "now" is not so easy as one might think at first glance. If it were merely a matter of differentiating recently constructed buildings from buildings constructed long ago, trees recently planted from full-grown trees, and so on, we would hardly be interested in so formal a problem. Skill and a clock. But if we seek the boundary between past and present, this just can't be done, because the boundary slips away with each second, each instant. Every step, every sigh is irretrievable, every written line has already been written, is no longer being written . . . In essence, the present *is* the boundary with the past. But if we draw this boundary at some very important historical dividing line (as we naturally draw it at 1917), the space between that line and today is always growing and being filled up with the past. By now that space can easily accommodate even a man's life and its personal past . . . as, for example, my life . . . and comparison becomes increasingly speculative and distant.

So only the "right now", or at most the "just recently" – that is my real material, that's what I can talk about in the present tense before it all hurtles away into the distant past. And is it so important just when a thing was created, if the creation still lives and breathes? If a building erected a thousand years ago and a building finished yesterday stand as neighbours today, they are contemporaries. In this sense, all living things are contemporary. "Now" means the fact that they stand side by side, not merely what didn't exist yesterday. The world is not inhabited by newborns alone.

Thus, no matter what I write about, only the present interests me, only the living: both what has just been born and what has long been alive, both what is emerging and what is departing into the past but hasn't yet departed.

Only the now, I thought, only the now . . .

And could see nothing, after Geghard.

QUIZ

. . . The next morning came, curtailing my trip by one more day, and I still hadn't attempted any work. But neither could I go on living, enjoying the things I'd enjoyed only yesterday.

This morning I had an appointment with a prominent Erevan official, a moving spirit in modern city planning – a remarkable man in many ways, according to all reports.

I was becoming more and more ashamed at the thought of all the people who had accommodated me: invented a topic so that I could come here, processed the trip authorization, signed for the cash, given me helpful advice, taken an interest in my living arrangements, provided me with a car from the editor's office.

Now they all expected something of me. I must not let them down by making a mess of things.

I strode through the morning city, happily noting that I had been wrong, I was liking the city better and better – I had merely been mired in subjectivity, et cetera, et cetera. And, indeed, the city looked its best in the morning. Clean and not too hot, with its shadows still long, it was quiet and modest. Its pinkish hue was becoming.

"Erevan should be seen very early in the morning" – that was how I would begin my essay. Yes, that's just how I'll begin, I told myself briskly as I crossed the threshold of a large institution.

At three minutes before eleven, gratified by my punctuality, I presented myself to a secretary. She vanished into the office and promptly reappeared: Would I please wait.

Nothing, so far, conflicted with the mental image that I had developed from various people's stories about this man. The stories were never anything but favourable. No one had a hard word for him, despite his exalted position. But always, along with the high praise, a gradual half smile would develop, a little grin, not mocking, not sceptical, more likely good-humoured – but not fully intelligible to me. "Yes, yes!" they all said. "Exceptional! Decent! Bright and knowledgeable!" The very unanimity on the subject of this official was exceptional. It certainly couldn't be attributed to fear or caution, which I would have noticed right away. And a decent, knowledgeable man in a position befitting his abilities is a phenomenon that truly deserves all manner of encouragement . . . But . . . now came the half smile. No, no one said "but", I'm the one saying "but" – instead of the "but", there was half of a smile. In some people it was wordless, the end of the matter. One man said, "He loves to play up his resemblance to N.; you'll see." This told me little, inasmuch as I had an even more remote conception of N.'s appearance (he was a remarkable Armenian poet) than of his verse. Another man said, "Oh, he's an actor!" The remark was devoid of sarcasm, however: He's just an actor, that's all . . .

"Ask him how many years since he took a vacation," someone advised, only deepening the mystery.

Something, vague in its features but definite in character, was emerging in my imagination, and I could hardly wait to compare my sketch with the original. So far, everything tallied: both the small, tidy, democratic waiting room – which suggested that the official before me was not one concerned primarily with the impressiveness of his setting, nor was he one who had no time to take care himself – and the secretary, who was neither a beauty nor a former beauty, but just right; neither haughty nor familiar, neither striking nor ugly, as if she were both there and not there . . . Everything, so far, was like a suit from an aristocratic tailor: a superlative fit, but you'd never notice the cut or the fabric.

Just then a petitioner, a venerable highland elder, emerged from the office. He all but wore a felt cloak, all but had a lamb scampering ahead of him. A representative of the people, a plain man . . . The secretary instantly picked up the receiver and asked me to go in. It was eleven o'clock on the dot.

He sat talking on the telephone, at the far end of a large, long office. I paused, shutting the door behind me. Our eyes met, and for some fraction of a second we seesawed, establishing an equilibrium, as if we were on the two ends of a board. Then he tipped the balance: with a precise nod, neither stern nor deliberately courteous, he invited me to approach. My end of the board rose, and I started for his desk easily, as if down an incline. This was time, while I crossed the space between us ... And it was literally space, because the office had nothing in it but his desk and a pair of armchairs. This, the most glaringly distinctive feature of his office, hadn't even hit me at first. There was neither a T nor a U in it. That is, no such conference table. No carafe, no glass. There was no television either. I don't remember for sure whether there was a model sailboat, but I don't think there was any picture above his head. This was an office from which everything had been removed. But ... how can I say it more precisely? ... it was not an office which had never had any of the things that weren't in it now. Again, I'm not sure whether there was actually a paler rectangle of parquet, signifying a vanished stick from the letter T, or whether there was only a square of less faded wallpaper, signifying a former picture. In any case, such was my impression: that he sat under a picture which did not hang above him, and that I walked around a T-shaped conference table which did not stand before him.

I approached his desk (this was an ordinary small office desk on the site of a previous, oceanic desk, and the desk had nothing on it) at the exact second that he finished his conversation, put down the receiver, stood up from his chair, and proffered his hand. He hadn't hurried to finish the conversation, any more than he had prolonged it until the instant I approached – he had simply managed to finish it by that moment. And he didn't proffer his hand while still talking, or point to a chair while pressing the receiver to his ear with his shoulder, or shrug, or spread his hands, or grimace impatiently at the invisible other party, he didn't fling down the receiver when he finished his conversation. No; he said goodbye to the other party, hung up, turned to me, and extended his hand, without keeping me waiting for even a second. Nevertheless ... how can I put it precisely? ... he had indeed *managed* to get it all done, and his pleasure in this, despite his reserve, was reflected on his face as a sort of bright shadow or highlight. If he didn't look at his watch to make sure that the second-hand stood at sixty, it was only because he knew how to control himself.

He was that kind of man.

We seesawed once more in equilibrium, this time up close, on more precise scales – the two ends of a handshake. Both his hand and its grip were irreproachable: the palm was dry but not rough, the grip was confident but not hard, and there was no doubt as to the cleanliness of his hands. He pressed his hand on my pan of the scales – and I sank into a chair.

During the handshake there was a brief and appropriate glance; the pause of it, a certain lengthiness, could hardly even be felt, but it was there. Once again we looked each other in the eye and seemed to understand each other. This is, either we really did understand each other, or each of us understood the other in his own way and resolved to stay within that understanding, drawing strength from it . . . At any rate, the glance signified that in joining the game called "interview" we had both undertaken not to deviate from the rules or go beyond the framework of our chosen convention, whereby each of us clearly saw what we must talk about and how, what to answer and what to ask (in just that sequence: the answer conditions the question). That being the case, it would plainly be unethical to measure him surreptitiously on some other, unstipulated level. Just as unethical as pestering him for an official favour in the sauna.

And that being the case, I am greatly at fault. But I dare say he was left with some secondary impression of me, too.

Well, he looked at me with clear green eyes, which went very well with his regular features and ivory skin. He tossed his forelock, as if with faint annoyance that this tossing motion, too, suited him very well. And then, with a slight, elusive gesture, he made as if to wipe a cobweb from his face. That gesture . . . I had already seen it.

With sudden and immutable conviction, I realized that this gesture was what belonged to the poet N. – of whom I now had a clearer conception, if only of his appearance. Yes, precisely: I was seeing not my city planner (whose outward appearance had become less clear to me at the moment) but the poet. I was astounded that a similarity is such an independent attribute, even when the object of the comparison is absent from one's field of vision. But that's beside the point.

He was a fine-looking man, very well preserved, and yet without the vulgarity of blooming health or a too youthful face: he was the ideal for his age, and only this idealness made him look a trifle younger. In general, he was a physical aristocrat. His shirt was ideal, as was the shave on his cheeks, and moreover ideal in the marvellous sense that the shirt didn't look as if it had just been taken out of the bureau drawer, just as his cheeks made you think of coffee and fine cigarettes rather than of the shaving brush.

He allowed me to begin. As I felt my way, trying to articulate a topic still vague even to me, he levelled his clear gaze on me, listened attentively, and refrained from comment, but only as a courteous man who knew how to listen without interrupting.

Though I bolstered myself emotionally by making a game of my ineptitude as I went along, the fact remained that I was stammering, drifting, and growing more and more uncomfortable under his wise and attentive gaze.

"You know," I said, the feeble words beginning to flow, "I'm not an expert on city planning at all. And what's more, not a journalist in the literal sense . . ." ("And what's more," I thought for him, "an idiot in the literal sense.") "Let's begin", I said, "with the fact that all I know is, Erevan is famous among other cities for its planning. And that I could hardly", I said, "become deeply acquainted with the subject in a short time, and naturally I don't want to write anything amateurish, and I doubt the reader is interested in coping with statistics . . . All of us, as ordinary people, see from the inside out, from the windows of our apartments and institutions, and our view is partial and fragmented, and what we'd be interested to learn is the opinion of a man who looks from the outside in – that is," I explained, "who doesn't forget the categories of the large and the whole. And what we'd be interested in would be . . ." I was running dry, but he kept listening. Finally – as if glancing at his internal watch, with the crisp, abrupt gesture of a man who wasn't in the habit of wasting time, who had understood me long ago, before I half finished, or even before I opened my mouth, and who had endured my vapid speechifying only out of courtesy – he entered the game.

Irreproachability was his only weakness.

"Architecture as a means for educating man, you say?" (When had I said that? My mental wheels began to spin.) "Yes, that's true. Positively, man is the primary factor in planning. Not *what* are we building, but *for whom* are we building. His spiritual world, his tomorrow

– that's what has to be our first concern, when everything's still on paper, in the blueprints, and not in stone. Not the things we're used to thinking about, not today, not deadlines and growth rates, but what will happen in fifty years!" His voice rang out. "Is this a question we often ask ourselves? We all say we're building in the name of the future – we use these words habitually, without ever probing what they mean. As a rule, we don't think about the future at all, what life will be like for people in the world we have built. When we're bogged down in worries about producing, economizing, and the yearly plan, tomorrow is exactly what we *don't* think about."

A startling word, that *we*!

He spoke as if he himself did the building . . .

He seemed ready for our encounter, more so than I had expected. He was telling me things I hadn't dared hope to hear. He had been ready before I appeared on his horizon. And therefore it would be naïve to suppose that I had somehow steered the conversation. As it turned out, what he was telling me was actually too much what I had wanted to hear from him. He had promptly appropriated even the thought and a half that had occurred to me in spontaneous connection with my assignment, the thoughts that I was already picturing typeset in the form of "A Writer's Reflections". For an accurate reconstruction of the interview – and since this man spoke for himself so completely and sensibly, it seemed appropriate to hold myself to his standard – for that kind of reconstruction, I simply didn't have the journalistic skills. I became slightly panicky, and for a moment I stopped listening to what he was saying. When I discovered this, I became even more flustered. With an inept, uncharacteristic flourish I opened my notebook and wrote down the first statistic, "50". (I would later spend a long time figuring out what it meant.) Like a cheating pupil – the horror of whose position is further multiplied by the fact that even as he copies he doesn't know whether he's copying the right answer, and by now he feels more ashamed to write something laughably stupid than to get a D, as honest and direct as an F – I cupped my hand to hide from him what I had written in my notebook.

None of this escaped him, but neither did he escape.

Perhaps because the pen is mightier than the sword, a normal, healthy person is stupefied and hypnotized by any form of minute-taking. If only in the first instant, the fact that the man opposite you has picked up his pen will give you a chill whiff of dungeons and guards. Even if it doesn't, an accountability-raising reflex will go to work – and you will stumble, tangled up in your grammar. As steam changes to water, and water to ice, a man changes from the state of speaker to answerer, and from the state of answerer to interrogatee.

The interrogatee looked down for a second. Since he allowed himself but few instinctive movements, that glance clattered like a chunk of ice. His speech stopped short. True, the sentence had been completed, and he was able to make this look like a natural pause. All in all, he quickly got control of himself – caught his fall, you might even say – and continued as if nothing had happened. But something, apparently, had. Because I can't even tell you how, but from that moment on, his speech seemed to have been slightly reorganized, adjusted for the record. And although I was always trying to decide which phrase to record next, and whenever I did decide I totally failed to hear what he was saying, nevertheless, I was twiddling the pencil in my hands . . . My companion did not allow himself to look at the pencil, but his gaze had been tethered by a thread. As I twiddled the pencil, I was twitching that thread.

I understood him better and better, but myself worse and worse. And I was less and less able to listen to what he was saying. I put myself in his shoes and felt embarrassed. Why the devil was I playing tricks on this earnest man? He had enough problems without me. Actually, if I had scribbled without pause, he might have forgotten my dagger. As it was, he had no way of knowing which phrase I would ambush.

"The environment is a means of education . . ." he said, and paused involuntarily for me to write it down. But suddenly I didn't write it down, and he was slightly thrown off. Then, by an effort of will, he banished the hallucination: ". . . to preserve ethnic traditions and create our today!" Still, every time he led up to an exclamation, the distinct apparition of the pencil arose before him, and he dropped his gaze. His speech was sensible and handsome; all the more, then, might he take offence on behalf of each phrase – why hadn't it been recorded? – and likewise feel astonished that another had been. The discrimination inflicted on his speech by my pencil was totally unjustified and unjust, like all discrimination.

As if honestly, as if absorbed in listening, I laid aside my pencil. I was so engrossed . . .

This wasn't long in producing an effect.

He told in a businesslike way about prospects for the growth of the city, and about the current idea of localizing the growth so that the city wouldn't bulge with irrational, shapeless outlying districts but would find inner resources through reconstruction, replanning, and the elimination of districts that were architecturally backward and unprofitable. He told about the difficulties that still stood in the way of this idea, about the stagnation in the thinking of other officials, about their ineradicable loyalty to yesterday, about administrative inertia and laziness . . .

Easily, without growing short of breath, he climbed the steps of his words to the very top of the precipice. Together we glanced back, a bit dizzy, and then slid quickly and smoothly down the spiral of his speech into the stillness and twilight of a pause, of a softened glance that lingered in reverie, and after resting there, under the branching canopy of the last sentence, we began to climb up again.

He was not the familiar type of orator who takes satisfaction in a neatly turned phrase, who plunges into his speech with the courage of a swimmer and spelunker . . . and behold! he finds his way out of the sentence! At the end of the phrase – a faint light, like the exit from a cave.

This man didn't crawl into the cave and grope frantically through the side passages of "which", "what", and "how" in search of the exit, he didn't get his sandals wet in a puddle of parenthetic words – he worked in the open air.

"As recently as five years ago the quantities would have seemed mythical. Every other day, a fifty-apartment building is ready for occupancy! But we mustn't let the very quantities confuse our minds, engulfing both our idea and our purpose. We have learned to pay heed to the exterior of a building, and even to its interdependence with the complex. But the interiors . . . Our task now is to eliminate this rupture between the room and the façade!"

"Rupture between the room and the façade" – suddenly I opened my notebook again and transcribed this brave phrase. A vague idea rose to mind when I was recording the word *rupture*, which he had spoken as confidently as though it were an established term. Although the phrase was ordinary at first glance, I took it down because I was struck by some elusive incongruity between its meaning and the alien vividness of its form . . . I never did capture the meaning I had paused for, especially as there was no time to delay. My companion, too, had lurched to a halt on this phrase – because my pencil, after a long interruption, had begun to record it, and this implied something – and now he darted aside like a man racing around a sudden obstacle, pretending that this was where he'd been heading. Fertilized by my pencil, the phrase became a flower, an ovary, and here was the fruit, already ripening, swelling. My sudden perplexity over the phrase was immediately answered by an entire speech growing up from it, and that speech explained a great deal to me . . .

"We require of a man that he work better and better with each passing day," he said with ever-increasing animation, as if planting himself more solidly and firmly on ground he had chosen once and for all, "and we take no interest in how he feels as he walks to work and back. We tell him constantly about his obligation and duty to his native city. And no one has yet formulated the question this way: Is the city obligated to the man?" He raised his hand, mildly but express-ively, as if to place this phrase just slightly above the level on which I had heard it. Up there, just to one side of the sound source, it took on a nickel-plated shine, like a giant paper clip. "A man is walking to work. What mood comes over him in ugly, squalid, identical streets? Or, on the contrary, are his spirits elevated by the beauty around him, and will he set to work with élan and a surge of strength? Surely it's worth giving thought to a man's route through the city? So that his passage will be orchestrated, as it were, and the city in motion will be exact and well considered, like music? The melody of the street . . ." He fell silent for an instant, as if listening. "This experiment –"

My hand twitched, and in spite of myself I wrote out the word *experiment*. A look of sheer passion appeared on my companion's face. The violin strings of his countenance tautened and began to sound, although without distorting his calm, pleasant pallor.

Just then the telephone rang.

At any rate, my notebook has a little square marked off somewhere near the word *experiment*, and in it is written "tel. conv". Frowning slightly, he listened without interrupting the other party. Then his face was smoothed by an explosion from within; once again it became calm and decisive.

"I said in the first place that it was an unprofessional sketch. Then I found out." His face froze in a hard smile. "The fact is, he's not even a practising architect – he's just a dilettante." Something was said to him at the other end. "No, I don't like the method itself," he replied, still maintaining the hard smile. "No, no. What we need here is creative analysis. The main thing is not to hurry . . ."

I was completely bewitched by the words *unprofessional sketch, method,* and *analysis* coming from his lips. Even more so because the words were used without special intent – they were spoken in a natural and unforeseen conversation. To stay abreast of a conversation and keep it going in such a way that one could also say something especially for the benefit of a third party who happened to be listening – such a threefold task, thrice interwoven, was beyond the strength of any man, I thought, especially such a nice one.

When he hung up, he again – wonder of wonders! – made no superfluous remarks. No inane apologies for interrupting our conversation, no explanations of the problem discussed on the line, no "Where were we?" – nothing of the sort. He glanced at me briefly and lucidly, as if he hadn't interrupted his speech in mid-sentence, and the glance said that it was over, he had expressed himself in full on the issue, he couldn't go into particulars, but carry on, ask anything that interests you. Work. You were sent here for a purpose, you know . . . And time is passing, dear comrade.

Much had already become clear to me: the zone of delight and the zone of doubt were increasingly distinct from each other and seemed to be moving apart. The delight, as an emotion, occupied the present; the doubt, as something rational and even bad, required rethinking. It existed rather in the future. There simply wasn't time to interpret the few words and phrases I had tripped over; I had probably just been irritated by the delay, the disruption of the harmony, and by suspicion of my own suspiciousness. I was painfully embarrassed by my own leisure and idleness vis-à-vis this man of affairs. In any case, I had absolutely no idea what else to discuss with him. My main concern was to ask a question that showed at least some intelligence, and to stay more or less on the conversational level he had set. In my considerable distress and confusion, a foggy idea suddenly dawned on me, and I seized on it gladly.

"To be perfectly frank with you," I said, blushing, "I didn't like Erevan very much at first. Of course I couldn't confess this to anyone. It wasn't until I learned a little about the country in which it lies that I began to get used to it. The paradox of Erevan" – in using the word *paradox,* I dropped a curtsy to the words *orchestrated* and *experiment* – "is this: Here you are, celebrating the 2,750th anniversary of its founding, and yet the city has no historical face. The individuality of a city takes shape over centuries. Cities that arise in our time can't even have a face; they can only be more or less in accord with our practical and aesthetic needs." My companion nodded. Encouraged, I promptly lost the thread. "I'm afraid my idea may strike some people as frivolous. But from all we've just said, I believe you will understand me correctly." This was a forbidden ploy. To say such a thing made me narrow my eyes to a slit. For the moment, however, I was alone in thinking myself clever; the gambit merely put my companion on guard. He had not, of course, been born yesterday. "The reason you could conceive a plan for the general reconstruction and rebuilding of the city, including even its central districts, is that none of Erevan's earlier buildings are noteworthy for their architecture. You want your city to look beautiful, you want to give it a unique, individual image . . ." My listener's face softened. He was increasingly ready to agree with me. And although I held the bank, while he was just taking the offered card – and moreover saw that I was cheating, slipping him an ace to go with his ten – he took the card. "But," I said, "however professional or even brilliant the plan, however fine the ideas that guide its creators, you're trying to create this unique new face for the city within a definite time limit. You can't incorporate thousands of years of history into your plan. You can't avoid creating the city in our era. And this imprint, barely visible to us now, will be noticed by succeeding generations. That is, the ancient city of Erevan will be a new city, built all at one time. This temporal monochromaticity – don't you suppose there's a possibility it won't quite suit those succeeding generations, of whom the people of Erevan, in contrast to many other cities, are ever mindful? I can't think of any cities that have managed to acquire vivid, individual architectural features in the space of a few years. As a rule, a city's individuality is shaped by the labour of time, rather than of its builders. How do you expect to solve this problem without the aid of time? You don't have time, you know, and your plans are so dependent on principle. Of the examples I'm familiar with, only Peter the Great succeeded in giving his city a face according to a plan and in a short time."

At Peter's name his eyes flashed, briefly and profoundly. The expression was promptly concealed by a timely gesture of weariness, as if by a theatre curtain, but either I had already gained experience in communicating with him, or I had so much faith in my own insight

that I saw only what I chose to, whether or not it actually happened
– whatever the case, that flash did not escape me.

"Yes," he said. His face paled and lighted up, not in the vulgar
sense of the word, but like a fluorescent lamp, perhaps. "Yes, you're
quite right. You mention Peter the Great with good reason. From
the very beginning, he managed to give his city an inimitable look.
Our department has solved a lot of problems, but we still haven't
worked out the character of the city. Leningrad, Tallin – these are
cities whose mere names call up an immediate image. We want to
achieve the same here in Erevan." He appeared to have missed my
bait about city planning and time, but for some reason he had bitten
where I didn't expect it, on Peter the Great. I grabbed my pencil.
Either his speech was an excited jumble or I took it down feverishly
and mindlessly, but the notes that follow are very incoherent. I've
spent a long time puzzling over them. "For the city to have educational
significance, too . . . Posters, display boards – they're all so formal,
so tasteless. And degrading to the idea itself, as a rule. Sometimes I
just feel like shouting: Why do you pollute the spiritual world of
man?!" (My notes say "spir. wor." It was quite a while before I understood this phrase, decoding it not as "spiritual world" but as "spirit
of the working man".) "What we've planned is experimental, of course
. . . The ring boulevard, designed in assorted ethnic architectural
styles, will symbolize the friendship of the peoples. Or *** Street, an
equally experimental design . . . You haven't been there? Do go. And
do at least notice that there are absolutely no memorial plaques. So
formal – I'm fed up with them, all those plaques . . . But suddenly
there's a work by a certain talented young sculptor of ours. No, not
a bust – a symbol, conceived in an elevated, lofty vein . . . Not pasted
on the wall like a building manager's report. Not like something on
a bulletin board, 'So-and-so lived here', 'Human beings lived here'.
No! 'Here is something divine!' – that's the idea that should occur to
the passerby . . . Monuments like this will inspire respect. They will
have an unwitting influence on the thinking of the passerby and serve
him inconspicuously as a sublime example of what man can achieve
. . . Let's say a father is walking with his son, he's picked him up at
kindergarten after work. And suddenly, this sculpture. The father,
tired and preoccupied, isn't looking around. But his little son notices.
He doesn't understand. 'What's this, Daddy?' he asks. And Daddy is
forced to explain, or walk over and read it himself, if he doesn't know:

'So-and-so lived and worked here . . .' 'But what did he do? Why did they put this art object here?' And now the father and son are having a conversation."

Somehow, in my delight, I completely missed the rest. Statistics, dimensions, skyscrapers . . . Demolish a million square metres – build a half million . . . Or vice versa. Suddenly I realized that he was silent.

I made as if to write the last phrase, and looked up.

I don't know whether he had glanced at his watch; I didn't see. But after a moment's hesitation he decided to do one more thing. He ran to the next room and brought back a tube.

We bent over the unrolled blueprints, our shoulders touching lightly. These were illustrations out of a science-fiction novel – a swimming pool *cum* aquarium, with a restaurant under the water, an aviary above the water, and fish swimming right toward us into our shot glasses. It would have been hard to believe, if the poolarium hadn't been scheduled to open next year.

I can truthfully swear that he didn't look at his watch at this point. But he froze for an instant, as if listening to it tick, and again swiftly disappeared into the other room. I couldn't quite see it from my chair, but I think it was small and much more cluttered than the one we were in. I even speculated that that was where they had dumped all the things that used to be in our room . . . At last he darted out with several cylindrical paving blocks clutched to his belly. All I could think was: Had there been a sudden explosion? And wasn't he getting his shirt dirty?

"Here." He dropped them on the desk. "Coloured asphalt! Experimental samples." Indeed, the blocks were different colours. "What a boring, tiresome colour we have underfoot! But now . . . Not to mention the lowered accident rate . . . Now the driver will never fall asleep at the wheel!"

Here his internal time expired. In such a way that he just managed to get everything done. We shook hands with profound sincerity and not a trace of familiarity.

As I shut the door behind me, I glanced at my watch. Exactly twelve.

BREATH ON STONE

In high spirits, with a sense of easily fulfilled duty, I hurried out of the shady park into the sunlight. During that hour the caressing warmth had become heat; the white-hot air had thickened and solidified in the middle of the street.

I looked at the streets with fresh eyes. Or that was what I should have done, so that my visual impressions could corroborate the propositions just expounded to me. But the day must have grown too hot: nothing looked very different to me.

Then I decided to review these propositions that needed to be corroborated with visual impressions, and realized with horror that I remembered nothing of the interview except for a few gestures. I grabbed my notebook – the precious little it contained made no sense.

I did come across the name of the experimental street in my notes and decided to find it. Luckily, it was not far off. The freshness and briskness inspired by the mere sight of my recent companion had mysteriously vanished. Melting in the heat, I was already wondering whether he existed. Had I invented all this?

I walked along the street, listening attentively for the moment when I would experience the sublime thoughts and the radiant, or at least cheerful, mood which must inevitably be induced by the design of this architectural complex.

The whole street had been built with variety, originality, and taste. Nothing was superfluous – all structures had been planned in relation to their neighbours. Horizontal harmonized with vertical, open space with closed. The visual effect was calm: nothing impeded or arrested the eye. I discovered with surprise that I had been walking for a long time and the street was about to end – as signalled by an ugly building, conspicuously inappropriate on the corner. That building was what I'd been seeing for some time now. I had walked the length of this street, listening to myself in vain: no thought, none at all, had occurred to me. Perhaps the day was too hot. Or perhaps you can't generally expect to have an idea on purpose . . . Here was a café, transparent through and through, and a department store like it, and even if the café had a coffee maker that worked and the department store were piled with jeans, and if, in addition, the department store and the café weren't closed for lunch, even so, everything would remain the same

– ready, empty, and waiting. A florist's shop in the shape of a vase; to get to it, you had to hop playfully along flagstones laid at random . . . Although I kept an eye out, I never did see the piece of art about the great man who had lived on this street, the memorial that was supposed to be so eye-catching. Agreeable colours, agreeable combinations of surfaces . . . Suddenly there were golden bubbles rising on one of the surfaces, as though from a water glass, or as though a large carp were breathing below it . . . And now – just like those bubbles, I told myself – a thought rose to my mind. The only one.

Why is this? Why do the planners think for me, why do they plan what and how I'm supposed to think? Which is it, are they thinking as a favour to me, or thinking instead of me? That's the question. In my interest, or at my expense? So that I'll be nice and comfortable – or so that *they* will, in their conception of me? There are a great many services I can dispense with. So far, I don't feel the bleak need to have anyone else think, love, eat, or sleep for me. So far, I'm coping with these things myself, as best I can. What I need is a place, so that none of these things will have to be done for me – neither the thinking nor the loving . . . A place where I can do these things myself.

Such was the resentful thought that came suddenly to mind. I felt almost gleeful when I looked at the undemolished eyesore, epochally conspicuous at the end of the street.

I had an appointment to meet a certain woman, a publisher. Not a business appointment – simply, there were still some things I hadn't had time to see: a park, a fountain, and an art gallery. I had no right to leave without seeing them, so we met. And perhaps I was truly annoyed, or perhaps, having met only my friend's friends for ten days, I missed feminine society and was now exploiting the opportunity, rare in Erevan, to be the escort of an interesting woman who wasn't anyone's relative – but, anyway, I began reporting my architectural tribulations to her with excessive passion. I blossomed with every phrase, I was such a fervent, earnest man . . .

"He totally failed to hear my question, you see. All he heard was Peter the Great. But the point I was making about Peter was a different one, and perhaps not the most flattering. Before leaving on this trip, you see, I visited Peter's house – for the first time, I'm ashamed to say, because after all I'm a native, my grandfather and my father and my great-grandfather all lived in Petersburg. I happened on it by chance. You won't believe this, but for thirty years I had no idea it existed. I thought Peter the Great's house and the Summer Palace were the same thing! But that's not my point. The house is Petersburg's earliest surviving building. I was stunned, overwhelmed. By its very lack of museum atmosphere – by the vividness and unity of the sensation that a man had lived here. This man, Peter. The house is not a palace, you know. In fact, it's a beggarly little house. 'The refuge of the miserable Finn,' as Pushkin said. Apart from its rarity, it has no architectural value for our day, and yet . . . Every object – and the place is modest, very modest! – speaks not of itself but of its owner. Do you understand what I mean? But I hadn't expected anything of the house – that's very important! I hadn't expected anything of Geghard, either. They gave me everything all at once, everything they had . . . And here I'm walking around Erevan, always expecting something . . . Well, about the house. Overwhelmed, I walked out to the Neva – and was stunned all over again. Walking out of Peter's tiny, dark lodge, I saw the Neva, and the Peter and Paul Fortress, and the Summer Garden. And all that lavish beauty suddenly struck me with fresh, unaccustomed force. I tried to understand what had happened, what had given me the strength to *see* it, this beauty a thousand times seen and by now invisible. And suddenly, again, I understood: Peter! That is, I had somehow touched his idea from within, and everything was illumined for me in a new light. The idea was beyond mere words and thoughts: it existed physically! That was the self-evident truth that suddenly came through to me. During his lifetime Peter didn't manage to build all that much, hardly even enough to constitute the face of the city. He built a whole lot more after he died. Historically, Petrine ideas quite soon came to nothing in his successors. Only the idea of Petersburg, the image of it, was powerful enough so that other people's thinking, for a long time, unintentionally followed the course set by Peter. Simply, no other thought occurred to them.

"The builders carried on Peter's work. Amid the forests of completely different, even opposite ideas, no one even suspected that the edifice of this half-forgotten idea was steadily rising. By the time the momentum of Peter's idea was finally spent, Petersburg stood; by its form, integrity, and uniqueness, it dictated the laws of its own continuation. Few things in Russia, perhaps only two, Petersburg and the Soviet regime, originate from a single idea. They have this in

common. It may even be that only Petersburg could have become the
cradle of the regime. (Only in this city, in this ossified idea, could the
idea of a straightforwardly and literally understood order and harmony have been put into practice, as inevitably and unswervingly as
its avenues.) And Petersburg, the most un-Russian city, the triumph
of Peter's idea, still stands, even in our most naïve of times, stands
with its frozen former face, and the new districts separate out from
it like oil from water. This is a marvel. A marvel not in the sense of
the miraculous but of the phenomenal, for we can still imagine the
idea arising in Peter's powerful mind, and yet the fact that the idea
was implemented is almost dizzying in its impossibility. Like a centaur
or a griffin – and suddenly, look! it's galloping and flying! . . . And
the city will go on standing, because Petersburg cannot be changed
gradually, it can only be destroyed, destroyed along with the idea that
created it. The two of them, the city and the idea, will disappear
only together. The other beautiful cities of Russia grew up gradually,
without careful planning; they were built by life itself, over the
centuries. Their suddenly achieved harmony and charm, unique and
elusive, are defenceless in the face of any constructive idea. Thus,
Moscow is vanishing. One felled pine does not mean the end of the
forest . . . nor the second pine, nor the third . . . and suddenly the
forest has been felled, the Arbat district has been cleared . . . And the
man who still remembers finding a Boletus mushroom there in his
childhood will soon be dead . . . What am I getting at? The word
build has sounded increasingly proud and elevated, of late. Whereas
this is a profession, a job. The builder should not be puffed up with
pride. He is building something, and for someone. As long as the
builder erects dwelling and temple, temple and dwelling, he builds
for himself, and he's outside of time. But as soon as he begins to build
for someone else – a palace for a king, a mansion for an aristocrat, a
hut for a slave – he belongs only to his own time. No matter how
brilliant he is, he will be encircled by time and will build nothing *for
the ages*. Only time itself builds for the ages. Time, preserving one
thing, burying another, and erecting a third, is what gives a city its
unique and beautiful face. It likens the trivial and temporary work of
human hands to nature and life itself. The city comes to resemble a
grove, its days and nights and seasons are just as natural . . . If we
build a city in a period of a few years (we do, and will, have occasion
to build in that way), at least we should be cognizant that the work

of the centuries is beyond our capabilities, and not flatter ourselves in this regard . . . For, when we proceed from even the most beautiful idea, but only the one, aren't we imposing it, already unwanted and inconvenient, on generations to come? We must not build for the future but for the present, with profound love. It's conceited, to say the least, to fit the voiceless man of the future into our schemes without his by-your-leave. He'll find it far more valuable to see how we lived than to study our naïve, fossilized concepts of how he would live someday after we were gone . . . What's achieved in relation to life is always greater than what's achieved in relation to an idea. Even in the most admirable instance (getting back to Peter), isn't it painful to be forced to live within an alien idea, even if harmoniously and beautifully expressed? The Petersburg melancholy – we have all kinds of literary examples, and, besides, our personal experience is enough. Petersburg is like music, a Petersburg Symphony. Isn't this the same indignation Tolstoy felt whenever he listened to the Kreutzer Sonata – whose creator, although long dead and gone, forced his alien and temporally remote listener into the world of his own passions and feelings, unexplained by anything in the listener's concrete experience? Isn't this the same feeling that will sometimes choke today's Leningrader when he sets foot on some crooked little bridge, looks at the dirty water in the canal, and can't understand what's happening to him? Incidentally, even Pushkin's *Bronze Horseman*. It's not really so much a hymn to Peter and Petersburg, as we were taught in school. Otherwise, why such a sharp boundary between the introduction and the story of poor Yevgeny? That boundary, that contrast, is the very idea of the poem. It's hard to say which is more significant: the poet's admiration for the beauty and the might of the city, or his sympathy for Yevgeny, casting about in that beauty –"

Here I felt someone take my hand. My heart leaped. I turned to my companion and caught the exceedingly feminine glance that may equally be understood as doubt or interest, sympathy or mockery . . .

"Come," she said.

I found myself in an old Erevan street at last. *Old* is the wrong word: the street didn't savour of millennia, or of centuries. It may have been a hundred years old. The two- and three-storey houses stood close together, with softly defined, rounded windows; they had a half-blind stare, like a nearsighted person without his glasses. Their attempts to be rectilinear, and not made of clay, looked naïve. In olden days, probably, the street hadn't been a poor one – the approaches to the main thoroughfare of a provincial city might have looked like this. The street had no architectural style. The houses reminded me of antique refrigerators, back when there was no electricity and the ice brought by a deliveryman was stored in galvanized boxes . . . The small, deepset windows suggested shadowed rooms and an after-dinner nap. The walls looked puffy. They appeared to have been drawn by a child's hand. Sometimes the line of windows slipped downwards, as in the work of a lazy schoolboy . . . There were no passersby.

"Look!"

I stooped slightly to peer under an arch. I needn't have bent down; a man of normal height might perfectly well have walked through standing up. But it didn't look that way. And besides, the place had a logic of peeping and spying . . . as if through a crack, as if through a chink, as if through the optical peephole device in a modern apartment door, where you see your guest in an unthinkable perspective, and he no doubt sees your terrifying eye.

The deep, shady little tunnel with its rounded arch was like a tube and diaphragm, and it gave an implausible, telescopic distinctness to the courtyard beyond. The air is never so clear as it was in that courtyard. In contrast with the entrance, the courtyard was brightly lit, though not, it seemed, by the officious, dull-witted sun that was beating down on our backs in the street. The light was tranquil and even. At the right there was a little stairway – four steep, narrow, hollowed-out steps, and an absurd railing with a curlicue at the end. Beyond, three children were playing a game I had forgotten – the painted knucklebones lay about on the ground . . . Farther beyond, there was a kind of veranda with a lean-to; grapes hung from a trellis, someone was asleep on a wooden lounge . . . A drooping tree showed from around a corner on the right . . . In its small shadow a tiny stove smoked, coals crackled . . . A black-clad grandmother at the end of the courtyard was gathering something, or perhaps strewing something on the ground . . .

There are things about which you cannot say that you ever saw them for the first time – they're in your blood. This was the first time I had seen such a courtyard, but the phrase is just for the record. I had always known this courtyard – that would be far more accurate. Mine was the kind of emotion with which a man returns to his homeland: One tree has snapped, but that bush – how it's grown! Everyone has died . . . That can't be Masha, so big! Why, I used to carry her in my arms! And that barrel, I remember it – don't tell me it's still around . . . You prostrate yourself on the ground. Still alive, old fellow!

We walked along, peering into these deep little gates. I had forgotten about my companion, although there was also some subtle significance in the fact that she was nearby and knew what she was showing me: I was not alone with my mute ecstasy.

No courtyard repeated any other, but neither did any differ, it seemed. None was more beautiful or more interesting than any other – each was perfect. How had this chaos of lean-tos, cul-de-sacs, trees, light, and shade developed? It was impossible to retrace or imagine. Evidently, when life organizes itself according to its own unpremeditated laws, it cannot create an imperfect form.

Only in the old Dutch masters could I remember such depth and clarity. A pregnant woman reads a letter by the window . . . What light! Oh, they understood what it meant to have a frame, a window! A world that you discover by peering into it, a framed world, is so much more serious and self-contained than the world on the street, on the highway, in the field . . . In a frame, it's already a concept. An idea of the world.

That was how each courtyard looked, framed by the black gate opening.

This was what it meant to say "Human beings lived here"! And no abstract "art object" was needed. People lived, loved, gave birth, got sick, died, were born, grew up, grew old . . . Someone plastered a wall, someone carried an unneeded three-legged table out of the house, someone planted flowers, someone tore down a barn and cleared the site, and someone built a henhouse next to it . . . The courtyard grew like a tree – old branches died off, new cul-de-sacs grew up – and the branches of a tree are never imperfectly arranged. It's thicker here, thinner there, crooked there, broken there – but it's a tree! Children chirp in its crown, lovers prop up its trunk, and a black-clad grandmother keeps busy at the roots, stooping down, kindling the stove, picking up bits of wood and dropping them. The perspective of the generations, each courtyard like a genealogical tree . . .

The meaning of life, before you and after you, is clear at last.

At each gate, you can't tear yourself away, yet neither can you spy. But the next one, too – when you're walking up to it, you can't believe it might be just as nice . . . but this next one, too, when you look in, is like a sigh, a sigh of relief, a sigh of meeting, a sigh of not parting, and the mysterious sweet faith that even you can have happiness . . .

Neither this street nor these courtyards have any historical or architectural value. They will be demolished. New buildings with all the conveniences will stand here, people will settle in them, they will love, give birth and die, suffer and rejoice. But I don't know: a hundred years from now, will these walls be so steeped in warmth and love, life and death, that as soon as you turn the corner and take the first step you will feel the same kinship and happiness you feel now, on this blurry clay lane? . . . Or will everything be reflected from surfaces full and shiny, regular and flat?

We value human labour, and we still value it too little. But do we value that which is even more precious, that which *is*, that which has come about without us, without our participation – the great harmony and art of nature and time? Lumber is more costly than unfelled pine, of course – but in monetary terms! We must not confuse cost with value, expensiveness with preciousness . . . The most brilliant creation of human hands is monosemantic and partial, compared with nature. Nature is a correctly and cleanly struck chord, overheard and borrowed from the absolute harmony and polyphony of life. Harmony cannot be measured by cost. The automobile is in no way more precious than the glade in which we have parked . . . And no effort of ours will ever create the early morning, or fabricate the sunrise, the dew, the blade of grass . . . No artist will ever, by mere force of imagination, be able to scatter the barns and huts as naturally, in relation to river, road, and sky, as they are scattered in any little village; he will never manage to place the lone cow or horse where it belongs, or the haystack or windmill, or to set the jars and earthenware pots in correct sequence on the pickets of the sagging wattle fence. He won't even be able to make the fence sag properly! All he can do is steal a glimpse.

A great textbook of harmony has been given to us by life – free, gratis. And we must remember that if we tear out all the pages, we will have nothing to study from.

Ah, Erevan! Did a bird sketch you? Did a lion
colour you like a child with a crayon box?

On this clay lane, when I bent my head and peered into a little courtyard, I saw that Erevan at last. Mandelstam was never inaccurate.

What does a man leave behind in objects? Merely the form he has
imparted to them? Or the warmth of his hands, the touch of his
glances, the dents from his words? Everything here spoke the language
of life, both past and future. Eternal life . . . I dared, I entered the
courtyard, and from all the doorways people who loved me came
running – great-grandfathers and great-grandmothers, great-
grandsons and great-granddaughters . . . People of the past and future
embraced me and formed a wordless column, tenderly grieving and
nodding, pitying me as I walked past them and wept with sorrow
and happiness . . .

Translated from the Russian by Susan Brownsberger

ANNA AKHMATOVA

Anna Akhmatova's poem "There Are Four of Us" celebrates the companion-ship of the four great Russian poets of the first half of the twentieth century: Osip Mandelstam, Boris Pasternak, Marina Tsvetaeva and, of course, Anna Akhmatova herself. Alongside "There Are Four of Us", we publish new translations of poems by each member of the quartet.

There Are Four of Us

Herewith I solemnly renounce my hoard
of earthly goods, whatever counts as chattel.
The genius and guardian angel of this place
has changed to an old tree-stump in the water.

Earth takes us in awhile as transient guests;
we live by habit, which we must unlearn.
On paths of air I seem to overhear
two friends, two voices, talking in their turn.

Did I say two? . . . There by the eastern wall,
where criss-cross shoots of brambles trail,
– Oh look! – that fresh dark elderberry branch
is like a letter from Marina in the mail.

NOVEMBER 1961
[in delirium]

Translated from the Russian by
Stanley Kunitz and Max Hayward

OSIP MANDELSTAM

Tristia

I have studied the science of saying goodbye
In a night of lamentations with hair unbound.
The oxen chew, and the wait drags on and on
Till the last hour of the city's vigil comes round,
And I ponder the ritual of that cockcrow night
When I lifted the load of sorrow I must bear
While eyes red from weeping stared somewhere out of
    sight
And the song of the Muses merged with a woman's
    tears.

Who can know, when he hears the word "farewell"
What kind of separation is before us,
Or what it is the crowing cock foretells
When the fire burns upon the acropolis,
And as some new kind of life is dawning,
While the oxen chew lethargically in their stall,
Why the cock, the herald of new life,
Flaps his wings on the city wall?

And so I cherish the familiar rituals of yarn:
The shuttle moves to and fro, the spindle hums,
Look there – running, like a fleck of swansdown,
Barefoot Delia comes!
Ah, this life of ours stands upon a base so thin,
And the language of rejoicing is so poor!
It all happened long ago, it all happens once more,
And nothing is sweet but the moment of recognition.

So be it: a fluid pattern
Spreads across a clean earthen plate
Like a squirrel skin someone has flattened,
Hovering over the wax, a girl waits.
It is not for us to speculate about Greek Erebus,
What wax is for women, bronze is for men.
Fate comes only in battle for us,
But their fate is to die in telling fortunes.

1918

Translated from the Russian by Robert Tracy

MARINA TSVETAEVA

An Attempt at Jealousy

What is life like with another, –
Simpler, no? – The stroke of an oar! –
Did the Memory of me soon
Fade away, a floating island,

Like the line of some sea shore,
(in the sky and not on the waters)?
Souls, O souls! You will be sisters,
You will not be lovers – you!

What is life like with a *simple*
Woman? *Without* deity?
You who have dethroned your princess
(And abdicated yourself),

What is life like – busying yourself? –
Do you curl up? How do you rise?
How do you cope, poor fellow, with the
Cost of the undying commonplace?

"Enough of palpitations and
Convulsions! I'll take a house."
What is life like with any other
Woman, you, my chosen one!

Is the food more eatable and
To your taste? If it palls, don't complain . . .
What is life like with any other
Woman, you, my chosen one!

What is life like with a stranger
From this world? In plain language,
Is she your love? Does not shame,
Like Zeus' reins, lay lashes on your brow?

What is life like? Are you keeping well?
Getting on? How do you sing?
How do you cope, poor fellow, with the
Ulcer of immortal conscience?

What is life like with market goods?
The price is steep, isn't it?
After the marble of Carrara
What is life like with pieces

Of plaster? (Out of a block God
Was cut – and smashed to smithereens!)
What is life like with one of a
Hundred thousand – you who have known Lilith!

Are you sated with new market
Goods? Now to witchery grown cold, and
Without a sixth sense, what is life
Like with a woman of this world?

1924

Translated from the Russian by Peter Norman

BORIS PASTERNAK

Night

Without lingering,
night begins to lighten and lift
as the pilot lifts
above the drowsing day

and dwindles in mist,
lost in the midst of light,
like the tiny cross
of a laundry mark,

leaving behind the all-night bars
in strange towns, sentry-go,
stokers, steam engines, stations —
all striking their spark.

The shadow of his aircraft
a silent skier on the cloud below.
And all the crowded stars
disperse in all directions,

strewn like the Milky Way
as everything suddenly banks.
Headlands shine out
over uncertain horizons.

The boiler house furnace flares
in the stoker's stare.
In Paris, Mars and Venus
stoop to the street

where a glistening poster
is pasted for the Opera.
High up, at a window
wide ajar on a mansard roof,

this sleepless soul
hypnotizes the far horizon.
He stares at the stars
as though they were the troubles

that kept him awake,
a constellation of cares.
Don't go to sleep. Work.
Work. Don't go to sleep.

Like a pilot, like a planet,
don't give way to drowsiness, poet.
You are the pledge we give eternity
and so the slave of every second.

Translated from the Russian by Craig Raine with
Ann Pasternak Slater

ANNA AKHMATOVA

Boris Pasternak

He, who compared himself to the eye of a steed,
Looks askance, glances, sees, recognizes,
And lo: like melted diamonds
Ice wastes away and puddles shine.

Backyards, platforms, beams and leaves
Repose with clouds in lilac mist.
Engines' whistles, the crunch of melon peel,
A timid hand in a fragrant glove.

Ringing, thundering, grinding, the crash of waves
And sudden quiet – all means he
Treads over the pine needles with trepidation
So as not to disturb the fragile sleep of space.

And it means; he counts the grains
In the empty ears; it means he has come
From some funeral once again
To visit the cursed, black Daryal grave-stone.

And once more the languor of Moscow burns,
The sleigh-bells of death ring out afar off . . .
Who has got lost two steps from home,
Where the snow is waist-deep and an end to everything?

For comparing smoke to Laocoon,
For singing of graveyard thistles,
For filling the world with a new song
In the new space of reflected verses –

He is endowed with eternal childhood,
With the generosity and sharpness of the spheres
And all the earth was his inheritance,
And he shared it all with everyone.

19 JANUARY 1936

Translated from the Russian by Peter Norman

CLAUDIO MAGRIS

From the novel *A Different Sea*

*Early in this century, Enrico, a young intellectual, leaves his native Gorizia,
the Autro-Hungarian city with its mixed population and culture, and sets
out across the ocean. He has been taught by his closest friend, Carlo, a
philosopher/poet who commits suicide in his early twenties, that his search
must be for an authentic life, free of social falsehoods. The scholarly Enrico
becomes a solitary gaucho in the* pampas . . .

Correspondence is difficult because of the distance and the unreliable
poste restante. Some letters addressed to Enrico care of Verzegnassi
the chemist in Buenos Aires were sent back again. His mother posted
him a cheque without adding a word: he returned it without a reply.
Carlo wrote to say that the thought that he would soon have news
of Enrico made him feel less miserable. Enrico reads his letter again:
"From you we are expecting a most important contribution to our
reality." He puts the letter away and looks at his feet resting on a log
next to the fire. For once he is wearing socks, as it is cold. Close by,
a calf, its muzzle nearly touching the ground, gives him a blank stare.
To graze, to ruminate, to die. It is a relief to lighten the load. His
talent is for reducing things, not for increasing them. Why do they
expect things from him that he cannot give? He gets to his feet and
goes for a walk, paying no attention to the animals that shy nervously
away.

He writes back and a few months later receives another letter from
Carlo, puzzled about his reticence which he attributes to the trials
and difficulties that his friend is having to endure "out there". But
the fact is that Enrico, "out here", is doing fine and has all he needs.
True, he has left his heart in Gorizia with Carlo, but one can survive
well enough without a heart – like having an artificial hand or leg.

All it takes is a bit of practice and then one can climb again into the saddle without difficulty. The problem lies only in explaining one's feelings.

Carlo's words arrive, large and peremptory, raining down like arrows in the void. "We have been inevitably drawn to you in our grey lives . . . we have come to understand the meaning of a confident and dignified conscience . . . you give definition to mankind and the material world . . . you, Rico, are a being of superior strength, like a saint, serene and assured in whatever circumstances of life or of death . . . you are showing us the way towards a true valuation of things." Dated 28th November, as he was leaving. A saint in Patagonia? Enrico lifts his eyes from the page to a large, dense cloud in the sky. It is as though it is his body floating away up there, leaving on its own account, while he himself, half reclining on the earth, is merely an empty form, the imprint of something that has been carried off.

Carlo wrote those words to him, Enrico. It should have been the other way round. His heart either contracts or swells. He understands little of these cardiac metaphors, but some part of him somewhere is definitely trembling. It isn't right. Their having been at school together means a great deal – but not everything. One of them is called Carlo, the other Enrico. Were it not for the time he had pointed out that thread of water falling down over the rock, perhaps Carlo would never have written that piece on life, how it flows and then is lost. But you cannot expect someone always to stay on the pedestal you make for him. Nino, too, always feels the need to rush ahead and reach the top of the hill during an otherwise enjoyable walk in the woods, while Enrico is happy enough lying on the grass and watching the daisies grow.

29th June 1910: "You, Rico, with your self-assurance, live your life ready for anything. Everything, whatever the peril, has a way of turning spontaneously to you. Because you ask for nothing. It is as though you do not notice the passage of time for, by acting in every moment, you are free of it. Thus too every word you utter derives from a life of freedom . . ." Carlo is right, Enrico asks for nothing. He does not even ask why and how it is that everything just seems to come his way – this letter, for instance, which is even, perhaps, too much.

When he is out riding, with that rush of excitement that brings colour to his cheeks, his troubled thoughts are forgotten. Sometimes after hours in the saddle he grows thirsty. So he lassos a wild horse and then slackens the rope, leaving the animal to lead him to some tiny spring it knows among the rocks with threads of cold, silent rust. At other times he has to kill a horse and drink its blood to quench his thirst.

He moves a little further south, towards San Carlos de Bariloche. He spends all day and every day in the saddle, careful to keep the herds from straying and getting lost. As soon as he can he will build a large corral, worry less about the animals escaping, and not wake up before they stir at dawn in the cold wind that comes, passing over few living things on its way, from the frozen distant wastes. But obtaining timber and building an enclosure are expensive, and right now he has no money. He must be patient and wait.

Wagon trains come past every so often. Enrico sells an animal and buys some tobacco, rice, biscuits, and coffee. Occasionally there are women travelling south with the wagons and then back up north, with a view to meeting men of his sort. One can afford to sleep with them for three days on the proceeds from the sale of a horse or calf, if the wagon trains stop that long; otherwise an hour is good enough. The women are fine mounts with strong flanks that know how to carry a good weight. And when minded they can show a bit of unexpected spirit that takes one by surprise. Yet whenever Enrico thinks about them, he can never conjure up any single one in all her particulars. He never remembers which face goes with which oversized breasts or with which gargantuan rump. There was one woman who, immediately it was over, would pull some flat maize bread and lard from her poncho and begin to eat, while he was still caressing her back, thinking it nicer to wind down slowly and not to have it over and done with all at once.

Occasionally too he sleeps with Indian women, but only rarely. He is stimulated by their harsh, closed faces, something which makes him feel rather ashamed. With them he rushes in like a nervous boy rather than relaxing and enjoying himself like a man. They twist like snakes and mutter incomprehensibly, while with the other women there is an amiable understanding that a poor devil doesn't have to make an effort to satisfy them. You and she understand and tolerate each other, whereas the Indian woman beneath him is beyond reach. Perhaps she is enjoying it but, if so, it is without noticing him. He might as well not exist: it is as though he simply isn't there. Only his pestle grinding away on its own account.

But it doesn't happen very often. People pass by so rarely. He admires the way the Indian women give birth without fuss. As soon as it is over they get to their feet and, if it's winter, break the ice of the frozen stream to wash themselves and the baby. If the child is healthy the cold does no harm, and if it dies – well it would not have survived anyway. Enrico doesn't stop to think about it, not least because he has never been able to endure babies, especially when they scream. The Indians he respects. But then the Indians respect each other. They harm nothing, neither man nor beast, without good reason. They strip life to the bone, like a leg of guanaco. His teacher Schubert-Soldern is an Indian too in his way. At times they defecate like horses, upright, with regal nonchalance, in their rapid stride across the prairie.

He has built himself a cabin, but just to sleep in, with a plank of wood for a bed. When hungry, he kills a sheep or shoots a rabbit. He has a good aim, and is in general capable and accurate – with horses as with the Greek aorist. Basic skill is only proper, since everything has the right to be treated with due care. It is right to know how to pick a flower without damaging it. To roast a piece of meat one only needs two stones and some firewood. And when it is months since the last wagon train, and he has run out of salt, he does not waste his meat. Instead he chews it, tasteless though it is, without spoiling it by wishing for the salt he lacks.

The milk too is good. He drinks it warm, straight from the bucket beneath the cow. He removes his sombrero to scoop out some milk – much easier than drinking from cupped hands. There is no need to lock up his cabin. It's enough to wedge the door with a stone to keep out the rain and the animals. From the Cordillera to the coast there is talk of outlaws, of Butch Cassidy, the Sundance Kid, or Evans, dead or resurrected. But no one ever passes by his way – for the past two years he hasn't seen a soul. He has no need of a lock on the door to protect two planks of wood, a couple of blankets, and five or six Teubner classical texts.

Enrico detests locks, as he does ties. But that does not mean that others could rifle through his kit. Absolutely not. In fact the letter from Tolstoy annoyed him for that reason. The grand old man replied magnanimously and irrevocably to him, an unknown lad from

Gorizia, and he kept those four sheets written in German, along with the letters from Carlo, among the pages of Sophocles. Enrico had written to Tolstoy – from the attic, of course. That was where they had read the works of Ibsen and Tolstoy. Those two Atlases, who propped up the world, had shaken it to its foundations by sundering themselves inexorably from the rhetoric in which they, like all the rest, had their roots. Truth was enshrined in their writing, as in the music of Beethoven. Enrico had written with reckless candour: he had wanted to become a follower, to enter the commune. The grand old man's reply had been brusque and majestic: he could come but first he should give all that he owned to the poor, as is written in the Gospels. It was easy enough for Tolstoy to give away his wife's possessions, but that did not go down at all well with Enrico. Better Schopenhauer, who kept a close watch on his purse and his food. Enrico prefers to own nothing, to undress on the banks of the Isonzo, to strip naked and throw himself into the water. But why should someone come along and carry off his rags and get praise for it? It is a senseless, empty gesture, as when his uncle Giuseppe gave away his townhouse in Gradisca and then sponged off his brothers.

No, Enrico has no time either for Socialists or Christians in catacombs. A Buddhist monk with his begging bowl and no shoes is all right; after all, it's nice to go around with bare feet. But those communes with their hearts on their sleeves must really be the limit, each more intrusive and irritating than the last. What is certain is that they make a great noise about it. What a crazy idea, living squashed altogether and sticking their noses into each other's affairs. Thank God he realized in time, and is now in Patagonia, not Jasnaja Poljana after helping a few layabouts.

Admittedly it can be seen as a fine gesture, a real act of largesse – and yet that other gesture, of replying to an impudent boy, is also great, perhaps even as fine as the one the old man expected of him. Sell off everything and give the money to the poor. Is that the true life? Why is it that everyone expects the impossible of him? Better Ibsen, who did not suffer from megalomania. And yet it is true to say Enrico never thinks of his father's mills in Gorizia, nor knows anything of his share of the inheritance or even how much money his family has.

Every so often the horses get sick with a fever that affects their lungs. He knows what to do. He opens a vein with his knife at the right place and bleeds it. Then he makes the horses gulp down *ginebra* or, if that doesn't do the trick, the whisky he bought off a Welshman, until they get drunk. Their heads droop with lolling tongues and rolling eyes, but then after a few days they recover. Once he finds himself face to face with a puma. His horse shies, and when he whips it furiously and even bites it, it throws and tramples him. For months afterward he pisses blood, until some Indians cure him with a decoction from the bark of certain trees.

He goes to Bahia Blanca for the big cattle fair. Thousands of animals are herded in from all over the country, and the earth pounded by their hooves is as slimy as grape pulp after the wine-making. The big traders are already there waiting and paying out money in huge wads.

There are prostitutes too from every corner of the country. For forty-eight hours money floods through the hands of the cattlemen, like the blackberries they used to cram into their mouths by the handful on the wooded slopes of San Valentin, bursting and crushing them with their teeth, careless of the juice running down their chins. Indian women, half-castes, negro girls with big red bows – all crowding round his horse like cows on the prairie, shouting and waving, with flashing eyes and white teeth. As evening comes on, a flask of wine breaks across the sky, spreading everywhere, even to the flushed and excited faces of the crowd.

The cattlemen throw bags of money into the hands raised and reaching towards them. Enrico does the same, not only for the sake of a barefoot girl with dark braided hair, but also for the sheer happiness of tossing something away, like throwing stones into the Isonzo and making them skip on the surface of the water. All around him is shouting, laughter, the lowing of cattle, the cracking of whips, fireworks going off, pomegranates erupting, their scarlet seeds spraying out into the night sky. With the girl in his saddle he loses himself for a while in the deafening jamboree. But he has soon had as much as he can take of the shouts, the lights, and the crush, and sets off for home. After a few days on the trail he reaches his cabin, moves the rock aside, and lies down to sleep.

He does not reckon up the days and the weeks. Instead he uses more elastic, indeterminate ways of measuring time – the first flurry of sleet, the grass's loss of colour, the rutting of the guanacos. There is always a wind, and after a while one learns to distinguish its different moods, from hour to hour and from season to season, a tugging, drawn-out whistle, a dry rasp like a cough. At times the wind seems coloured – golden brown in the scrub, black on the desolate plain.

Large clouds float by and are gone, a cow tugs free a clump of grass, the earth turns yet also stands still, a daisy lasts a month, a mayfly just one day, the evening star is the morning star. Sometimes the sky opens out like a sphere of blown glass, grows distant and vanishes.

Enrico fires. The wild duck plummets to the ground, one moment in heraldic flight, the next a piece of rubbish tossed from a window. The law of gravity makes nature clumsy. Only words are protected – such as those printed in the Teubner Greek and Latin texts from Leipzig.

The shot's echo dies out among the rocks. Carlo shot himself with Enrico's pistol. The final curtain has been lowered. There is nothing more to say – for Enrico that is, not for Carlo, over whom that instantaneous gesture can have no power, just as the cerebral haemorrhage has no power over Ibsen, or pneumonia over Tolstoy, or hemlock over Socrates. Carlo is the conscience of his age. Death has power only over the verb "to have" not over the verb "to be". Enrico has his herds, his horse, and a few books.

He learned of Carlo's death a year after it happened, in the September of 1911. The news was waiting for him on his arrival at Puerto Madryn on the coast after a journey of six hundred kilometres. Nino had written to tell him and had enclosed a copy of the poems Carlo had written since Enrico's departure, in the last year of his life. "I have had the good fortune, denied you, of being close to him, of seeing him, of sharing his life right to the end. Now we are alike, and his death binds us even more closely. What he taught me, you have learned in a different way by yourself. How life seemed then and how it seems now! All that is over, for ever. No life, no joy will ever equal that for which I believed I only had to wait."

Translated from the Italian by Stephen Spurr

JOSE SARAMAGO

From the novel *The Gospel According to Jesus Christ*

The Gospel According to Jesus Christ *follows the life of Christ from his conception to his eventual crucifixion, but Saramago's version focuses on a naïve, human Jesus whose doubts and fears are rooted in the confusion surrounding the events of his birth, his father's troubled life and untimely death, and in the unknown identity of the mysterious yet compassionate beggar with whom he subsequently spends his formative years. At pains to understand the path of saintly martyrdom which his tyrannical God has paved for him, Jesus resolves to find the answers to the numerous questions which have caused him such disquiet.*

A MISTY MORNING. The fisherman rises from his mat, looks at the white space through a chink in the door and says to his wife, I'm not taking the boat out today, in such a mist even the fish lose their way under the water. This is what he said and, using more or less the same words, all the other fishermen echoed his sentiments from one bank to another, puzzled by the rare phenomenon of mist at this time of the year. Only one man, who is not a fisherman by profession although he lives and works with fishermen, goes to his front door as if to confirm that this is the day he has been waiting for and, looking up at the dull sky, says to himself, I'm going out fishing. At his shoulder, Mary Magdalene asks, Must you go, and Jesus replied, I've waited a long time for this day to come, Won't you cat something, Eyes are fasting when they open in the morning. He embraced her and said, At last I shall know who I am and what is expected of me, then with surprising confidence, for he could not even see his own feet in the mist, he descended the slope to the water's edge, climbed into one of the boats moored there and began rowing out towards that invisible space in the middle of the sea. The noise of the oars scraping and hitting the sides of the boat, the disturbance and dispersal of water as it escaped, resounded over the entire surface and kept awake those fishermen whose anxious wives had told them, If you can't go out fishing, at least try to get some sleep. Restless and uneasy, the villagers stared at that impenetrable mist in the direction where the sea ought to be and waited, without knowing, for the noise of the oars to stop so that they might return to their homes and secure all their doors with keys, crossbars and padlocks, even though they knew that a simple puff of air would knock them down, if he who is yonder is who they imagine him to be and should decide to blow this way. The mist allows Jesus to pass, but his eyes can see no further than the tip of the oars and the stern with its simple plank which serves as a bench. The rest is a blank wall, at first dim and grey, then, as the boat approaches its destination, a diffused light turns the mist white and lustrous, and it quivers as if searching in vain for a sound amidst the silence. Moving into a wider circle of light, the boat comes to a halt, it has reached the centre of the lake. God is sitting on the bench at the stern.

Unlike the first time, He does not appear as a cloud or column of smoke which in this weather would get lost and merge with the mist. This time, He is a big man, elderly, with a great flowing beard spread over his chest, head uncovered, hair hanging loose, a broad and powerful face, fleshy lips, barely moving when He begins to speak. Dressed like a wealthy Jew, in a long, magenta tunic, under a blue mantle with sleeves and gold braiding, the thick sandals on his feet are clearly those of someone who walks a lot and whose habits are anything but sedentary. Once He has gone, we shall ask ourselves, What was His hair like, without being able to remember whether it was white, black or brown, judging by His age, the hair must have been white, but there are people whose hair takes a long time to turn white and He might be one of them. Jesus shipped the oars and rested them inside the boat as if preparing for a lengthy conversation and simply said, I'm here. Slowly and methodically, God arranged the folds of the mantle over His knees and added, Well, here we are. The tone of voice suggested that He might have been smiling but His lips hardly moved, only the long hairs of His moustache and beard were quivering like the vibrations of a bell. Jesus said, I've come to find out who I am and what I shall have to do henceforth in order to fulfil my part of the contract. God said, These are two questions, so let's take them one at a time, where would you like to start, With the first one, said Jesus, before asking for a second time, Who am I, Don't you know, God asked him, Well I thought I knew and believed myself

to be my father's son, Which father do you mean, My father, the
carpenter Joseph, son of Eli or was it Jacob for I'm no longer certain,
You mean the carpenter Joseph whom they crucified, I didn't know
there was any other, A tragic mistake on the part of the Romans and
that poor father died innocent having committed no crime. You said
that father, does this mean there is another, I'm proud of you, I can
see you're an intelligent lad and perceptive, There was no need for
any intelligence on my part, I was told by the Devil. Are you in league
with the Devil, No, I'm not in league with the Devil, it was the Devil
who sought me out, And what did you hear from his lips, That I am
Your son. Nodding His head slowly in agreement, God told him,
Yes, you are my son, But how can a man be the son of God, If you're
the son of God you are not a man, But I am a man, I breathe, I eat,
I sleep and I love like a man, therefore I am a man and shall die as a
man, In your case I wouldn't be too sure, What do you mean, That's
the second question, but we have time, how did you answer the Devil
when he said you were my son, I said no more, simply waited for the
day when I should meet You, and drove Satan out of the possessed
man he was tormenting, the man called Himself Legion and said he
was many, Where are they now, I have no idea, You said you exorcised
those demons, Surely You know better than me that when demons
are driven out of someone's body, nobody knows where they go, And
what makes you think I'm familiar with the Devil's affairs, Being God,
You must know everything, Up to a certain point, only up to a
certain point, What point is that, The point where it starts to become
interesting to pretend that I know nothing, At least You must know
how I came to be Your son and for what reason, I can see you're
getting somewhat more confident, not to say impatient, since I first
met you, In those days I was a mere boy and rather shy, but I'm
grown up now, And you're not afraid, No, Don't worry, you will be,
fear always comes, even to a son of God, You mean to say you have
others, What others, Sons, of course, No, I only needed one, And
how did I come to be Your son, Didn't your mother tell you, Does
my mother know, I sent an angel to explain things to her, and I
thought she would have told you, And when was this angel with my
mother, Let Me see, unless I'm mistaken it was after you left home
for the second time and before you miraculously changed the water
into wine at Cana, So, Mother knew and never said a word, when I
told her I had seen You in the desert, she didn't believe me, but she

must have realized I was telling the truth after the angel's appearance
yet she never confided in me, You know what women are like, after
all you live with one, they have their little susceptibilities and scruples,
What susceptibilities and scruples, Well, let Me explain, I mixed my
seed with that of your father before you were conceived, it was the
easiest solution and the least obvious, And since the seeds are mixed,
how can You be sure that I am Your son, I agree that it's usually
unwise to feel certain about anything, but I'm absolutely certain for
there is some advantage in being God, And why did You want to
have a son, Since I didn't have a son in heaven, I had to arrange one
on earth, which is not all that original because even in religions with
gods and goddesses, who could easily have given each other children,
we have seen some of them descend upon earth, probably for a change,
and at the same time benefit mankind with the creation of heroes and
other wonders. And this son who I am, why did You want him,
Needless to say, not for the sake of change, Why then, Because I
needed someone to help Me here on earth, But surely being God,
You don't need help, That is the second question.

In the silence that followed one could hear somewhere in the mist,
without being able to determine from which direction, the noise of
someone swimming this way, and judging from the puffing and panting, he was no great swimmer and fairly close to exhaustion. Jesus
thought he saw God smiling and felt sure He was deliberately giving
the swimmer time to appear within the circle clear of mist which had
the boat at its centre. The swimmer unexpectedly surfaced on the
starboard side when one might have expected him to arrive on the
other side, a dark, ill-defined shape which, at first sight, Jesus mistook
for a pig with its ears sticking out of the water, but after a few more
strokes he realized it was a man or something with human form. God
turned His head towards the swimmer, not out of mere curiosity but
with genuine interest as if anxiously encouraging him to make one
last effort, and this gesture, perhaps because it came from God, had
an immediate effect, the final strokes were rapid and regular and it
was hard to believe that this new arrival had covered all that distance
from the shore. His hands grabbed the edge of the boat although his
head was still half-submerged in the water and they were huge, powerful hands with strong nails, hands belonging to a body which like
that of God must be tall, sturdy and advanced in years. The boat
swayed under the impact, the swimmer's head emerged from the

water, then his trunk, splashing water everywhere, then his legs, a Leviathan rising from the lower depths, and he turned out to be Pastor, reappearing after all these years. I've come to join you, he said, settling himself on the side of the boat equidistant between Jesus and God yet, strange to relate, this time the boat did not lean over to his side, as if the weight had gone from Pastor's body or he were levitating while appearing to be seated, I'm here to join you, he repeated, and hope I'm still in time to take part in the conversation, We've been chatting for some time but we still haven't come to the heart of the matter, replied God, and turning to Jesus He told him, This is the Devil whom we have just been discussing. Jesus looked from one to the other, and saw that without God's beard they could pass for twins, although the Devil looked younger and less wrinkled, but it must have been an optical illusion or mistake on Jesus's part. Jesus said, I know very well who he is, after all, I lived with him for four years when he was known as Pastor, and God replied, You had to live with someone, it couldn't be with Me, and you didn't wish to be with your family, so that only left the Devil. Did he come looking for me or did You send him, Frankly, neither one nor the other, let's say we agreed that this was the best solution, So that's why he sounded so certain when he spoke through the possessed man from Gadara and called me Your son, Precisely, Which means that both of you deceived me, As happens to all humans, You've already said that I'm not human, And I can confirm it, but you have been what might technically be described as incarnated, And now what do both of you want from me, I'm the one who wants something, not him. Both of you are here and I noticed that Pastor's sudden appearance came as no surprise, so You must have been expecting him, Not exactly, although in principle one should always count on the Devil, But if the problem You and I have to resolve only affects us, what is he doing here and why don't You send him away, One can dismiss the rabble in the Devil's service if they start being troublesome in word and deed, but not Satan himself, So he's here because this conversation also concerns him, My son, never forget what I'm about to tell you, everything that concerns God also concerns the Devil. Pastor, whom we shall sometimes refer to as such, rather than constantly be invoking the Enemy by name, overheard their conversation without appearing to listen or be aware that they were discussing him, thus appearing to deny God's closing and all-important statement. However it soon became clear that his inattentiveness was mere pretence, because Jesus only had to say, Let's now turn to the second question, for Pastor to prick up his ears. But without uttering a single word.

God breathed in deeply, looked at the mist around Him and murmured in the hushed tones of someone who has just made an unexpected and curious discovery, It would never have occurred to Me, but this is just like being in the desert. He turned His eyes towards Jesus, paused awhile and then, like someone resigning himself to the inevitable, began speaking, Dissatisfaction, my son, has been put into the heart of men by the God who created them, I'm referring to myself, of course, but this dissatisfaction which like all the other traits which made them in my image and likeness, I myself pursued in my own heart and rather than diminish with time it has grown stronger, more pressing and insistent. God stopped for a moment to consider the effect of this preamble before going on to say, For the last four thousand and four years I have been the God of the Jews, a quarrelsome and difficult race by nature, but on the whole, I have got along fairly well with them because they now take Me seriously and are likely to go on doing so for the foreseeable future, So, You are satisfied, said Jesus, I am and I'm not, or rather, I would be were it not for this restless heart of mine which is forever telling Me, Well now, a fine destiny you've arranged after four thousand years of trials and tribulations which no amount of sacrifices on the altars will ever be able to recompense, for You continue to be the god of a tiny population which occupies a minute part of this world You created with everything that's on it, so tell Me, my son, if I can derive any satisfaction from this depressing sight which is constantly before my eyes, Never having created a world, I'm in no position to judge, replied Jesus, True, you cannot judge but you could help, Help in what way, To spread my word, to help Me become the god of more people, I don't understand, If you play your part, that is to say, the part I have reserved for you in my plan, I have every confidence that within the next six centuries or so, despite all the struggles and obstacles ahead of us, I shall pass from being God of the Jews to being God of those whom we shall call Catholics as in Greek, And what is this part You've reserved for me in Your plan, That of martyr, my son, that of victim, which is the best role of all for propagating any faith and stirring up fervour. God uttered the words martyr and victim as if His tongue were made of milk and honey, but Jesus suddenly felt a chill go through his limbs as if the mist had closed over him and the Devil looked at him with an enigmatic expression which combined scientific interest with grudging compassion. You promised me power and glory, stammered Jesus, still shivering with cold, And I intend to keep that promise, but remember our pact, you shall have them after death, What good will it do me to have power and glory when I'm dead, Well, you won't be dead in the absolute sense of the word, for as my son you'll be with Me, or in Me, I still haven't finally decided. In the sense You've just mentioned of my not being dead, That's right, for example, you'll be venerated in churches and on altars to such an extent that people will even forget that I came first as God, but no matter, abundance can be shared, what is in short supply should not. Jesus looked at Pastor, saw him smile and understood, I can now see why the Devil is here, if Your authority is to extend to more people in more places, his power will also spread, for Your limits are exactly the same as his, You're quite right, my son, and I'm delighted to see how perceptive you are for most people overlook the fact that the demons of one religion are powerless to act in another, just as any god, directly confronting another god would neither be able to vanquish him nor be vanquished by him. And my death, what will that be like, It is only fitting that a martyr's death should be painful and, if possible, ignominious, so that believers may be moved to greater fervour and devotion. Come to the point and tell me what kind of death I can expect, A painful and ignominious death on a cross, Like my father, You're forgetting I'm your father, Were I free to make a choice, I'd choose him despite that moment of infamy, You have been chosen and therefore have no say, I want to end our pact, to have nothing to do with You, I want to live like any other man, Empty words, my son, can't you see you're in my power and that all these sealed documents we refer to as agreements, pacts, treaties, contracts, alliances, and in which I figure, could be reduced to a single clause, and waste less paper and ink, a clause which would bluntly state that, Everything prescribed by the law of God is obligatory, even the exceptions, and since you, my son, are something of a notable exception, you, too, are as obligatory as the law and I who made it, But with Your power would it not be much simpler and ethically more honest for You to go out and conquer those other countries and races Yourself. Alas, I cannot, because it is forbidden by the binding agreement between the gods ever to interfere directly in any dispute, can you imagine Me in a public square, surrounded by gentiles and pagans, trying to persuade them that their god is false and that I am their real God, this is not something one god does to another, and, besides, no god likes another god to come and do in his house what he is forbidden to do in theirs, So, You make use of humans instead, Yes, my son, man is a piece of wood that can be used for everything, from the moment he's born until the moment he dies, he's always ready to obey, send him there and he goes, tell him to halt and he stops, tell him to turn back and he retreats, whether in peace or in war, man, generally speaking, is the best thing that could have happened to the gods, And the wood from which I'm made, since I'm a man, what use will it be put to, since I'm Your son, You will be the spoon I shall dip into humanity and bring out laden with men who shall believe in the new god I intend to become, Laden with men You will devour, There's no need for Me to devour those who devour themselves.

Jesus lowered his oars into the water and said, Farewell, I'm off home, and you can both go back the way you came, you by swimming, and You by disappearing as mysteriously as You came. Neither God nor the Devil stirred, whereupon Jesus added ironically, Ah, so you prefer to go by boat, better still, I'll row you ashore myself so that everyone may see how alike God and the Devil are and how well they get on together. Jesus turned the boat to face the bank from where they had come and, rowing with vigorous strokes, penetrated the mist which was so thick that he could no longer see God nor so much as the Devil's face. Jesus felt alive and happy, and unusually energetic. From where he was sitting the prow of the boat was invisible but he could feel the boat rising with each stroke of the oars like the head of a horse in a race threatening to come apart from the rest of its body yet having to resign itself to pulling that weight to the last. Jesus rowed and rowed, they must be almost there and he wonders how people will react when he tells them, The one with the beard is God, the other is the Devil. Taking a backward glance at the coast, Jesus could make out a different light and announced. We're here, and rowed some more. Any second now he expected to feel the bottom of the boat softly gliding over the thick mud near the shore, the playful grazing of tiny, loose pebbles, but the prow of the boat which remained invisible was pointing out to the middle of the lake, and as for the light he had seen, it had become like that of the brilliant magic circle, the glowing snare from which Jesus thought he had escaped. Exhausted, his head fell forward, he crossed his arms over his knees, one wrist resting on the other, as if waiting to be bound, and even forgot to retrieve the oars, convinced as he was that any further move would be completely futile. He would not be the first to speak, he would not acknowledge defeat in a loud voice, nor ask to be forgiven for having disregarded God's will and mandate and indirectly prejudiced the interests of the Devil, the natural beneficiary of the subsequent rather than the secondary consequences of the exercise of the Lord's will and the effective realization of His plans. The silence following this frustrated act of defiance was short-lived. Sitting there on His bench, God arranged the folds of His tunic and the hood of His mantle and then with mock solemnity, like a judge about to pass formal sentence, He said, Let us start from the beginning and go back to the moment I revealed that you are in my power, for until you humbly and peacefully submit to this truth you will be wasting your time and mine, Let's start again then, agreed Jesus, but be warned, I refuse to work any more miracles and without miracles Your plans will come to nothing, a mere shower from heaven incapable of satisfying any real thirst, You would be right if it were in your power to work or not to work miracles, Don't I have the power, What an idea, I work miracles both great and small, naturally in your presence so that you may reap the benefits on my behalf, you're superstitious at heart and believe the miracle-worker has to be at the patient's bedside for the miracle to take place, but if I so wished, a man dying all alone with no one by his side, abandoned to utter loneliness without a doctor, nurse or beloved relative within reach or hearing, if I so wished, I tell you, that man would be saved and go on living as if nothing had happened to him, Then why not do it, Because he would imagine he'd been cured by the strength of his own merits and would start boasting, The likes of Me could not possibly die, and with all the presumption there is already in this world I've created, I have no intention of encouraging any such nonsense, So all these miracles are Yours, All those you have worked and will work, for even supposing you were to persist in opposing my will, to go out into the world and deny that you are the son of God, I should cause so many miracles to happen wherever you passed that you would be obliged to accept the gratitude of those thanking you, and thereby thanking Me. So, there's no way out, None whatsoever, and don't play the restive lamb that resists being taken to be sacrificed, becomes agitated and bleats in the most heart-rending manner, for your destiny is sealed, the sacrificial sword awaits you, Am I that lamb, You are the lamb of God, my son, which God Himself will carry to the altar we are preparing here.

Jesus looked at Pastor, not so much for help as for a signal, for his understanding of the world must perforce be different, since Pastor is not nor ever has been man, god he has never been nor is ever likely to be, so perhaps a mere glance or raising of eyebrows might suggest some suitable reply which would allow Jesus to play for time and extricate himself, at least for a while, from the difficult situation in which he finds himself. But all Jesus reads in Pastor's eyes are the words he spoke to him when he banished him from the herd, You've learnt nothing, begone with you. Now Jesus realizes that to disobey God once is not enough, that he who refused to offer Him his sacrificial lamb must also refuse Him his sheep, that one cannot say, Yes, to God, and then say, No, as if Yes and No were one's left and right hands, and the only good work were that which is done with both hands. For notwithstanding His normal manifestations of power as the universe and the stars, the lightning and thunder, voices and flames on top of mountains, God could not force you to slaughter the sheep and yet out of ambition you killed the animal, and its blood could not be absorbed by all the soil in the desert, see how it has even reached us, that thread of crimson liquid which will follow in our tracks whenever we leave this place and pursue you and God and me. Jesus said to God, I shall declare before men that I am Your son, the only son God has, but I do not believe that even in these lands of Yours, this will be enough to enlarge Your kingdom as much as You would wish. At last you're speaking like a true son, now that you've given up these tiresome acts of rebellion which were beginning to anger Me, now that you've come round to my way of thinking without any prompting, amongst the many things one could say to men, whatever their race, colour, creed or philosophy, only one thing is common to all, only one, namely that none of these men, wise or ignorant, young or old, rich or poor, would dare to say, This has nothing to do with me, And what might that be, asked Jesus with undisguised interest, All men, replied God, as if imparting wisdom, whoever and wherever they may be and whatever they may do, are sinners, for sin, in a manner of speaking, is as inseparable from man as man from sin, man is like a coin, turn it over, and what you see there is sin, You haven't answered my question, Here is my answer, the only word no man can reject as having nothing to do with him, is Repentance, because to all men who have succumbed to temptation, had an evil thought, broken some rule, committed some serious or minor crime, spurned someone in need, neglected their duty, offended religion and its ministers, or turned away from God, to all such men you need only say, Repent, repent, repent, But is it really necessary to sacrifice Your own son's life for so little, surely all You had to do was to send some prophet, The time when people listened to prophets has passed, nowadays one needs to administer stronger medicine, to apply shock treatment in order to touch men's hearts and arouse their feelings, Such as a son of God hanging from a cross, Yes, why not, And what else am I supposed to say to these people, besides enjoining them to dubious repentance, if they get tired of hearing Your message and turn a deaf ear, Yes, I agree, it may not be enough to ask them to repent, you may have to use your imagination and don't make any excuses because only today I had to admire the way in which you cunningly avoided sacrificing your lamb, That was easy enough, the animal had nothing to repent, A subtle reply but meaningless, although that, too, has its charm, people should be left worried and perplexed, be made to believe that if they don't understand, they are at fault, So, I'm to make up stories, Yes, stories, parables, moral tales, even if it means distorting Holy Law ever so slightly, don't let that bother you, the timid always admire daring liberties when taken by others, and I myself, while anything but timid, was impressed by the way you saved the adulteress from death, and that's saying a lot, for it was I who put justice into the commandments I handed down, It's a bad sign when You start allowing men to tamper with Your commandments, Only when it suits Me and proves to be useful, you must not forget what I told you about the law and its exceptions, for whatever I may will instantly becomes obligatory, You said, I shall die on the cross, That is my will. Jesus looked askance at Pastor who seemed to be absorbed as if he were contemplating some moment in the future and could not believe his eyes. Jesus dropped his arms and said, Then do with me as You will.

God was about to rejoice, to rise to His feet and embrace His beloved son when Jesus stopped him with a gesture and said, On one condition, But you know perfectly well you cannot lay down conditions, God replied angrily, Then let's call it a plea rather than a condition, the simple plea of a man sentenced to death, Tell me, You are God and, therefore, can only speak the truth when asked a question, and being God, You know the past, the present, what lies between them, and what the future will bring, That is so, I am time, truth and life, Then tell me, in the name of all You claim to be, what will the future bring after my death, what will the future bring which would otherwise not be there unless I had accepted to sacrifice myself because of your dissatisfaction, and this desire of Yours to reign wide and far. God responded angrily, as if trapped by his own words, and made a half-hearted attempt to shrug it off, Now then, son, the future is infinite and would take a long time to measure, How long have we been out here in the middle of the lake and surrounded by mist, asked Jesus, perhaps for a day, a month, a year, well then let's stay here for another year, month or day, allow the Devil to leave if he wants to, for in any case his share is guaranteed, and if the benefits are proportionate, as seems just, the more God prospers, the more the Devil will prosper, I'm staying, said Pastor, and these were the first words he spoke since revealing his identity, I'm staying, he said for a second time before adding, I myself can see certain things belonging to the future, but I'm not always certain if what I see there is true or false, that's to say, I can see my lies for what they are, in other words, my truths, but I don't know to what extent the truths of others are their lies. This tortuous outburst could have been rounded off nicely if Pastor had said something more about the future he envisaged, but he abruptly fell silent as if aware of having said far too much already. Jesus, who had not averted his eyes from God, said with a note of wistful irony, Why pretend to ignore what You know, You realized I would ask this question, and know very well You will tell me what I want to hear, so postpone no longer my time for dying, You began dying the moment you were born, True, but now I shall die all the sooner, God looked at Jesus with an expression which in a person we would have described as respectful, His whole manner became human, and, although the one thing did not appear to have anything to do with the other, we shall never know the deep links that exist between things and actions, the mist advanced towards the boat, surrounded it like an insurmountable wall in order to keep from the world God's words about the effects and consequences of the sacrifice of Jesus whom He claims as His son and that of Mary, but whose real father is Joseph, according to the unwritten law which commands us to believe only in what we see, although, as everyone knows, we humans do not always see things in the same way and this has undoubtedly helped to preserve the relative sanity of the species.

God said, There will be a Church which, as you are aware, means an assembly or gathering, a religious society which will be founded by you or in your name, which basically comes to the same thing, and this Church will spread far and wide throughout the world and be called catholic, because universal, although sadly this will not prevent discord and misunderstanding amongst those who will see you rather than Me, as their spiritual leader although this will only last for several thousand years, for I was here before you and I will continue to be here after you cease to be what you are and will be, Speak clearly, interrupted Jesus, It's impossible, said God, for human words are like shadows, and shadows are incapable of explaining light and between shadows and light there is the opaque body from which words are born. I asked You about the future, It's the future I'm talking about, What I want to know is how the men who come after me will live, Are you referring to your followers, Yes, will they be happier, Not in the true sense of the word, but they will have the hope of achieving happiness up there in heaven where I reign for all eternity, and where they may hope to live eternally with Me, Is that all, Surely it is no small thing to live with God, Small, great, or everything, we shall only discover after the Day of Final Judgement when You will judge men according to the good or evil they have done and until then You reside alone in heaven, My angels and archangels keep Me company, But You don't have any human beings there, True, and you must be crucified in order that they may come to Me, I want to know more, said Jesus vehemently, anxious to shut out the mental image of himself hanging from a cross, covered in blood and dead, What I'd like to know is how people will come to believe in me and follow me, don't try to tell me that anything I may say to them or those who come after me may say to them in my name will be enough, take the Gentiles and Romans, for example, who worship other gods, surely You don't expect me to believe they will give them up to worship me just like that, Not to worship you but Me, But You yourself said that You and me comes to the same thing, however, don't let's play with words, just answer my question, Whoever has faith will come to us, Just like that, as easily as You've just said, The other gods will resist, And You will fight them, of course, Don't be absurd, such things only occur on earth, heaven is eternal and peaceful, men fulfil their destiny wherever they may be, Let me get this straight, even though words are but shadows, men will die for You and for me, Men have always died for the gods, even for false and mendacious gods, Can the gods speak false, They can, And You are the one and only true god amongst them, Yes, the one and only true god, Yet You are unable to prevent men from dying for You when they should have been born to live for You on earth rather than in heaven where You have none of life's joys to offer them, Those joys, too, are deceptive for they originated with original sin, ask your friend, Pastor, he'll explain what happened, If there are any secrets You and the Devil do not share, I hope one of them is what I learned from him even though he insists I've learned nothing. There was silence, God and the Devil confronted each other for the first time, both giving the impression of being about to say something, but nothing happened. Jesus said, I'm waiting, For what, asked God, as if distracted, For You to tell me how much death and suffering Your victory over other gods will cost, how much suffering and death will be needed to justify the battles men will fight in Your name and mine, You insist on knowing, Yes, I do, Very well then, the assembly I mentioned will be founded, but in order to be truly solid, its foundations will be dug out in flesh, and the bases made from the cement of abnegation, tears, suffering, torment, every conceivable form of death known or as yet unrevealed, At long last, You're starting to make sense, carry on. Let's start with someone whom you know and love, the fisherman Simon, whom you will call Peter, like you, he will be crucified, but upside down, Andrew, too, will be crucified on a cross in the shape of an X, the son of Zebedee, known as James, will be beheaded, And what about John and Mary Magdalene, They will die of natural causes when their time comes, but you will make other friends, disciples and apostles like the others, who will not escape torture, friends such as Philip who will be tied to a cross and stoned to death, Bartholomew who will be skinned alive, Thomas who will be speared to death, Matthew, the details of whose death I no longer remember, another Simon who will be sawn in half, Judas who will be beaten to death, James stoned, Matthias beheaded with an axe, also Judas Iscariot, but as you will know better than me, spared death but strung from a fig tree by his own hands, Are all these men about to die because of You, asked Jesus, If you phrase the question in that way, the answer is Yes, they will die for my sake, And then what, Then, my son, as I've already told you, there will be an endless tale of iron and blood, of fire and ashes, an infinite sea of sorrow and tears, Tell me, I want to know everything. God sighed, and, in the monotonous tone of someone who preferred to suppress compassion and mercy, He began a litany in alphabetical order rather than offend any susceptibilities about order of pre-cedence, Adalbert of Prague, put to death with a pikestaff with seven points, Adrian, hammered to death over an anvil, Afra of Augsburg, burnt at the stake, Agapitus of Praeneste, burnt at the stake hanging by his feet, Agnes of Rome, disembowelled, Agricola of Bologna, crucified and impaled on nails, Agueda of Sicily, stabbed six times, Alphege of Canterbury, beaten to death with the shinbone of an ox, Anastasius of Salona, strung up on the gallows and decapitated, Anastasia of Sirmium, burnt at the stake and her breasts cut off, Ansanus of Siena, his entrails ripped out, Antonius of Pamiers, drawn and quartered, Antony of Rivoli, stoned and burnt alive, Apollinaris of Ravenna, clubbed to death, Apollonia of Alexandria, burnt at the stake after her teeth have been knocked out, Augusta of Treviso, decapitated and burnt at the stake, Aurea of Ostia, drowned with a millstone round her neck, Aurea of Syria, bled to death by being forced on to a chair covered with nails, Auta, shot with arrows, Babylas of Antioch, decapitated, Barbara of Nicomedia, likewise, Barnabas of Cyprus, stoned and burnt at the stake, Beatrice of Rome, strangled, Benignus of Dijon, speared to death, Blandina of Lyons, gored by a savage bull, Blaise of Sebasta, thrown on to iron spikes, Callistus, put to death with a millstone round his neck, Cassian of Imola, stabbed with a dagger by his disciples, Castulus, buried alive, Catherine of Alexandria, decapitated, Cecilia of Rome, beheaded, Christina of Bolsena, tortured again and again with millstones, tongs, arrows and snakes, Clarus of Nastes, decapitated, Clarus of Vienne, likewise, Clement, drowned with an anchor fixed round his neck, Crispin and Crispinian of Soissons, both decapitated, Cucuphas of Barcelona, disembowelled, Cyprian of Carthage, beheaded, young Cyricus of Tarsus, killed by a judge who knocked his head against the stairs of the tribunal, and on reaching the end of the letter C, God said, from now it's all much the same with few variations apart from the odd refinement which would take forever to explain, so let's leave it at that, No, go on, said Jesus, so, reluctantly, God continued, abbreviating wherever possible, Donatus of Arezzo, decapitated, Eliphius of Rampillon, scalped, Emerita, burnt alive, Emilian of Trevi, decapitated, Emmeramus of Regensburg, tied to a ladder and put to death, Engratia of Saragossa, decapitated, Erasmus of Gaeta, also called Elmo, stretched on a windlass, Escubiculus, beheaded, Eskil of Sweden, stoned to death, Eulalia of Merida, decapitated, Euphemia of Chalcedon, put to the sword, Eutropius of Saintes, beheaded with an axe, Fabian, stabbed and spiked, Faith of Agen, beheaded, Felicitas and seven sons, beheaded with a sword, Felix and his brother Adauctus, likewise, Ferreolus of Besançon, decapitated, Fidelis of Sigmaringen, beaten to death with a spiked club, Firminus of Pamplona, beheaded, Flavia Domitilla, likewise, Fortunas of Evora, probably met the same fate, Fructoasus of Tarragon, burnt at the stake, Gaudentius of France, decapitated, Gelasius, likewise with more iron spikes, Gengolf of Burgundy, cuckolded and assassinated by his wife's lover, Gerard Sagreda of Budapest, speared to death, Gerean of Cologne, decapitated, the twins Gervase and Protase, likewise, Godleva and Ghistelles, strangled, Gratus of Aosta, decapitated, Hermenegild, clubbed to death, Hero, stabbed with a sword, Hippolytus, dragged to his death by a horse, Ignatius of Azevedo, murdered by the Calvinists who are not Catholics, Januarius of Naples, decapitated after being thrown to wild beasts and then thrown into a furnace, Joan of Arc, burnt at the stake, John de Britto, beheaded, John Fisher, decapitated, John of Nepomuk, drowned in the river Vltava, John of Prado, stabbed in the head, Julia of Corsica, whose breasts were cut off before she was crucified, Juliana of Nicomedia, decapitated, Justa and Ruffina of Seville, the former killed on the wheel, the latter strangled, Justina of Antioch, thrown into a cauldron of boiling tar and then beheaded, Justus and Pastor, not our Pastor but the one from Alcalá de Henares, decapitated, Kilian of Würzburg, decapitated, Léger of Autun, also decapitated after his eyes and tongue had been torn out, Leocadia of Toledo, thrown to her death from a high cliff, Livinus of Ghent, decapitated after his tongue had been torn out, Longinus, decapitated, Lawrence, burnt on a grid, Ludmila of Prague, strangled, Lucy of Syracuse, beheaded after having her eyes plucked out, Maginus of Tarragon, decapitated with a serrated scythe, Mamas of Cappodocia, disembowelled, Manuel, Sabel and Ismael, Manuel put to death with an iron nail embedded in each nipple and an iron rod driven through his head from ear to ear, all three of them beheaded,

Margaret of Antioch, killed with a firebrand and an iron comb, Maria Goretti, strangled, Marius of Persia, put to the sword and his hands amputated, Martina of Rome, decapitated, the martyrs of Morocco, Berard of Carbio, Peter of Gimignano, Otto, Adjuto and Accursio, beheaded, those of Japan, all twenty-six crucified, speared and burnt alive, Maurice of Agaune, put to the sword, Meinrad of Einsiedeln, clubbed to death, Menas of Alexandria, also put to the sword, Mercurius of Cappadocia, decapitated, Nicasius of Rheims, likewise, Odilia of Huy, shot with arrows, Paneras, beheaded, Pantaleon of Nicomedia, likewise, Paphnutius, crucified, Patroclus of Troyes and Soest, likewise, Paul of Tarsus, to whom you will owe your first church, likewise, Pelagius, drawn and quartered, Peter of Rates, killed with a sword, Peter of Verona, his head slashed with a cutlass and a dagger driven into his chest, Perpetua and her slave Felicity of Carthage, both gored by a raging bull, Philomena, shot with arrows and anchored, Piaton of Tournai, scalped, Polycarp, stabbed and burnt alive, Prisca of Rome, devoured by lions, Processus and Martinian probably met the same fate, Quintinus, nails driven into his head and other parts of his body, Quirinus of Rouen, scalped, Quiteria of Coimbra, decapitated by her own father, Renaud of Dortmund, bludgeoned to death with a mason's mallet, Reine of Alise, put to the sword, Restituta of Naples, burnt at the stake, Roland, put to the sword, Romanus of Antioch, strangled to death after his tongue had been torn out, Are you still not satisfied, God asked Jesus who retorted, That's something You ought to be asking Yourself, carry on, So God continued, Sabinian of Sens, beheaded, Sabinus of Assis, stoned to death, Saturninus of Toulouse, dragged to his death by a bull, Sebastian, pierced by arrows, Secundus of Asti, decapitated, Servatius of Tongres and Maastricht, killed by a blow to the head with a wooden clog, Severus of Barcelona, killed by having nails embedded in his head, Sidwell of Exeter, decapitated, Sigismund, King of Burgundy, thrown into a well, Stephen, stoned to death, Symphorian of Autun, decapitated, Sixtus, likewise, Tarcsius, stoned to death, Thecla of Iconium, mutilated and burnt alive, Theodore, burnt at the stake, Thomas Becket of Canterbury, a sword driven into his skull, Thomas More, beheaded, Thyrsus, sawn in half, Tiburtius, beheaded, Timothy of Ephesus, stoned to death, Torquatus and the Twenty-Seven, killed by General Muça at the gates of Guimaraes, Tropez of Pisa, decapitated, Urbanus, Valeria of Limoges, and Valerian and Venantius of Camerino met the same fate,

Victor, decapitated, Victor of Marseilles, beheaded, Victoria of Rome, put to death after having her tongue pulled out, Vincent of Saragossa, tortured to death with millstone, grid and spikes, Virgilius of Trent, beaten to death with a wooden clog, Vitalis of Ravenna, put to the sword, Wilgefortis, or Livrade, or Eutropia, the bearded virgin, crucified, and so on and so forth and all of them meeting similar fates. That's not good enough, said Jesus, to what others are You referring, Do you really have to know, I do, I'm referring to those who escaped martyrdom and died from natural causes after having suffered the torments of the world, the flesh and the devil, and who in order to overcome them had to mortify their bodies with fasting and prayer, there is even the amusing case of a certain John Schorn who spent so much time on his knees praying that he ended up with corns on his knees, of all places, and he's also reputed, and this will interest you, to have shut the devil inside a boot, ha, ha, ha, Me, in a boot, said Pastor scornfully, these are old wives' tales, any boot capable of holding me would have to be as vast as the world, and, besides, I'd like to see who would be capable of putting the boot on and taking it off afterwards, Perhaps only with fasting and prayer, suggested Jesus, whereupon God replied, They will also mortify the flesh with suffering and blood and grime, and innumerable other penances, with hairshirts and flagellation, there will even be some who scarcely ever wash and others who throw themselves on to brambles and roll in the snow to suppress carnal desires which are the work of Satan who sends these temptations with the intention of luring souls from the strait and narrow path which leads to heaven, visions of naked women, terrifying monsters, abominable creatures, lust and fear, weapons used by the Demon to torment the wretched existence of mankind, Is this true, Jesus asked Pastor, who replied, More or less, I simply took what God didn't want, the flesh with all its joys and sorrows, youth and senility, bloom and decay, but it isn't true that fear is one of my weapons, I don't recall having invented sin and punishment or the terror they inspire, Be quiet, God interrupted sharply, sin and the Devil are one and the same thing, What thing, asked Jesus, My absence, How do You explain Your absence, is it because You retreat or because mankind abandons You, I never retreat, never, Yet You allow men to abandon You, Whosoever abandons Me comes looking for Me, And when they cannot find You, I suppose You blame the Devil, No, he's not to blame, I'm to blame because I'm incapable of reaching out to those who seek Me, words uttered by God with a poignant and unexpected melancholy, as if He had suddenly discovered the limitations of His power. Jesus told Him, Go on, There are others, God continued slowly, who withdraw into the wilderness where they lead a solitary life in caves and grottoes and with nothing but animals for company, others who choose a monastic existence, others who climb to the top of high pillars and live there year in year out, others, His voice fell and died away, God was now contemplating an endless procession of people, thousands upon thousands of men and women throughout the world entering convents and monasteries, some rustic dwellings, many of them palatial buildings, There they will remain to serve you and Me from morning until night, with vigils and prayers, all with the same mission and destiny, to worship us and die with our names on their lips, they will use different names, be known as Benedictines, Cistercians, Carthusians, Augustinians, Gilbertines, Trinitarians, Franciscans, Dominicans, Capuchins, Carmelites, Jesuits, and there will be so many of them that I should dearly like to be able to exclaim, My God, why so many. At this point, the Devil said to Jesus, Note from what He has told us that there are two ways of losing one's life, either through martyrdom or by renunciation, it wasn't enough for all these people to have died when their time came, in one way or another they ran to meet their death, crucified, disembowelled, beheaded, burnt at the stake, stoned, drowned, drawn and quartered, skinned alive, speared, gored, buried alive, sawn in two, shot with arrows, mutilated, tortured, within or outside their cells, chapter-houses and cloisters, doing penance and mortifying the flesh God gave them without which they would have nowhere to rest their soul, these punishments were not invented by the Devil who is talking to you. Is that all, Jesus asked God, No, there are still the wars, and the massacres, No need to tell me about the massacres, I might even have died in one, and thinking it over, what a pity I didn't, for then I would have been spared the crucifixion awaiting me, It was I who led your other father to the place where he overheard the soldiers' conversation and therefore saved your life, You only saved my life in order to ordain my death at Your pleasure and convenience as if prepared to kill me twice, The end justifies the means, my son, From what You have told me so far I can well believe it, renunciation, cloisters, suffering, death, and now wars and massacres, what wars are these, One war after another and everlasting, especially those waged against you and Me in the name of a god who has yet to appear, How can there possibly be a god who still has to appear, any true god can only have existed for ever and ever, I know it's difficult to understand or explain, but what I'm telling you will come to pass, a god will rise against us and our followers, entire nations, no, no, there are no words to describe the massacres, bloodshed and slaughter, try to imagine my altar in Jerusalem multiplied a thousandfold, replace the sacrificial animals with men, and even then you will have no idea what those crusades were like, Crusades, what are they and why do You refer to them in the past if they still have to take place, Remember, I am time and so for Me all that is about to happen has already happened, all that has happened goes on happening every day, Tell me more about these crusades, Well, my son, these parts where we now find ourselves, including Jerusalem, and other territories to the north and west, will be conquered by the followers of the god I mentioned who has been slow in coming, the followers of those on our side will do everything possible to expel them from the places you have travelled and I constantly frequent, You haven't done much to rid this place of the Romans, Don't distract me, I'm talking about the future, Carry on, then, Furthermore, you were born, lived and died here, But I'm not dead yet, That's irrelevant for, as I've just explained to you, as far as I'm concerned, for something to happen and have happened comes to the same thing, and please stop interrupting otherwise I'll say no more, All right, I'll be quiet, Now then, future generations will refer to these parts as the Holy Places, because you were born, lived and died here, so it didn't seem fitting that the cradle of the religion you will represent should fall into the unworthy hands of infidels, this was sufficient reason to justify the invasions of those great armies from the west who for almost two hundred years tried to conquer and preserve for Christianity the cave where you were born and the hill where you will die, to mention only the most important landmarks, Are these armies the crusades, That's right, And did they conquer what they wanted, No, but they slaughtered many people, And what about the crusaders themselves, They lost just as many lives if not more, And all this bloodshed in our name, They will go into battle crying out, God wills it, And no doubt died crying out, God willed it, Such a nice way to end one's life, Once again, the sacrifice isn't worth it, In order to save one's soul, my son, the body must be sacrificed, I've heard You use much the same words before, and what about you, Pastor, what do you say about these amazing events which lie ahead, No one in his right mind can possibly suggest that the Devil was, is, or ever will be responsible for so much bloodshed and death, unless some villain brings up that wicked slander accusing me of having conceived the god who will oppose this one here, It strikes me that you are not to blame and should anyone hold you responsible you need only reply that if the Devil is false then he could never create a true god, Then who will create this hostile god, asked Pastor. Jesus was at a loss for an answer and God, who had been silent, remained silent, but a voice came down from the mist and said, Perhaps this God and the one yet to come are one and the same god, Jesus, God and the Devil pretended not to hear but could not help looking at each other in alarm, mutual fear is like this and readily unites enemies.

Time passed, the mist did not speak again and Jesus asked, now with the voice of someone who only expects an affirmative reply, Nothing more. God hesitated, and then, in a tired tone of voice, said, There is still the Inquisition, but if you don't mind, we'll discuss that at some other time, What is the Inquisition, The Inquisition is another long story, Tell me more, It's best you shouldn't know, But I insist, You will only suffer remorse today which belongs to the future, And You won't, God is God and suffers no remorse, Well, since I'm already bearing this burden of having to die for You, I can also withstand the remorse that ought to be Yours, I wanted to protect you, You've done nothing else since the day I was born, Like most children, you're ungrateful, Let's stop all this pretence and tell me about the Inquisition, Also known as the Tribunal of the Holy Office, the Inquisition is a necessary evil, we shall use this cruellest of instruments to combat the disease that will persistently infiltrate the body of your Church in the form of wicked heresies and their harmful consequences along with a number of physical and moral perversions, which if lumped together without regard for order or precedence will include Lutherans and Calvinists, Molinists and Judaizers, sodomites and sorcerers, some of these plagues belonging to the future, others which can be found in every age, And if the Inquisition is a necessary evil, as You claim, how will it go about eliminating these heresies, The Inquisition is a police force, a tribunal, and will, therefore, pursue, judge and sentence its enemies like any other tribunal or police force, Sentence them to what, To prison, exile, the stake, Did You say the stake, Yes, in days to come, thousands upon thousands of men and

THE GOSPEL ACCORDING TO JESUS CHRIST   179

women will be burnt at the stake, You mentioned some of them earlier, They will be burnt alive because they have believed in you, others because they will doubt you. Isn't it permitted to doubt me, No, Yet we're allowed to question whether the Jupiter of the Romans is god, I am the one and only Lord God and you are my son, You say thousands will die, Hundreds of thousands of men and women will die and on earth there will be much sighing and weeping and cries of anguish, the smoke from charred corpses will blot out the sun, human flesh will sizzle over live coals, the stench will be nauseating, and all this will be my fault. You're not to blame, your cause exacts this suffering, Father, take from me this cup, My power and your glory demand that you should drink to the last drop, I don't want this glory, But I want that power. The mist began to lift and around the boat water could be seen, smooth, sombre water without so much as a ripple of wind or the tremor of a passing fin. Then the Devil interrupted, One has to be God to enjoy so much bloodshed.

The mist started advancing again, something else was about to happen, some revelation, some new sorrow or remorse. But it was Pastor who spoke, I've a proposal to make, he said, addressing God, and God, taken aback, replied, A proposal from you, and what proposal might that be, His tone was cynical and forbidding and would have reduced most people to silence, but then the Devil was an old acquaintance. Pastor remained silent as if searching for the right words before explaining, I've been listening carefully to all that has been said here in this boat and although I myself have caught glimpses of the light and darkness ahead, I never realized the light was coming from the burning stakes and the shadows from innumerable corpses, Does this bother you, It shouldn't really bother me since I'm the Devil and the Devil always profits from death, even more than You do, for it goes without saying that Hell is much more crowded than Heaven, Then why are you complaining, I'm not complaining, I'm making a proposal, Go ahead but be quick for I cannot be loitering here for all eternity, No one knows better than You that the Devil also has a heart, Yes, but you make poor use of it, Today I intend to use it by acknowledging and hoping that Your power will spread to the ends of the earth without any further need of so many deaths, and since You insist that anything which thwarts and denies You is the fruit of the Evil I represent and govern in this world, I propose that You should receive me into your Heavenly Kingdom, my past offences redeemed by those I shall not commit in future, that You accept and preserve my obedience as in those happy days when I was one of Your chosen angels, Lucifer, You called me, the bearer of light, before my ambition to become Your equal consumed my soul and made me rebel against Your authority, And would you care to tell Me why I should pardon you and receive you into my Kingdom, Because if You were to do so and grant me that same pardon which one day You will promise so readily right and left, then Evil will cease at once, Your son will not have to die, and Your Kingdom will extend beyond the land of the Hebrews to embrace the entire world, whether known or yet to be discovered, Good will prevail everywhere and I shall sing amongst the lowliest of the angels who have remained faithful, more faithful than all of them now that I have repented, shall sing Your praises, all will end as if it had never been, all will start to become what it should always have been, I've always known you have a talent for confusing and losing souls, but I have never heard you make such a speech with such conviction and eloquence, you've almost won Me over, So You won't accept or pardon me, No, I neither accept nor pardon you, I much prefer you as you are and, were it possible, I'd prefer you to become even worse than you are, But why, Because the Good I represent cannot exist without the Evil you represent, it is inconceivable that any Good might exist without you, so much so that it defies imagination and, in short, if you were to come to an end, so would I, for Me to be Goodness, it is essential that you should continue to be Evil, unless the Devil lives like the Devil, God cannot live like God, the death of the one would mean the death of the other. Is that Your final word, My first and last, first, because that was the first time I said it, final because I have no intention of repeating it. Pastor shrugged his shoulders and addressed Jesus, Never let it be said the Devil didn't tempt Jesus one day, and getting to his feet, he was about to pass one leg over the side of the boat when he suddenly paused and said, In your knapsack there is something belonging to me. Jesus could not remember having brought the knapsack on to the boat, but, in fact, there it was, rolled up at his feet, What thing, he asked, and, on opening the knapsack found there was nothing inside apart from the old black bowl he had brought from Nazareth, That's it, that's it, replied the Devil picking up the bowl with both hands, One day this will be yours again, but you won't even know you have it. He tucked the bowl inside his shepherd's tunic of coarse cloth and

lowered himself into the water. Without looking at God, he simply
said, as if addressing an invisible audience, Farewell for evermore,
since that is what He has ordained. Jesus followed him with his eyes
as Pastor gradually moved off in the direction of the mist, he had
forgotten to ask him what had possessed him to swim all the way
here and back, Seen from afar, he once more looked like a pig with
pointed ears and he was panting furiously, but anyone with a keen
ear would have had no difficulty in noticing that there was also a note
of fear there, not of drowning, what an idea, for the Devil, as we
have just discovered, has no ending, but of having to exist forever.
Pastor was already disappearing behind the broken fringe of the mist
when God's voice suddenly rang out bidding an abrupt farewell, I
shall send someone called John to help, but you will have to prove
to him that you are who you say you are. Jesus looked round, but
God was no longer there. Just then the mist lifted, vanished into thin
air, leaving the sea clear and smooth from point to point between the
mountains, there was no sign of the Devil in the water, no sign of
God in the air.

Translated from the Portuguese by Giovanni Pontiero

YURY DOMBROVSKY

From the novel *The Faculty of Useless Knowledge*

The Faculty of Useless Knowledge is Dombrovsky's masterpiece. The novel is set in the year of the Terror, 1937, in the central Asian republic of Kazakhstan. A group of archaeologists find themselves caught up in an ambitious Cheka investigator's attempt to set up a show trial in Alam-Ata to rival those taking place in Moscow. Dombrovsky's hero, Zybin (the Keeper of Antiquities, and hero of the earlier novel of the same name), is already in the hands of the secret police. In this central section, his assistant Kornilov and a priest with a weakness for vodka, Father Andrei, discuss the betrayal of Christ. Each has been approached by the Cheka, and each knows that he teeters on the edge of the abyss into which they fear Zybin has fallen.

They drained one glass and poured another. Father Andrei began talking about the North. He was an accomplished raconteur and pronounced the broad "a" with an actor's skill. Kornilov was in stitches throughout. He was especially tickled by the story of the co-operative cook – Baroness Serafima Bark. Her arms were as rough as bark too, but some days she wore bracelets and a signet ring. Once in his presence, with a fisherman's oath she had seen off a brawny tough who had come in for vodka; she at once turned to Father Andrei and explained in French: "It's awful the way one has to talk to these people but alas (*hélas, hélas*), it's the only language they understand. Now he realizes that it's a definite refusal, he'll turn round and take himself off." And so he did.

"Incidentally this Fimka woman caused a real mix-up," said Father Andrei. "Some Institute organized a folklore expedition about five years ago. They were looking for old story-tellers all along the coast. But where could they find them? There weren't any! Anyway, somebody, whether out of stupidity or mischief, sent them along to Fimka. She sang them a couple of dozen songs. Cribbed them straight out of Avenarius, the one who wrote the children's book about the Kievan heroes. Their eyes fairly stood out on stalks. What material! They sat there day and night. They did reams of writing and saw off a bucket of vodka. The old woman was making a profit out of them! So they went away. Then they came back again. So she told them fairy tales from Sakharov, served up the naughtiest ones there are. In the North, there's no shortage of that kind of thing! Again they covered page after page with this stuff. Then on the very last day, as they were leaving, after the champagne and the toasts, she told them who she was, and where she came from – she was a wicked woman, may God forgive her. The leader of the expedition nearly took a fit! He clucked like a broody hen! 'But-but how can that be? What, what? The Smolny Institute.* But that's government money! But that's . . . but that's . . .' What do you think of that?" Father Andrei roared with laughter, flapping an arm.

"But what if he knew where I've been with his manuscript," thought Kornilov and abruptly blurted:

"You see, I've been called in." He was instantly stricken and thrown into confusion. Not knowing what to say, he repeated urgently: "There! There! In there!" and followed the example of the scientific secretary in pointing to the ceiling.

Father Andrei glanced at him, tipped the glass down his throat and shook his head.

"D-damnation!" He whispered. "It's blasted strong! Seventy degrees shouldn't wonder." He caught his breath and got to his feet. "Well, what of it, Vladimir Mikhailovich, we'll all be there! 'To this favour we must come.' Wait a minute, I'll pop and get the gherkins."

It was odd, but the almost raw spirit had no apparent effect on Kornilov. An extraordinary sobriety and clarity had descended upon him. He sat and mused.

"This is all very well, of course, both the priest and his cherry brandy; and what I said, it's all right – but what happens next? The director will be back soon. I'll settle up and get away, head off somewhere and leave them looking silly. What about Dasha? Lina? Zybin? Well, to blazes with Lina, but there is Dasha."

* *The Smolny Institute*: before 1917, a famous institution for daughters of the nobility.

At this he began to consider seeing Dasha again and what he would say to her. It was pleasant to think about. He even smiled.

Father Andrei came out with a plate of gherkins.

"Just try these," he said. "All my own work! They call everybody in. They called me in."

"What?" Kornilov was stunned. "You too!"

"Me too. Go on, eat up, eat up, please! Yes, they called me in. But what could I possibly know? Georgi Nikolaevich in the museum is up there," he pointed to the ceiling. "And I'm down here." He pointed to the floor. "Who am I, a priest! Flogger of dead horses. Georgi Nikolaevich is persona grata. He gave us an instructional talk once on how to fill a card in and that was the only time I saw him. That's what I said and they didn't even bother writing it down."

"Who was it interrogated you?"

"Interrogated!" Father Andrei smiled, shaking his head and sighing. "Lord, such words! They didn't interrogate me. They interrogate accused persons. They ta-alked to me. It was a Lieutenant Golikov who did the talking. It wasn't him who asked for you?"

"No, not him."

"Well, naturally, there's lots of them there. The size of the place. Well, what of it? I get one, you get another; they ask me about one, they ask you about another – then perhaps the truth will emerge."

"What truth is that, pray," Kornilov scowled. "Why do you think they arrested Zybin?"

Father Andrei smiled and shrugged his shoulders.

"Still, come on, why?"

"I don't know, Vladimir Mikhailovich, and I'm not even interested. Earthly powers – they're tricky things. People like your boss are usually arrested not for something they've done but for some reason."

"What was that again?"

"Or in the name of something. So they don't get in the way of things, I mean. The authorities think up something and he doesn't agree and obstructs it. Or has the capacity to do so. Therefore they pick him up in good time, on the principle: 'It is better for us that one man should die for the people, rather than the whole people should perish.' They arrest him on that principle."

"What's that from?"

"Oh, it's the gospels again. The celebrated John, chapter eleven. Well, from the point of view of the earthly powers it's perfectly logical."

"Terrific," Kornilov looked at him and suddenly felt roused to fury. "'Better for us'. And who are 'You'? I'd love to get a look at your bright, shining face just for one minute! Just to find out in the name of whom or what you're acting like gangsters! Benefactors indeed! Although, yes, yes!" He brandished an arm. "'There is no power but of God.' You've got a quotation for every occasion! Oh you priests!" He smiled obscurely and paused and shook his head. "But you are right about one thing. If a man is dangerous, they eliminate him. Click – and that's the end of him. So, someone has demonstrated to someone else that Zybin was dangerous; that's the long and short of it. But it's something else that I don't get – take you. You're a dangerous individual too, one of the former – pre-revolutionary folk, and yet here you are sitting drinking vodka with me, writing an obscurantist work, and they don't touch you. Why? There's a reason for that, is there?"

"Hmm!" Father Andrei smiled wryly. "Since when have I been a dangerous character? It's true I'm a priest, an obscurantist, a harmful element. Harmful, though, not dangerous! I would ask you to mark that! I am in no way a threat to anybody. I've been suppressed, that's all. And nowadays I'm useful, not harmful at all. Because I work for a living. I chop down trees, I go to sea, I break my back for my father's and grandfather's sake. What on earth am I to do? I have to eat. Now, don't go frowning, I can see my priestly lack of principle annoys you. I won't harp on about it. Anyway, why have we got onto this? Tell me what you thought about my book, then."

Kornilov gripped his cut-glass tumbler till his fingers started going numb.

"I enjoyed it," he said softly, though his eyes still flickered. "I enjoyed it very much. And not only me; comrade Surovtsev did too."

"Who is this comrade Surovtsev?" asked Father Andrei, slicing the gherkins.

Kornilov had been rising higher and higher; he was now soaring above creation. It was from this height that he felt bound to disgorge everything that was struggling to be free. He was really exhausted by now.

"I don't know who he is," he said, smiling ironically. "An investigator or an operative; well, anyway, he sits in the big house and takes a special interest in you."

"And he asked you for the manuscript?" enquired Father Andrei peaceably.

"He didn't have to. I brought it to him myself. As soon as I got it from you, I took it along. He's called me in and asked me: 'Who is this Kutorga?' I answered: 'A priest.' 'What's he doing these days?' 'He's working on a book about Christ.' 'What sort of a book is it?' 'I can bring it along if you like.' 'Do that.' So I took it. He put it in his drawer and a week later rang me: 'Come and collect your gospel.' I went there and got it. That's all."

He blurted all this at once, in cold bitterness, but in an almost feverish haste, afraid to stop for a second in case he cooled down and then he would say nothing more. Now he talked and talked, unable to call a halt. He did not simply want to talk about this, he wanted to go on talking. Talking about himself and his absurd, ludicrous existence; where he had been born, how and from whom he had learned things; how he had been married off unsuccessfully at the age of twenty-one. And all the rest of it too, about his father and mother, his elder sister and her husband, a prominent military man; how much they loved him, looked after his interests, sent him packages and parcels; how he didn't need anything just so long as he was left in peace, so long as he was left alone! Yes, in peace, in peace. That was why he was bursting to talk, simply had to talk about his first investigator and how the swine had tricked him back then. He would have started talking about it even if Father Andrei had been short with him and cut him off, saying that decent folk don't do such things – who had given him permission to take his manuscript along to that building? Ah, then he would have simply overwhelmed him with words! Positively awash with indignation! Ech, Andrei Ernestovich, Andrei Ernestovich! Governor's confessor! Hell, what sort of a spiritual father are you if you can't even make sense of that?

But Father Andrei was looking at him in a perfectly commonplace fashion, and Kornilov couldn't read anything in that direct gaze. He simply ran up against it and subsided.

"Earthly powers!" said Father Andrei pensively. "What can you say about them? But put us in their place and in a couple of months we'd send the whole enterprise to the bottom. Yet you see the little ship's still afloat, still afloat . . ." He thought for a moment, tapping his fingers on the table. "As for showing them my manuscript, that was the right thing to do. They'll feel easy now. A priest's a priest, what else can you expect! They'll turn me out of the museum no doubt, but let that pass."

"What do you mean, Andrei Ernestovich!" Kornilov was outraged. "Why talk like that? Our director would never agree to that!"

"He will, that director of yours, he will," said Father Andrei with the suspicion of a smile. "Why, you ask? It stands to reason: to keep obscurantism out of cultural enlightenment. Well, well, it's not the first time and it won't be the last! I'm used to things turning out this way. It's all right. I'm not afraid of work. Take a look at my palm here. No, feel it, feel it! Like wood, isn't it? Another month and it'll be just my time of year – I'll go and get a job with the forestry. I'm not a priest in that field, I'm a professor! Now then, where's your glass, let's drink to that profession of mine. Still, why stick to tots? Wait a minute and I'll fetch proper glasses."

"Earthly powers", said Father Andrei, as he snorted and pushed away the empty glass. "They're very tricky things. You can't make head or tail of them. They're governed by a thousand and one considerations. In that context, the story of Pontius Pilate is very instructive. There's no fathoming what his attitude to Christ was, even now, is there? Opinions have divided diametrically, one might say. Take you: 'President of the military tribunal! – condemned him and washed his hands of it! What does that mean? Although he crucified a man, he is blameless?' And, I, mark you, wouldn't laugh. I would have understood that such things also happen. Because they are tricky, very tricky, these earthly powers! Spiritual powers now, they're much more straightforward. In the Christ story it was all only too straightforward in that regard. They didn't like Christ, he was seized, judged, condemned, and put to death, that's all there was to it. Although it was no easy task condemning him."

"Not easy?"

"At first it was not at all easy. Later on, things went more smoothly, but at first the thing almost fell through altogether. You don't resort to false witness straight away, do you, there have to be some promptings of despair. During investigations too, they don't start bawling at you straight off, an interval has to elapse while they get used to the prisoner, as it were, look their fill at him. In those times it was all a thousand times more difficult. Listen to the way the presiding judge spoke to the witnesses." Father Andrei went across to the writing-desk, opened a folder and took out a sheet of paper. "'Perhaps what you say is based on supposition or on rumours, the words of others, and you do not realize that before we can accept your testimony, we will test you by way of question and answer. Remember that if the case concerns money, restitution can be made in money, but in this case, the blood of an innocent man, and all his unborn descendants for ever and ever will lie upon the false witness, for it was not in vain that the Lord God said of Cain: "The bloods of your brother Abel cry out unto me." (Mark that, 'bloods', not 'blood'! 'The bloods of the unborn posterity of Abel.') This is why Adam was created unique, in order to teach you that he who destroys one soul, destroys the whole world, and he who saves an innocent man, saves all mankind. For if a man makes a thousand impressions from his seal-ring, they will all be identical, whereas God took the image of all people from Adam, so that although they are equal, no one is like unto another. This, therefore, is what you have to decide; whether the whole world was created only for the sake of the man who now stands before you and whose life depends on your word.' Those were his final remarks. After that begins the questioning of the witnesses; they come in one at a time. The circumstances are as follows: dead of night (the cock crew a second time, so the whole business took place between two and three o'clock), seven-branched candlesticks burning; the hall is vast, stone-built and empty, half of it always in darkness; seventy-two judges on cushions on the floor, in two semi-circles, facing one another, so that everyone can see the others' eyes. Three secretaries in the centre – one to note down the words of the accused, two others the testimony of the witnesses. One for the prosecution witnesses, the other for the defence. Well it's obvious that false witnesses in circumstances like that will tend to lose their way and get confused: 'For many bear false witness against him . . . but their witness agreed not together,' says Mark's gospel – that is, not one of the witnesses could wholly confirm the words of any other. And now two witnesses spoke individually whose testimony seemed to coincide."

"Judas and this other?"

"I don't know, perhaps it was them. After all, everything concerning this nocturnal court is obscure. Who could know what took place there? The court was secret, with no outsiders present – and the accused isn't here now either, having been executed. So, two witnesses spoke, both testifying that Christ had reviled the temple. A more heinous crime could not have been imagined but this evidence too was rejected. According to Mark, Jesus is supposed to have said: 'I will destroy this temple that is made with hands, and within three days I will build another made without hands.' In Matthew, it has a different sound: 'I am able to destroy the temple of God and to build it in three days.' Ah! You see the contradiction there!"

"No, I don't," said Kornilov. "It's the same thing in my opinion."

"Ha! In your opinion! You're a poor lawyer, then. There's an enormous divergence. Just think now: 'I will destroy this temple.' This one! Terribly precise – that is, the one we are talking about at this moment! The definite article is there. The one in which is preserved the tabernacle of the Lord, the holy of holies for the people of Israel – the temple of Solomon. And I will build another not made with hands. Which is that then, may one ask? Your own? The temple of Jesus? The son of Joseph and Mary? The one who has brothers called Jacob, Joseph, Judas and Simon, as well as several sisters? What sort of temple are you promising, prophet, to build for us in your name in place of this one of Solomon's – that was the meaning of the testimony of the first witness."

"Well, what about the second?"

"The second testified thus: 'I can destroy a temple of God and build it in three days.' Meaning of course, not that I can, but that I could – the subjunctive mood there, but never mind. As if to say: 'This is how strong I am.' What temple? There is no definite article, so then, any temple! And of course there was an abundance of them. All temples were sacred after all! So in three days, you can build us a synagogue? You are a braggart of a builder indeed! Got a lot of money out of fools probably. They would have a good laugh and walk away. And that was it. So the two testimonies could not be combined. The accusations petered out and Jesus had to be released."

"Where to? Back to His beloved disciples? To Peter? Thomas and Judas?" Kornilov could not understand why, but the fact that his confession had apparently made not the slightest impression on Father

Andrei, who had simply heard him out, then upped and talked about something else, had been a severe shock to his nerves. Better if he had abused him or struck him, or thrown him out; otherwise it made it look as though nothing else could have been expected of Kornilov.

"Why have you taken against Peter?" Father Andrei grinned. "After all, say what you like, he was the only one who did not abandon his teacher. The others, as Mark tells us, 'all forsook him and fled'. Do you know why that whole sad story strikes me as thoroughly authentic? Everything about it is so bitterly and unattractively human. Could these really be apostles? Or martyrs? More than that, could they really be Christians? A Christian is supposed to

> March to death singing hymns,
> Into the jaws of ravening beasts
> Look without flinching.

"Or as Saint Ignatius said, 'I am Godly wheat and let me be ground by the teeth of beasts and become the bread of the Lord.' Or again. 'Even a robber chief, the leader of a band of villains, even he is never betrayed by his swinish followers, unless he has first betrayed them.' So says Porphyry, a bitter foe of Christ and Christianity, about the apostles. You're not the first to be ironic about Peter. 'How could he be the foundation of the church if on hearing the word "Jesus" from the mouth of some wretched rabbi, he was so terrified that he broke his vow three times?' That was Porphyry again. What of Christ himself? Remember: 'My soul is exceeding sorrowful, even unto death: tarry ye here and watch with me.' And again: 'Father, all things are possible unto Thee; take away this cup from me.'

"And on the cross: 'Eli, Eli, lama sabachthani. My God, My God why hast thou forsaken me?' and in some manuscripts, even more harshly: 'Why dost thou humiliate me?' And then that prayer: 'I thirst!' And the kind-hearted executioners offer him the sponge of vinegar. Where will you find anything like it in the lives of the saints? No wonder that other hater of Christianity, Celsus, is maliciously direct: 'If he has himself decided to accept execution, in obedience to his father, why call on him for help and pray to be released?: "Father, let this cup pass from me"? Why didn't he endure his thirst on the cross, as any one of us often has to?' And Porphyry also adds: 'All these speeches are unworthy, not only of the son of God, but even of a sage who despises death.' Alas, all this is so. And there is only one answer: 'Ecce homo!' And the evangelists could do nothing with this man. They didn't dare!"

"But they wanted to?"

"Well of course they did! 'Three and four times over,' writes Celsus, 'they re-wrote the first copy of the gospel, to avoid revealing it!' Yes, the most terrible revelation of all, that of the truth. And yet they didn't dare wipe out this weak, panicking, aching, utterly human element. And God, feeble and weak as he was, remained God. The God of men. You understand? No, no, how could you?"

"Yes, yes, I do understand," Kornilov assured him earnestly. "And you know what I've just remembered? Lessing wrote somewhere that a martyr is the most undramatic figure in the world. You can't write a tragedy about him. He performs no feats, he does not hesitate or suffer – he simply endures. He is tortured and he endures, he is tempted and he prays. Tfu! How depressing! But let us return to our muttons. So the witnesses got themselves mixed up?"

"So much so that the prisoner had to be released. But as the saying goes, they don't pull you in just to let you go again. The presiding judge addresses Jesus: 'I adjure thee by the living God,' he says, 'that thou tell us whether thou be the Christ, the Son of God?' Oh! This is a gross violation of the law! He should only have addressed the witnesses in that way. If Christ had now disavowed it or had answered in a vague or ambiguous fashion, they would have had to release him. But he honoured his life's work above life itself, above mother, sisters and brothers, the law and the temple, and in that most dreadful moment of his life, he did not dare – you hear? He simply did not dare! – to betray it. If he had just said: 'No, I am certainly not the man you take me to be,' that would have ended the matter. He would have beaten the sanhedrin. The seventy-two judges, followed by the guards, witnesses, secretaries, lay-brothers, altogether about a hundred of them, the whole crowd, would solemnly lead him out onto the square. And on that same square where he had preached, place him before the crowd and his disciples, and proclaim: 'We have judged this man and found him innocent. He never gave himself out to be the Christ, and he did not promise you the kingdom of heaven in his name. He merely preached the prophets to you according to his lights and understanding and you did not comprehend him.' And that is all. And Christ would vanish from our sight. The world remain unchanged. History would pass by. But he knew that this temptation would one day come and he would have to overcome it by death – but dying consciously and of his own free will, not like Seneca, the precursor, but like the son of man."

"You mean you don't think Seneca died of his own free will?"

"Perhaps he did, but not in that way. He fled rather than died. For Seneca, death was a release from compromise. And oh, Seneca was guilty of that! Acknowledging it fully, he once wrote this. Very finely. He could write beautifully. 'Wherever you look – you see the end of your torments everywhere. You see that ravine? In its depths lies your freedom. That crooked tree – stunted and twisted? Your freedom hangs from it. You see that river, the sea, that well? At the bottom of them is your freedom.' But Jesus felt himself to be perfectly free all his life in any case, free as the wind, like God. The gospels have brought to us that feeling. 'Here is a man who liked to eat and drink wine,' others wrote of him. 'I am come that they might have life, and that they might have it more abundantly,' he said of himself. Life for him was joyous, an exploit not a torment. That was precisely why he did not deign to answer 'no' to the presiding judge's question; he said 'yes'. The evangelists convey his answer in different ways, but at all events he answered very simply, monosyllabically – anything to have done with it all. Porphyry reproaches him for that. It seems to him that at such a decisive moment a man should grow to be as granite, break out in thunder and lightnings and with his tongue sear the judges' hearts. 'The same way,' he says, 'that Apollonius of Tyana accused the emperor Domitian! The fur flew!' But Christ was not Apollonius; he was worn out and weary unto death; he was sickened by all that had been happening. At that moment he wanted just one thing – let it be over quickly, quickly! Perhaps he was afraid that he wouldn't be able to stand it and collapse. But the judges were also in a hurry. 'Thou hast said.' The presiding judge ripped his garments open to the waist. This was equivalent to breaking his judge's rod. 'Guilty of death,' he said. 'Guilty of death,' confirm the seventy-one. The end. 'And the whole multitude rose and led him to Pilate.' Rome now enters the case – the proconsul of Judaea, Pontius Pilate.

He came of a rich Samnite family and therefore was never accounted a man out of the top drawer. The Samnites after all, were so-called allies, not Romans. They even had different emblems: the Romans had a wolf, but they had a bull. If you remember, there had even been three Social wars,* when the bulls had gone for the wolves as a herd. But all that was over and done with. Now Pontius Pilate, at any rate in Judaea, felt himself to be a Roman patrician, a white man in a savage eastern land. By nature he was a vigorous and active individual. Such people were known in Rome at that time as "homo novus", "new man". There's something untranslatable in that sobriquet – a hint of scorn, a light flip on the nose. Nouveau riche, upstart, le bourgeois gentilhomme, rags to riches, that sort of thing. Eusebius writes that Pilate was sent to Judaea by Sejanus – there was a cruel villain of that name at Tiberius' court. Later on, naturally, he also was executed. So, Sejanus is supposed to have appointed Pontius Pilate as proconsul precisely because of his detestation of the Jews. Very possibly. At all events, Judaea had never before experienced such a tyrant. 'Bribery, violence, execution without trial, endless horrible cruelties' – so, according to Philo, wrote Herod Agrippa to Tiberius. Very well, that was probably no more than the truth. But all the same, he did not want to execute Christ. Why? This is where the confusion arises. The Christian writers have complicated the issue dreadfully. I recall here a conversation I had with an academician long ago. He said to me: 'But what do you find inscrutable about him, father? There really is no mystery about it. In our education work for instance, we're up to our ears in people like Pilate. He's a typical middle-ranking official of the imperial era. Harsh but not cruel, shrewd and worldly-wise. In minor and uncontroversial matters – just, even principled; in more important matters, evasive and indecisive. In every other regard he was extremely crafty in his dealings. Therefore, although he realized where the truth lay, he would start squirming at the slightest hint of complexity, wash his hands of it, so to speak. In the incident with Christ, this was demonstrated especially clearly. That was all there was to it.' But in this, as I now realize, the academician was not altogether correct. Special factors were at work."

"What were they then?"

* *The Social Wars*: fought between 90–88 BC over the issue of extending the Roman franchise to all Italians.

"Well, I've already mentioned the first of them. He couldn't stand these filthy Jews. And since they reciprocated the feeling, everything got inextricably tangled up. And in these stratagems, Pilate at times positively lost his head. The shrewd, sober man was so on edge all the time that occasionally he would forget all about constraints. And at such moments he could be recklessly foolish. A bull beset by jackals! He dealt out humiliation where he could – and annihilation too. Luke describes in one place: Christ was told of some Galileans whose blood Pilate mingled with that of their sacrifices during divine service. And Christ answered calmly: 'Do you think those Galileans were more sinful than others?' You see the terseness, the simplicity of it! No point at all in enquiring about why these innocents were slaughtered; they had been killed, that was the point. A run of the mill incident. So commonplace in fact that it wasn't worth talking about. But the grateful populace, while allowing themselves to be killed, had taken due note of this and had sent 'lamentations' to Rome. And when they came to the eyes of the emperor, Pilate received a telling-off. Explanations were demanded of him. Tiberius was an experienced administrator and couldn't stand a lot of fuss being made over nothing. Yes 'O, race of slaves!' Yes, the people were flatterers, slaves, cowards and traitors, but one had to be able to deal with them. With me they don't shout even when I suffocate them. Why do they shout with you, proconsul?"

"It was him who brought in penalties and punishments for every word of opposition, I believe?"

"It was, it was him. The law of AD 15. 'Criticism of the actions of the emperor is tantamount to insulting the majesty of the Roman people.' For that you lost your head at once."

"Some experienced administrator!"

"What was wrong with it? Tiberius, unfortunately, was far from being the only idealist in history. They haven't diminished much over two thousand years. However that might be, Pilate came to a bad end. Some sources say he took his own life under Caligula. Others say he was put to death by Nero; still others that he was banished to Switzerland where he drowned in Lake Lucerne. There is a mountain in the Alps called Pilatus. On Good Friday, the day of the court hearing, a great shadow appears on it and everyone washes their hands over and over. It was in Switzerland, in 1912, that I saw a mystery play – an enactment of our Lord's passion. There were around ten thousand spectators. It all took place under the open sky in an alpine valley. A meadow amid dazzling snowy heights. And below them moves the procession: legionaries, the brigands and a large white figure – Christ. Then I recalled Shakespeare. His chronicles. He's the one who could have written a tragedy about Christ! And you know, he would hardly have needed to invent anything. It's all there in the gospels. Images, characters. circumstances, deathless dialogue, where one line says it all. Borrowing something from the apocryphal writers, it might go like this:

PILATE: Art thou the King of the Jews?

JESUS: Askest thou this thyself or art thou repeating what others have told thee?

PILATE *smiling derisively and shrugging his shoulders*: Am I a Jew then? That is thy people. Thy high priests have brought thee here to me. What hast thou done then? Art thou a king?

JESUS: If my kingdom was of this world, my subjects would surely not have allowed me to be seized and brought before thee?

PILATE *insistent*: But art thou then a king?

JESUS: Thou sayest it. What I say is: I came to the world to establish the truth.

PILATE *grinning peevishly*: Truth, truth! And what is truth?

JESUS: It is that which is from heaven.

PILATE *grins*: So then it does not exist on earth?

JESUS: Thou hast seen what is done on earth to people who speak the truth! They are delivered unto such as thou.

PILATE: Whence art thou? *Christ does not reply.* Why dost thou not reply then? I can either crucify thee or release thee.

JESUS: Thou seest – thou canst, and thou wouldst not have that power if it had not been sent to thee from on high! But then thou art not to blame, judge! The sin is upon those who have brought me before thee.

PILATE *deliberates and comes to a decision*: Let us go!

He goes out of the hall into a yard filled with people and takes his place on the judgment seat – the judge's raised marble chair. The soldiers bring Jesus in after him. Hubbub.

PILATE: Here is your king. *A thunder of shouting: "Death to him, death! Crucify him, crucify!"*

PILATE *impatiently*: Quiet! Listen! You have delivered him to me as an agitator of the people. I questioned him in your presence, investigated all the circumstances and did not find him guilty. I sent him to Herod and he also found him not guilty. So therefore I will punish him and let him go. *Indignant cries.* Wait! Easter is upon us. Your custom is that I should release a prisoner of your choice. At the moment I have Barabbas. He has been convicted of murder during a revolt. Whom then should I release unto you. The brigand or Jesus, called the Christ?

SHOUTS: Barabbas! Barabbas! Crucify him! Death to him!

PILATE *Shouting in rage*: I see! I'm to crucify your king am I, wretches? *One of the high priests approaches, saying quietly, insidiously and insistently: "We have no king but Caesar. Anyone calling himself king is an enemy of Caesar, proconsul."*

SHOUTS: Crucify him, crucify! Barabbas! Barabbas!

PILATE *beside himself, almost hopeless*: But what evil has he done you?

SHOUTS: Crucify him, crucify! *Pilate surveys the crowd in silence. He then makes a sign and brings a vessel and towel.*

PILATE *washes his hands*: I am not guilty of the blood of this just person: see ye to it.

Howling of the crowd, the soldiers take Jesus away. At this moment a high priest approaches him.

HIGH PRIEST: Eh! Destroyer of temples and builder of them in three days! Now save thyself, come down from the cross!

Laughter from the crowd and shouts: "Let him be crucified! Let him be crucified! Let his blood be upon our heads! On ours and those of our children!"

"That's approximately how it would sound if you were to set out the gospel story dramatically. I've only put in the stage directions and filled out the very obscure place about what is truth, from the apocryphal gospel according to Peter. And so, the Jews disliked Pilate. They kept writing and writing to Rome and their constant lamentation and complaining finally had its effect. Pilate was recalled. One can imagine the exasperation that had developed on both sides. Hence Pilate's initial hesitation. He simply didn't want to execute anyone for the benefit of the Jews. But there was a second consideration. Reasons of state this time. The fact of the matter was that Christ, or someone like him, suited Pilate's book very well. Surprised? It's quite simple really. He had thoroughly assimilated two aspects of Christ's teaching. In the first place, this wandering preacher did not believe either in war or revolutionary upheaval; no, man must refashion himself from within, and then everything would happen by itself. Therefore he was against rebellion. That was the first point. Second: the only thing that Jesus sought to destroy and actually was undermining all the time, were the authorities. The authority of the Sanhedrin, the Sadducees and the Pharisees, and so, perhaps unwittingly, the authority of Moses and the temple. And it was in the monolithic and unquestionable nature of these that the greatest danger to the empire resided. Clearly Rome needed precisely the sort of subversion that Jesus represented. And this was an intelligent subverter too. He knew perfectly well that if you wish to destroy something ancient and cherished, you never say, I have come to destroy this. No, say you have come to support this sacred edifice, renew it, replace the decayed elements in it; then, when you are trusted, you may wreak your will, and drive the people as hard as you want, and no dawdling! Crush and smash! Take the well-known beginning of the sermon on the mount: 'I am not come to destroy the laws but to fulfil' and then the ending: 'Ye have heard that it was said by men of old time: "hate thine enemy", but I say unto you, love your enemies, bless them that curse you, do good to them that hate you and persecute you.' Grand? And all this taken together comes under 'till heaven and earth pass, one jot or one tittle shall in no wise pass from the law.' An iota? The whole thing was shaken to pieces. Now imagine the state of the world at that time and ask yourself whether or not such utterances in the mouth of the Galilean did not suit Pilate? Didn't it mean a prescription to pray for and love him, the occupier? Surely Pilate, a state official who knew the East and the land he was attempting to pacify, realized that this was the very force on which he ought to rely? That Christ was indeed a force – this he did sense. He also had a vague intuition of something else: any kind of meekness was immensely powerful. You don't recall who said that?"

"Tolstoy I expect?"

"No. Dostoevsky. In his last years he thought a great deal about Christ: he didn't know quite how to treat him, and so essayed various experiments with him. In one of these he left him with meekness and love, and took away his sword and scourge as being superogatory. The result was Lev Nikolaevich, Prince Myshkin – a personality not only lacking vitality, but destructive of all who love him. After that he returned the sword to him and threw out all the rest. The result of that was the Grand Inquisitor, that is, Christ putting Christ to death. But in that regard Pilate was much more realistic than Dosto-evsky and his Inquisitor: he understood Christ as he was, and that Christ suited him well."

"You mean he didn't even suspect the revolutionary destructive power of Christ's preaching?"

"Who could have suspected it then? Even long afterwards, nobody could see their way clearly in that regard. A hundred years later, the younger Pliny made an attempt to comprehend what it was, but apart from 'a savage superstition taken to absurd lengths', he could see nothing in it. This is what he wrote to the emperor Trajan. Tacitus was even more to the point than that: 'people hated for their nastiness and evil deeds, whom the mob called "Christians"'. And further (speaking about the burning of Rome): 'they were accused not so much as having started the fire, as for the hatred they bore towards the human race.' I am quoting from memory, so I can't be quite exact. That is the way the most refined, intelligent, enlightened human minds thought and wrote about Christianity many years after Christ's execution. But Pilate didn't think like that. He knew: this wandering preacher was very necessary to Rome. He was listened to, people believed in him and followed him. He was capable of founding a new cosmopolitan religion, acceptable to the authorities. Whether he was mistaken in this view, is still unclear. Opinions have differed sharply on the point. So much for the second reason, but there was still a third: why the devil should they be trying to frighten and blackmail him? Why should he play the role of synagogue executioner? They had been deprived of the *jus gladii*, the right of the sword, so now they wanted to cut off an inconvenient head using his hands. The hands of a Roman patrician! To Beelzebub with them! The dirty tricks they had played on him too! Hadn't they disrupted work on the aqueduct? Indeed they were pigs, they had no use for clean water. They used to wash in ponds and here was he wanting to bring in water from the Jordan! They wouldn't let him. Just think, Caesar's image, the Roman military banners – they wouldn't allow them into Jerusalem! Wouldn't allow it and that was flat. Even the shields had to be removed from Herod's palace – they bore the emperor's portrait, you see. And they got away with everything – he was the one who got the blame – didn't know how to approach them. And who the devil were they? Liars and traitors! Filthy eastern dogs. And now he – the representative of the emperor, the first man in the land, had to put this wretch to death at their whim and behest, simply because he, Pilate, had need of him and he was therefore hateful to them. And there was nothing for it – he had to do it. Ah, if he had only been Gallio! Do you know who he was? Seneca's own brother. Proconsul of Achaia. His residence was in Corinth, and this is what had taken place there on one occasion. I remember this place by heart: 'The Jews made insurrection with one accord against Paul and brought him to the judgment seat, saying: this fellow persuadeth men to worship God contrary to the law.' You see, just as it was with Christ. But this was Gallio, and this was the upshot. 'If it were a matter of wrong or wicked lewdness, O ye Jews, reason would that I should bear with you: but if it be a question of words and names, and of your law, look ye to it; for I will be no judge of such matters.' And he drove them from the judgment seat. And all the Greeks took the chief ruler of the synagogue and beat him before the judgment seat. And Gallio cared for none of those things. A grand scene and a grand patrician. 'Look ye to it,' but that was something Pilate couldn't say; he simply didn't dare. Palestine wasn't Greece, Jerusalem wasn't many-columned Corinth, and he wasn't Gallio, just Pontius Pilate 'homo novus'. So that when he heard the dreaded: 'If you release him you are Caesar's enemy', he caved in, washed his hands and carried out the execution. Just like you and I! My dear friend," Father Andrei seized Kornilov by the shoulder, "You say: they summoned you and took my manuscript from you. They took it, you say, because they don't want to crucify me. That means you were talking to people just like Pilate, wretched people like Pilate on whom absolutely nothing depends. With murderers and cut-throats in the name of an alien god! With poor Judas, whom it is impossible even to forgive, because there is nothing to forgive! For it is not they who are guilty, but rather those nonentities who sit behind seven walls and send them coded messages: 'Seize, judge, kill!'"

"Oh," Kornilov grimaced, wincing from nausea and a ringing pain in his temples. "Whom do you mean?" Father Andrei loomed over him, tall, angular, with his gaunt sallow face and weird, absolutely circular all-engulfing eyes.

And once more it seemed to Kornilov that this was all a dream, that any minute there would be a tremor, a shift in the delicate rainbow veil on which all this was being depicted; it would split asunder and he would wake up in his own bed. All he had to do was want it to happen.

"Whom do I mean?!" asked Father Andrei with quiet menace. "You understand whom! Those two. The florid dwarf and the half-witted Moses. The two vampires I'm talking about."

"Yes, a dream," thought Kornilov. "A horrible, drunken dream; it'll burst in a minute and I'll wake up."

And mumbled: "What are you talking about Father Andrei? What dwarf is this? What Moses? Better just pour me out a drop more."

Here Father Andrei suddenly began to weep. He sat down, dropped his head on his hands and, ever so quietly, began crying like a child. This brought Kornilov round completely. "It's all right," he thought. "The dacha's empty. Nobody to hear anything. It's all right."

"Father Andrei," he called softly.

The priest sighed, slowly raised his head and all of a sudden fixed Kornilov with a piercing stare. His eyes were normal again, old man's eyes, glinting with tears.

"Oh, my dear chap," he said with simple bitterness. "No matter how many times I tell that story, no one ever understands what it means at all. And nor have you. But really, it's quite simple. Very simple. Yet people die or betray because of it!" For a minute more he regarded Kornilov with a smile of ineffable bitterness, then sighed lightly, slid the decanter over and said: "Very well then, yes! Let's have one more! For the road!"

Translated from the Russian by Alan Myers

YASHAR KEMAL

From the novel *Suleiman the Solitary*

Suleiman the Solitary is the story of Ismail Agha, who is driven from home when the Ottoman Army fails to repel the invading Russians. Ismail's struggle to retain his humanity in a world of savagery, and his difficult friendship with the young outcast Suleiman, is the dominant thread running through this powerful evocation of Turkish pastoral life. In this excerpt, Ismail Agha and his family are first uprooted from their ancestral homeland by the shores of Lake Van.

Lake Van is surrounded by the mountains of Süphan, Nemrut and Esrük whose peaks, snow-capped all the year round, shed a white radiance on the mirror of the lake. Its shores as well as the mountain slopes are entirely bare, and so are the plains of Muradiyé, Patnos, Chaldiran and Van that stretch beyond.

The village was situated on the banks of the lake, just below Mount Esrük, at the approach to the Sor Valley. A long file of man-tall stones marched along this valley from Esrük to the lake. All the dwellings were underground. One descended into them through an opening like the mouth of a well. The sheep and goats, cattle and horses also went in through this entrance and slept inside along with the inmates. On freezing winter nights their breath warmed the whole house and their dried dung served as fuel for cooking. There was only one habitation above the ground and that was the Bey's two-storied, sixteen-roomed mansion, built of well-hewn stones culled from ancient edifices.

The Bey was a handsome, dark-complexioned man, very tall, with broad shoulders and a long white beard. His brothers and relatives resided in strange houses half buried in the earth, with no windows at all, only a largish hole on the mud roof which served both to let in the light and let out the smoke from the hearth.

The Bey had studied in Istanbul and Salonika. His brothers, too, were literate men which was rare in these parts. Ismail Agha was the Bey's nephew, the eldest of three brothers, stalwart youths renowned all over the lake country for their good looks. Ismail Agha's father had sent him to high school in Van. He had felt oppressed, somehow, in this city of goldsmiths and jewellers, set right on the shores of the lake and surrounded by walls of sun-dried brick. Surmounting the city was the ancient citadel, its bastions of the same solid sun-dried brick as the city walls. Hundreds of years, thousands perhaps, had done nothing to impair these earthen walls and bastions, they had only grown sturdier with time.

Hüseyin Bey, the Bey's youngest brother, was a student at the Military Academy in Istanbul. He was Ismail Agha's only friend in the village and just as handsome. Together they would go riding to take part in a game of *jerid* and hunt for deer in the mountains. It was not only ties of blood that linked them, their friendship dated from their years at high school in Van where they had both stayed at the house of a relative. They were closer than brothers and had not parted until the day Hüseyin Bey left for Istanbul. After that Ismail Agha never set foot in Van again. He remained in the village, tilling his fields, growing honeydew and water-melons and hunting the deer. He would return from the hunt on Mount Esrük, bearing huge-antlered deer, sometimes more than a dozen, and these were brought down by the mountain people. With the help of the village youths Ismail Agha would skin them and distribute the meat in equal parts to all the families in the village. Even the Bey never got more than his share. Winter was the season for hunting partridges. They flocked in from far and wide to shelter in the crevices of the Sor Valley. However, it was not everyone who could tackle the drifts of snow that blocked the valley during the long winter months or brave the blizzards and the violent storms that never let up and could be heard way off from the shores of the lake like the rumble of distant thunder. But nothing could deter Ismail Agha. Penetrating into the Sor Valley with a few dauntless companions, he soon uncovered coveys of partridges huddled in a shelter or scattered over the snow like buckshot. He and his men advanced towards them waving their arms and the partridges started up and alighted some five hundred paces further off. The men flushed them again and this time the birds settled less than two hundred paces away. At the third go, the partridges were unable to fly and Ismail Agha and his friends could gather them without further ado. Back in the village it would be a feast day. From every home rose the odour of partridges being broiled over acrid smouldering dried dung, and greasy fumes swirled through the air mingling with the smell of snow and of Lake Van which smelled like no other lake, not swampy at all, but more like a white-foamed spring surging from gnarled roots in a pine forest.

In the summer the village moved up into the high pastures of Mount Esrük, leaving Lake Van far below with its many shades of blue, shot with evanescent streaks of orange, and the snow-white reflection of Mount Süphan, and also Patnos plain with its flocks of cranes, its pelicans, its tall graceful poplars, and the snakes that swarmed in thousands in the white heat of the summer. The long black tents of goat hair were pitched on the plateaux between the tarns that abounded with red and blue speckled trout. The villagers, men and women, were expert at fishing for trout, for they had been doing it since their childhood. They caught so many that they could not eat them all and had to salt them away in barrels to take back down to the village.

A thousand and one flowers bloomed on Mount Esrük, the grass was knee-deep, a cool breeze blew constantly and gentle sunlight bathed the meadows. Musicians with pipes and drums flocked into the uplands and every day was a day of festivity. Half the villagers were Armenians, but they spoke Kurdish too and, until the killings and enmity, lived in perfect harmony with their neighbours. Moslem Kurds would dye eggs and celebrate Easter together with the Armenians and the Armenians in their turn offered sacrifices along with the Kurds during the Kurban Bairam. So it had been for centuries. The Armenians would worship their own god in the mosque, and Moslems would perform the *namaz* in the church. For Ismail the time of the killings was the most painful in all his life. He could never forget his neighbour Onnik's face, stunned, distressed, incredulous . . .

"Save me, Ismail," he had cried, his eyes wide with fear. "They're after me. To kill! Our own Bald Riza! Riza with whom we grew up together! Riza who spent more time in our house than in his own . . . And now he wants to kill me!"

Ismail Agha had tried to reassure him, but Onnik was much too frightened and, that night while the household was asleep, he fled into the mountains.

"Why on earth d'you want to kill Onnik?" Ismail Agha had asked Riza.

"I'll kill him. I'll find him even if he's hiding in the pit of hell," was all he could get out of the man. He lost his temper. "If you kill him, then I'll kill you too," he shouted. "Just you try!"

On the flowering meadows youths and maidens, Kurdish and Armenian, dressed in bright-coloured clothes, lined up arm in arm for the *gövend*. Their bodies moved with incredible litheness, with joy and pride to the slow rhythm of this ancient dance. It was always Ismail Agha who led the dance, a handsome figure, tall and willowy, his large eyes shining like black diamonds in his swarthy face. And all the people of the uplands came to watch him and joined in the dance, swaying like a slumbering sea, delicate as a wisp of smoke trembling up into the sky . . .

Famous bards came from far and wide to visit the Bey's majestic seven-poled tent. They were installed on a throne-like elevation outside the tent and everyone crowded around on brightly printed felt mats to listen to the telling of age-old epics. The most renowned of these bards was Abdalé Zeyniki, the Bey of Malazgirt's own private minstrel. Apart from his own ballads and songs, he recited traditional epics like no other bard ever could. Blind until the age of sixty, Abdalé Zeyniki had suddenly recovered his sight, and this he attributed to a miracle, which he celebrated in a ballad sung by all the minstrels of the region. The Bey had an immense respect for two bards. One was Abdalé Zeyniki and the other the Armenian, Hachik. He would rise to greet them, which he did for no one else, and never sit down until they had done so first. Indeed, these two bards were revered in villages and encampments from Kars to Van, from Van to Diyarbakir, Erzinjan and Erzurum. The household or village which they visited would ever after boast of their coming. Even Ismail Agha, the most modest of men, would proudly recall Abdalé Zeyniki's stay in their house. "This homestead," he would say, "has been honoured with the presence of the Abdal, the great Zeyniki . . ."

When Hüseyin Bey arrived from Istanbul to spend the summer in the high pastures, he would quickly shed his black city suit, so outlandish in these parts, to don the wide trousers and waistcoat of the local costume called the *shal shapik* and join with Ismail Agha in the merrymaking.

Were they happy, these people? Ismail Agha? Or unhappy? Such a thought never crossed their minds. Wars and massacres they had known, famines and pestilences that decimated men and beasts, and that was perhaps for them the meaning of unhappiness. But even then they still knew how to laugh and though there was much suffering, there were just as many joys.

Unhappy was a word Ismail Agha heard for the first time from the lips of Hüseyin Bey.

"I'm unhappy, Ismail," Hüseyin Bey said with a deep sigh one day after he had come from Istanbul.

Ismail Agha was puzzled. "You're not ill, are you?" he asked.

"Ill? No," Hüseyin Bey replied. "I wish I was . . . Consumptive, leprous, anything . . . I'm unhappy."

Ismail Agha concluded that this was a kind of sickness, and worse than any other. Indeed, as from that day Hüseyin Bey did not go back to Istanbul. He kept out of the village activities and was never heard to speak to anyone again, not even Ismail Agha.

East of the village were some tall crags that fell steeply into the lake. Each day Hüseyin Bey would get up before dawn, boil his milk and tea and eat his breakfast all alone. In the winter he would don a thick shepherd's cloak, in the summer his blue *shal shapik* then he would make off for the crags, there to sit till nightfall, motionless, his huge dark eyes fixed steadfastly on the lake, and when it was too dark to see he would return home, eat the meal that was kept ready for him in front of the hearth and go straight to bed. Such had been Hüseyin Bey's whole existence for five or six years. Neither the snakes that swarmed over the crags in the scorching summer heat, nor the frost that cracked the rocks, the snows that hid even the telegraph poles, and the black *bora* that uprooted the trees could make him stir from his post on the crags. Vast as a sea, situated at five thousand four hundred feet above sea level and surrounded by mountains, Van Lake is sometimes swept by tidal bores, and waves as high as minarets beat against its shores. None of this seemed to touch the man nailed to his rock. At the most, as though on some blind impulse, he would move a little higher up the crags when a waterspout sucked at the shore.

And so the story went:

Istanbul is a city on the sea, just like the city of Van, with many islands too. One day, on one of these islands, an island like Aghtamar Island on Lake Van, Hüseyin met a girl and it was love at first sight for both of them. They made love, but suddenly the girl drew away and rushed straight into the sea. Hüseyin caught a glimpse of her hair floating on the water before she sank away out of sight. After this he was unable to drag himself from that island. He remained there for months on end, his eyes glued to the spot where the girl had disappeared, and one day the girl's head rose out of the water. In a rush of emotion Hüseyin Bey fainted away and when he came to, there was not a trace of the girl. But he waited, for days, for months he waited and then at last she appeared again. This time Hüseyin Bey jumped into the water. He was unable to catch her, but she spoke to him. I am a fairy, she told him, and I love you true. Go to Van. There, in the lake, I have a sister. I'll come and join her and, though I won't be able to get out of the water, I'll be there where you can see me every day from dawn to nightfall. After the sun sets I must go back to my father, the *Peri* King who lives in the castle of Van ... Hüseyin was overcome with joy. Lake Van is where I live, he said. I know, the girl said. Van is my home too, that's where I first saw you, on the steep crags below the castle of Van, and when you left for Istanbul I followed you ... So that is why Hüseyin Bey hurried back home. That is why each day when the east begins to pale he goes to the lake and the girl's head appears on the surface of the water, so beautiful that Hüseyin Bey can never have his fill of looking at her. And the fairy, too, is so enraptured with Hüseyin's handsome countenance that she remains there all day long, oblivious of waves and storms and waterspouts.

For days on end the villagers flocked to the shores of the lake, stealthily they hid among the rocks, not to be seen by Hüseyin Bey, eagerly they waited and watched, but no one ever saw the beautiful head of the fairy. At last they gave up. "She's visible to none but her lover," they concluded, and left Hüseyin Bey and his fairy love to themselves.

Cranes in bevelled formation fly through the sky, shedding their shadow on the blue of the lake. At every moment of the day Lake Van is imbued with a wealth of colours. Suddenly, a lightning flash of orange shoots across the water from east to west and the whole lake is an orange dream on which rests the head of the fairy. Next, a flash of mauve tinges the lake. Sweeping white-foamed wavelets before it, it reaches the flanks of Mount Süphan and casts a mauve blanket over the richly flowering Patnos plain. Sometimes the rippling surface of the lake is bright red on one half and deep blue on the other and sometimes the majestic shape of Mount Süphan, with its snow-capped peak soaring far into the sky, is reflected on the lake in a white immaculate splendour that irradiates even the darkest night.

And there he sits, Hüseyin Bey, singing in an undertone. He sings for his fairy love whose head only he can see on the water and he sings to the unending columns of cranes flying past, sometimes very low, their wings skimming the surface of the lake, sometimes soaring high into the vast blue sky. He sings to the red earth and green pastures of Mount Esrük, and the breeze blows down to him from the mountain, laden with the fragrance of a thousand and one flowers and grasses. His sad eyes are riveted on the lake and over his pale, mournful face flickers the reflection of the ever-changing colours of the waters, now foaming and tempest-tossed, now smooth and calm as though no wind had ever touched them. And as the sun sets, colours and lights, rocks and flying cranes fade into the gloom and out of the night rise the cries of wild beasts and birds, the noise of many waters and the booming of the mountain.

One night, Hüseyin Bey gave ear to an officer who had lost both feet in the war and for the first time in many years he was shaken to the core.

"Defeated!" the officer was saying. "Ninety thousand men left there on the snows of Sarikamish! And most of them devoured by lice. By lice! It's the lice defeated the Turkish soldiers, not the Russians. Lice!" he shouted, and repeated in Arabic, in Kurdish, in Syriac. "The great Ottoman Empire eaten up by lice, finished!" He hid his face in his hands and wept, then went on with a bitter smile. "The battle of Sarikamish will go down in history as the battle where the Turks were vanquished by lice. Ninety thousand men lying there, dead on the snow. Run, my friends, get away from here, the Russian army is coming, burning, destroying, killing, and before it, shielding it, is its greatest weapon, swarms of lice. Quick, my friends, empty the villages, for when they arrive they will leave nothing standing, no one alive . . ."

The Bey and his guests stared at him as though he had gone out of his mind. How could the great Ottoman army be defeated? It was inconceivable.

A few days later survivors of the routed Hamidiyé regiment entered the village and at once began to plunder and kill. It was terrible. The dregs of the Hamidiyé regiment, the last remaining soldiers of Enver Pasha, had turned into a wild, desperate horde, hounded by lice and the Russian army. All over the mountain, deserters ravaged the villages, making away with the cattle, abducting the women, stealing their gold necklaces, bracelets and rings, and burning those villagers who tried to resist. And so it was everywhere in the eastern provinces, swarms of marauders pillaging and killing, and most of all it was the Yezidis and Alevis* and Armenians that they killed. The villagers themselves were not always idle. They struck at these remnants of the Ottoman army whenever they could.

At the first burst of cannon to be heard from behind Mount Süphan the deserters took to their heels. But still the stragglers came, weary now, sick, wounded, all skin and bones, with nothing human left about them. Their ragged capotes were stiff with blood.

Then one evening just before sunset, a cannonball fell plumb into the hot water spring that flowed in the middle of the village. The waters gushed high into the air and a deep pit was formed that soon filled up with water. After this cannonballs began to fall all over the place. Pandemonium broke loose, people screamed, cattle bellowed, horses neighed and there were many killed and wounded. People lay around with severed legs and arms. Nothing could be done to relieve them and they just bled to death.

From where he sat by the lake Hüseyin Bey could hear the burst of cannon, but he never stirred. For all he cared, the cannonballs that exploded near him might have been so many falling autumn leaves. Only at his appointed hour, after the sun had set, he rose, stood a while as he always did, his eyes fixed on the darkening waters, then set off for the village, oblivious to the shells that whistled and fell about him, striking up flames from the trembling soil and raising columns of water poplar-high from the lake.

The Bey came to meet him half-way. "My dear Hüseyin," he said very gently, as he took his hand and drew him along, "we have to leave this place tomorrow before daybreak. The enemy is advancing, burning the villages, killing everyone, young and old. Can't you hear the shells hitting our village? So many killed already . . . Tomorrow morning you must not go to the crags for we shall be leaving very

* Yezidi and Alevi: two Moslem sects.

early. Who knows," he sighed, "if we shall ever see our home again, our village, the lake, our high pastures . . ."

Darkness fell and the shelling stopped. But the villagers did not sleep. They spent the night gathering their belongings and loading the packs onto donkeys, horses, cows and oxen. When they finally set out at daybreak, the cannonade started again and soon after, the first of the enemy forerunners entered the village.

The Bey anxiously sought out Ismail Agha. "What am I to do?" he said. "Hüseyin's nowhere to be found."

"He must be there by the lake," Ismail Agha said.

"But I told him not to go! He knew we were leaving."

"Don't worry, uncle. It's on our way. I'll run and fetch him and catch up with you all."

Utter confusion reigned in the countryside. Long trains of fugitives pressed on, shouting and wailing and moving slowly in the pale dawn light.

Ismail Agha quickly reached the crags, but he saw with sudden misgiving that for the first time in all these years Hüseyin Bey was not in his usual place. He looked around and his eyes fell on the figure lying prone on the water about fifty strokes offshore. It was Hüseyin, wearing his black Istanbul clothes and swaying gently on the pale blue of the lake. Ismail Agha plunged into the water and swam up to him. Hüseyin Bey's body was rigid, his eyes fixed in a bulging stare. The gold chain of his watch, a watch which he had not worn for years, gleamed dully in the water. Ismail Agha heaved him onto the shore and sat him down in his old place facing the lake, his back against the rock. And there he left him and ran back to join the trek. But there was something that troubled him, some change in Hüseyin Bey. The watch, he knew about. His shoes were the patent leather shoes he had worn on his return from Istanbul, the shirt, embroidered, also from Istanbul . . . Then it came to him. The gold wedding ring on his long slim finger! Ismail Agha had never seen it before, neither on the day Hüseyin Bey arrived from Istanbul, nor at any time in the years that followed.

The Bey gave a cry of pain when he saw Ismail Agha return alone. "Where is he?"

"He's gone," Ismail Agha said. "Maybe he's already ahead of us. We'll meet him on the way."

The tears ran down the Bey's face. "He's lost, alas," he sighed.

That night they did not stop to sleep, but were carried along with the flow of refugees, and it was only towards morning on the second day that they were able to slip away into a little valley and disburden the beasts under a spreading walnut tree. There they bethought themselves of food and cooked their first meal.

Ismail Agha's mother was an invalid and he had carried her on his back up to here. His brothers had offered to take her in turns, but he would not let them. His younger brother was still a bachelor. The youngest, Hassan, was married though it was unusual in these parts for younger brothers to get married before their elders. Ismail Agha himself had taken a wife late in life and only very recently.

They remained there one day at the foot of the walnut tree, then set off again, the noise of cannon still ringing in their ears. Ismail Agha's mother was on his back again, silent, uncomplaining, bearing it all with the patience of a saint. Though over seventy she was still beautiful, her face without a single wrinkle. Her only worry now was that she had to be carried, that she was wearing down her son. She never showed her distress, but Ismail Agha guessed it and did his best to give her the lie. He laughed and sang and every now and then he repeated: "Why mother, how light you are! Just as if a bird had come to perch on my shoulder!"

A month and a half later they reached the plain of Diyarbakir. Thousands of refugees were streaming into this torrid plain, strewn with black, incandescent rocks, its waters like warm blood, its swamps spreading malaria. People died like flies and the survivors did not have the strength to bury them. And still they came, fleeing, dying . . . The family had nothing left to eat. Some of their cattle had been stolen by the deserters, some they had to kill for food and the remainder were dropping dead in the blistering heat of Diyarbakir. The whole plain, the roads and ditches, the River Tigris reeked with the stench of carrion. People began to flee into the hills and to loot the villages up there. Famished hordes swooped down on the hamlets and small towns like swarms of locusts and when they departed there was not a morsel of food to be found, not a crumb of bread or a drop of water. The grass did not grow again on their passage. In the town and hamlets the men armed themselves and massacred the invaders. But nothing could stop the human flood. Day after day, like a torrent overflowing its banks, this ragged famished multitude poured into the plains, the valleys, the hills, and pursuing them were the deserters, the fires, the roar of cannon. The war with the enemy, they had left behind in Van, but a fiercer war was raging in Diyarbakir and the surrounding provinces, a merciless war between the deserters and the refugees, between the local inhabitants and the invaders who scorched the earth they stepped on. Those whose homes had been plundered began to pillage other villages and towns, thus swelling the bands that fluctuated from the plain of Diyarbakir to the desert of Mardin, and from there to Urfa and the plain of Harran, naked, starving, dying, but ever more numerous. They had grown accustomed to the dead strewn on their way, to the putrid odours, intensified by the heat that hit them like a blow in the face, to the eagles and vultures and other birds of prey that fell upon the corpses, tearing them to pieces, their wings and beaks and talons red with blood. And the birds of prey, too, did not shy away from these exhausted, half-dead creatures. The dead and the living, the eagles and vultures, all were merged in a constant flux. Throughout the southeastern lands and on the vast Mesopotamia plain, crazed multitudes milled around, sometimes walking a whole day for a drop of water, the weaker ones, the sick, falling or dragging themselves along. And when they found no one to despoil, these homeless, starving people attacked and killed one another until scenting food in some town, they marched upon it, leaving nothing but desolation in their wake. They themselves were reduced by half, but others came to take the place of the dead.

Ismail Agha never recalled by what miracle they escaped from this inferno, nor how they reached the Gavur Mountains. One fine morning, they found themselves in a pine grove by the side of a mountain spring. A year and a half had gone by since they had left their homeland. At Bitlis they had got separated from the Bey and the others. Ismail Agha's younger brother had died on the way. With bitter weeping and laments they had buried him there, south of Mardin, this handsome man, lithe as a gazelle, and left him under a mound on the wide plain. The father of Zéro, Ismail Agha's wife, had also died, and more were left behind to sleep their last sleep among the yellow thistles at the foot of the black-pocked rocks.

Translated from the Turkish by Thilda Kemal

GEORGES PEREC

From the short story *Les Revenentes*

After writing his novel La Disparition, *Georges Perec found he had a large number of e's at his disposal, because he had written this novel without using this vowel so much as once. (The challenge of translating that e-less text into English has been undertaken by Gilbert Adair, and it will be published by Harvill as* A Void.*) Perec therefore determined to expend his stock of e's in a story which would contain no other vowel. To begin with he was meticulous in abiding by his rule, but gradually he resorted to a little creative cheating. In his ingenious translation, Ian Monk has followed Perec first in his scrupulous adherence to the rule, then in his propensity to bend it, often with most comical effect. The excerpt here reproduced comprises the opening pages of the story.*

Deep dentelle screened, the seven green Mercedes Benzes resembled pestered sheep. They descended West End Street, swerved left, entered Temple Street then swept between the green vennels' beeches, elms 'n' elders. These trees enkernelled Exeter's See's svelte, yet nevertheless erect, steeples. Pecked men were pressed between the thermes' entrées. The screened Mercedes' secrets perplexed them:

"See them?"

"Them's yer excellence. Yer Reverend Excellence."

"Peeweet! Them's screenmen!" the set's teethless shrew yelped.

"Let's bet three pence Mel Ferrer's here!" the demented Western expert decreed.

"Excrement! Peter Sellers's the better bet!" jeered, ensemble, the TV septet.

"Mel Ferrer? Peter Sellers? Never!" yelled enreddened me. "She's Bérengère de Brémen-Brévent!"

"Bérengère de Brémen-Brévent!!" the yet reperplexed set reblethered.

"Yes! Bérengère! Bérengère 'The Qween'. Bérengère 'The Legs'.

Dresden, even Leeds cheer her. The Rex, the Select, the Pleyel revere her! Bérengère, the scene's Hebe, the crème des crèmes, French fêtes', French sprees' best belle! Endless brethren cense her; when she enters the scene then sheds her dress, meteless men degender themselves!"

"Then tell me her present schemes. Peter see me? Her genre, meseems, never seek vespers," the spencer-beret enshelled jerk reflected.

"Nevertheless, Bérengère's ever present chez the Reverend Excellence. He's Herbert Merelbeke's brer, see? Herbert's Thérèse Merelbeke's engenderer's engenderer; then Thérèse Bérengère's best ephebe!"

The perplexed geezer's heben fettered specs were deflexed, then reset: "These brers, engenderers, best ephebes seem well enmeshed!"

The jerk's senseless speech vexed me, led me where these men grew fewer, thence chez Hélène's . . .

Then, meseemed, the breeze between the deserted streets blew me these excerpted speeches:

". . . the See effervesces . . ."

". . . her recent endebtedness deepens . . ."

". . . she sells her jewels . . ."

"Pecks?"

". . . where's her fence?"

"Her fence's the Reverend Excellence's cleverness!"

". . . teehee . . ."

Then the breeze blew west. The rest deserted me . . .

Hélène dwelt chez Estelle, where New Hemlstedt Street meets Regents Street, then the Belvedere. The tenement's erne-eyed keeper defended the entrée. Yet, when seven pence'd been well spent, she let me enter, serene.

Hélène greeted me then served me Schweppes. Cheers! Refreshments were needed. When she'd devested me, she herd me eject:

"Phew! The wether!"

"Thertee-seven degrees!"

"Septembers swelter here."

She lent me her Kleenexes. They qwenched the cheeks' fervent wetness.

"Feel better then?"

Hélène seemed pleesed, yet reserved, expectent re the recent news. En effect, she then begged me:

"Bérengère's entered the See yet?"

"Yes."

"Perfect! Events present themselves well."

These eyes begged her tell me the deserts she expected. Free jewels?

"Heck, Bérengère's gems 'n' bezels tempt me!" she yelled.

Her extreme effervescence needed relentment, meseemed:

"Yet the gems' theft'd be reckless! The See's screened. Endless tents're there, where expert peelers 'n' shrewd 'tecs dwell. We'd be demented . . . !"

"We'll never be checked! We'll detect the defences' breech, then enter. The rest'll ensew."

Next, she let me redeter her, then tell her the excerpted speeches the breeze'd sent me between the deserted streets: meseemed rebel men eke lechered Bérengère's jewels. We regretted the news. Hélène set her teeth. Her deep verblessness lengthened. The news'd depressed her? Never, she reneged, then sed she'd persevere ne temere. Where led her secret, fervent reverees?

"Ernest's relentless cheek!" she yelled.

"The jerk? The self-seeker?"

"Yes, the jerk 'n' the seven Greek henchmen!"

"Let's skewer them!"

"Never!" sed vehement Hélène. "The deed'd be senseless, then we'd get endless pen sentences. We'd better deter them."

Her phlegm checked me. Nevertheless, her preference seemed effete.

"Ernest 'n' the henchmen's deterrent represents deep perplexedness. The weekend's here! We're stewed! We'll never enter Bérengère's den. We need the pretext."

"Feeble feller! Thérèse'll be the perfect pretext!"

"Thérèse? Thérèse Merelbeke?"

"Herself! She's deep between these sheets. The Reverend Excellence's present scheme's the weekend spent between tender wenches' sweet empressements. She's expected there!"

"Yes, Thérèse!"

Hélène's perverse yet clever scheme cheered me.

"Nevertheless, she's chez elle. Rennes's endless versts hence!"

"When'll Clement get clever? Telex her!"

The telepheme clerk preened her teeth, redressed her tresses, deterged her scent-cells then respelt the skew-lettered texts strewn between her ledgers.

"The telex pleese?"

"We're shet."

"Then when'll the telex serve me?"

"Retern efter seven."

"Yet the need's emergent!"

"The extreme emergence?"

"The emergentest extreme. These terms've been well selected."

She then let me send the telex express:

THÉRÈSE MERELBEKE. SEVEN JETEE DES FRÈRES FERRET. RENNES. WE NEED, STRESS, NEED THEE. SCHNELL! CLEMENT.

The clerk redd the telex then entered the expense: twelve pence.

"Twelve pence! Strewth! The exces seem extreme."

"The telex never extends decrements." The severe cheerless teller sneered.

Her twelve pence were then threwn between her eyes.

Fecklessness led me hence between the Elster's scented evergreens, the fennel, the feverfew. There, meek mereless men weeled the fresh creek. They netted tench, kelt, flecked perch. Herb Bennet vended green beens, fermented crèpes; the geezer's feet reeked Chester cheese. Deshevelled, vehement Celts crew the rebec's re, the crwth's te. Between the shet crèches, temp. hens fed chestless fleglets Nestlé teets. Ewes wheepled. Wrens beppered the resplendent elm trees. Bees, then sphenxes swerved between the elders. Tedesche shepherds smelt red setters' ends. The steps drew me between the steep steles where we remember the Stefenssens (Zen sect members, yet even then Effel & Perret's welders), when they smelted the twentee-seven steel fletches the Greek, then the Mede sect members decreed.

The scene's sweetness sent me! Ellesmere, the elden demesne, seemed there! The creeks. The scree. The petrels. The tempests. Then melt there! Be free! Where the ether reflects celeste resplendence, the

bens' green crests, the September hemp seeds! The demesne set
between the mere's, then new Tempe's cwm. Clement Theleme: there
we'd resee Sceve, Sterne, Mersenne, Wegener! . . .

Tlemcen, September the seventh, MCMXXXVJJ, Mme Merelbeke
engendered Thérèse. Her begetters were French. The père, René,
served between Gen. Leclerc's men. He, the tested regent, defended
the dey's, then the bey's sceptres when Berber rebels pretended they
were free. These events effects were: Thérèse'd been kept chez her
begetter's begetters: Herbert Merelbeke, Exeter's Reverend Excellence
Serge's brer; & Pernelle Merelbeke, née Bescherelle. Herbert
shepherded sheep. The herd fed the wee wenches 'n' men. Ewes'
blether blessed Thérèse's sweet sleep.

Yet, René Merelbeke detested the rebels. He sed he'd skewer them.
Leclerc, the serene regent, grew nettled. He felt René's schemes were
extreme: be severe, yet reserved, he decreed. René seethed. He clept
Leclerc "The Berber's Bender". These vexed men then went berserk.
René belted Leclerc; Leclerc beweltered then felled René.

The French HQ herd Leclerc's messenger retell these events. They
expelled René. He left the French reserves then selected the Metz
express. Nevertheless, Mehmet ben Berek (he led the Berber rebels)
fettered Thérèse, enjeeped her, then kept her tethered between the
desert tents. Next, René's tether ended. He re-emerged between
the French reserves.

"Seek the rebels," he begged Leclerc.

"Never. Thérèse's dedd. Berek slew her," Leclerc pretended.

René deserted then rented seventeen fez-dressed henchmen.
Between the jebels, the deserts, the ergs where the steppes' breezes
seeded then deleted defenceless weeds, here erred these henchmen,
needleless brens, spent stens, nerveless épées, depleted steeds, kneeless
gee-gees, bereft jennets, Thérèse's feckless seekers. Then Mehmet ben
Berek's Berbers penned themselves between the secret crests. The
desert steppes were mere creekless versts, endless extents: Kef,
Meknes, Zemzem, Yemen; René sensed he grew demented when he'd
see the wenchless henchmen seek ewes then eschew Thérèse.

Translated from the French by Ian Monk

JAAN KROSS

The Ashtray

Shall I tell you the most improbable story which actually happened to me?

Several different types of improbability exist. For instance – I do not know what professional probability theorists would think of my classification, but be that as it may – intrinsic improbability and statistical improbability would be reached if I were to start telling about my encounter with a UFO. In terms of statistical improbability, however, this encounter need not appear especially improbable – judging by all those typed pages on UFOs, every third or at least three-hundredth open-minded person round here seems to have spotted UFOs with his own eyes, whether on the island of Saaremaa or in the Sayan* Mountains.

Although it may be possible to prove anything you like with statistics, statistical probability or improbability has one important quality: it evokes the illusion of measurability. In other words, in the case of statistically improbable occurrences, it would seem to be in some way possible to get a feel of *how* improbable any given occurrence becomes. For that reason, I choose to tell my story at the level of statistical improbability.

It was late November 1947 and our train was travelling along the Vorkuta railway line, first due north from Kirov,† then north-east. And that event at least was far removed from any type of improbability, be it intrinsic or statistical. Not even our senses took it for improbable. Quite the contrary, it was all too damnably real.

The historical Twentieth Congress of the Communist Party of the

* A range of mountains in Central Siberia.
† Mining centres. Vorkuta is in the Pechora coalfield in the Komi Autonomous Republic, Kirov in the Russian Federation.

Soviet Union has, in the meantime, been superseded by so many even more historical ones, that it begins to be almost improper to remember what was said at this most historical congress of all. It was, at any rate, at that congress that the subject of the illegal repression of millions was first aired at such a gathering. Repression was a catch-all phrase meaning anything from being sacked from one's job to being shot. But in the majority of cases it meant the illegal despatch of millions to prison camps plus an incalculably smaller proportion of executions. Legal executions and prison camp sentences were undoubtedly carried out against criminals parallel to what occurred illegally. And for a number of reasons, certain years enjoyed a veritable boom in both legal and illegal acts of repression.

The year 1947 was, in any case, one of these boom years. And although I will gladly leave any research into the more immediate causes to historians, I am obliged to mention the most significant events for the sake of those interested in following the course of history. Obliged, since such people could very well be under the age of forty, and would therefore understand *even less* when consulting existent official sources than would have those who also have some personal memories of the events in question to go on. So, one of the main reasons for the boom taking place in 1947 but stretching back a couple of years in time and continuing a couple of years thereafter was the shift that had taken place on the map of Eastern Europe. A gigantic tract of land from Leningrad to Stalingrad, Petsamo to Beltsy and, to a certain extent, Berlin to Sofia had – according to taste – moved over, ended up, fallen to, or been returned to Soviet power. That is to say to the power of Stalin and Beria. And with all the mental rigidity of these two, with all their wooden imaginings devoid of logic, investigations were instituted into how the millions of people of these regions had lived and fared before the arrival or return of Soviet power. *Investigations*, not in the sense of collating psychological data and drawing tactical conclusions or using it for self-education, but investigations with a view to punishment. And this unfortunately occurred all the more inevitably and dramatically since there were simply *bound* to be criminals of a pettier or more major sort among these millions, whatever criminal code was being employed as a yardstick.

Hardly ever have the investigatory bodies worked with such smooth efficiency as during that period, where attaining formal results is concerned. Hardly ever in a civilized country, or one which purports to be, has the division made by the investigatory bodies, by way of illustration of their work, been as telling as then. Hardly ever has the percentage of those declared innocent or freed by the courts been so minimal, practically non-existent, and those subjected to punishment so well-nigh omnivorously huge. The investigatory bodies had become almost ideal in their infallibility!

For at that time, no one had as yet divided up those subjected to punishment into those punished legally and those punished illegally. No one other than those who were punished themselves, that is. Which made such division a highly subjective affair.

The mass of those to be punished, quite undifferentiated in this respect, were pressed through troikas and tribunals and were then allowed to trickle unhurriedly through the various transit prisons and camps, moving in a mainly easterly and north-easterly direction, into the realms of wood and coal, ensuring a new base for the enrichment of society. If not in their millions, then at least in their hundreds of thousands.

Thus the statistical probability of finding the young internationalist (ha-ha-ha-haa) Peeter Mirk in a train winding its way from Kirov to Vorkuta during late November 1947 was so high that I indeed happened to be on such a train.

The train journey was, on the one hand, limitlessly boring but on the other, simply delightful. Kirov Prison, to which we had been moved a month previously from the large mill on Konstantingradskaya Street in Leningrad, was a pathetic Noah's Ark of wooden barracks surrounded by a plank fence, and during the rainy season, drowning under its burden in the mud and filth beyond the railway line and the outskirts of the town. The room in which I had spent the month seemed to be typical of the average cells in this building. Owing to the lack of space, life went on day and night on the two-level bunks. Because of the low ceiling, the top level had, at best, sitting room only. So that days and nights were spent either lying down or crouched. Of the forty to fifty men, about one quarter could manage to stand between the bunks and the only exercise consisted of making one's way to the latrine. The far corner of the room was hot and stifling, while by the window it was cold since the glass panes had been knocked out back in the time of Arakcheyev* and since, during

---

* Alexander Andreyevich Arakcheyev (1769–1834) was Minister of Defence under Tsar Alexander I. Notorious for his repression of free thought, his violent and venal régime and his general cruelty.

the second week of our stay, the temperature outside had reached around a dozen or so degrees below zero. All of this – crouching in the cold to the left, dripping with sweat to the right, the turfy bread and the slop-like skilly, a naked Ilyich-bulb hanging from the ceiling in a constant battle against the smoke and gloom-laden stench of the latrine, the lack of close personal contact owing to the fact that the politicals were mixed in among common criminals and the fact that some of the politicals attempted to adopt the tone and manner of the *blatnois** to mask in some way the accursed fact that they were intellectuals and to provoke less derision – all this was quite within the bounds of statistical probability. Even the only eccentric in our cell more-or-less kept within these bounds: Nikolai Nikolayevich. A fellow-prisoner. A former field surgeon's assistant. A large man with deep-seated burning piggy-eyes, who had rapidly lost weight and who was already, or on the way to becoming, mad. Who from morn till eve, and even at times through our fitful night's sleep, could be heard preaching: "Comrades – you know full well: when you're on the job it is absolutely *forbidden*, do you hear, the most absolutely evil thing you can do is to knead a woman's tits! Kneading a woman's tits amounts to killing her! A slow death, admittedly, but you'll kill her in the end nonetheless. I mean – you over there Vassili Vassilievich – come on, now – admit how you've kneaded your wife's tits or those of any other woman you may have gone to bed with? Confess! All men knead tits. Because they simply don't know any better. But there are those who do so perhaps just because they do know: that's the only way women get breast cancer. I know it's a scientifically proven fact: sooner or later every woman whose tits have been kneaded gets breast cancer. And it kills them –"

Even Nikolai Nikolayevich with his delusion was within the bounds of statistical probability. In so far as field surgeons' assistants are represented in any society, they must occur to the same extent in the repressed portion of that society – since you could also say that absolutely every type from society-at-large was also represented here. And in so far as they, surgeons' assistants that is, have any medical knowledge, this knowledge must, given the circumstances, be transformed into something of a phantasmagoria. In another tale I would be quite prepared to tell of how I myself, and not in such an exotic location as

* (Russ.) A common criminal.

now in Kirov but in the almost homely surroundings of Tallinn Central
Prison, managed to work out a grammatico-logico-social world order.
But let us return to Nikolai Nikolayevich. Everything in what he said
was within the bounds of statistical probability. Despite undernourish-
ment and depression, erotic imaginings kept stirring within us and
many of us had, thrashing about in the cellars of our mind, a guilt complex about what we had at some time or another done with our own
wives, someone else's, or with God knows what other people. In a word,
Nikolai Nikolayevich's *idée fixe* and the Kirov Prison as a whole had an
oppressive influence on us. Even an unbearable one. And if you could
stand it, this was only thanks to an awareness of the temporary nature
of affairs. In so far as you could, in our circumstances, speak of *knowing*
anything about your prospects. So let us rather put it this way: it became
bearable owing to the hope of the temporary nature of affairs. For we
were always unfailingly ready to spin together all manner of infallible
hopes for ourselves, realistic or unrealistic.

Oh yes, indeed, I can remember how we used to hope, some time
before the commencement of this train journey I have begun describing, back during the time we were in Leningrad in the large transit
prison on Konstantingradskaya, quite a civilized place in comparison
with Kirov, for the most favourable things to happen in the near
future. I mean my God, the Thirtieth Anniversary of the Great
October Revolution would soon be knocking on our door! To celebrate such anniversaries there were always amnesties, were there not?!
Indisputably! Well – mumbled those more experienced fellow-
prisoners who tried to cover up the surge of hope within themselves
with words of wise scepticism – such amnesties exist but they're bound
principally to affect criminals, being of rather limited compass as
regards politicals. OK, be that as it may. But hitherto none of those
anniversaries had been the Thirtieth! And you cannot compare one
anniversary with its predecessor – two years is no time at all – since
such a liberating event as the victory in the Great Patriotic War!
The only possible conclusion: an opportunity for announcing such a
widespread amnesty, covering political prisoners as well, had never
before presented itself! Under the terms of such an amnesty as was
now imminent a good half of the prisoners, well, almost half of the
prisoners or perhaps one quarter, would almost certainly be released.
But among this half to be released, or this quarter, or even one tenth
who were dead certain to be amnestied, there was room for each and

every one of us. And, painful to relate, for a while there was also room for me! My short but rather compact life experience and some legal training notwithstanding.

For, owing to my relative professionalism, I should have seen things in a larger context than many others and should have kept myself aloof from childish hopes. And at the same time I could, strictly professionally speaking, see with my relatively well-trained lawyer's eye that, considering the crimes I had been accused of, I had got off with a baby-sentence of a mere five years, making my case appear one of the more hopeful ones.

Of course the amnesty, news of which finally reached us by way of scraps of newspaper, affected only criminals, pickpockets and minor recidivists, only the "friends of power" as we would call them ironically, and even they from that margin whose misdemeanours were of the least gravity and then only to the very least extent. Or perhaps a little greater. God only knows. But it could not be said in general terms that the ensuing disappointment was in proportion to the hopes so recently raised. Soon we were hoping for other things. And in the Kirov we were hoping that we would leave the place as soon as possible, to enjoy conditions which could not be other than incomparably better than those we were living under at the time.

And then, one morning, it really happened: the column was drawn up, Mirk, Pyotr Ivanovich included, bundle in hand. And off we went.

I cannot say how far our march took us. Maybe four or five kilometres. From the prison to the siding behind the main railway station. I cannot remember what the surroundings looked like. But I can clearly recall walking over the snow-covered sleepers of the railway embankment in a column of a couple of hundred men, guards with their dogs in front, at the sides and behind, like one great big black centipede, jointed and winding, over white snow, and I recall the smell of rotting which we suddenly smelt close beside us and the clean wind which blew in gusts into our mouths. And one tall swarthy Rumanian next to whom I happened to be walking.

He was a stately thirty-five-year-old of the Ancient Roman type, against whom I harbour strong prejudices as well as downright aversion. Maybe this is based on jealousy as to imagined prowess with women, perhaps it is jealousy of their culture, which they just happen to possess and which they trample on with indifference, maybe jealousy based on the collating of information of a genetic origin, based on the fact that men of such physique tend to turn out to be impostors. But my one-hour acquaintance with this man was, at any rate, a pleasant one. He spoke French well, too well for my liking, and he managed fearlessly, for four of the five kilometres we had to walk, to recite Baudelaire from memory. And I felt that for the sake of his Baudelaire the distance could have been twice as long. My French was – as those who remember my school reports will appreciate – pretty weak, but thanks to Monsieur Ledoute with his special method I had managed to commit to memory six or seven Baudelaire poems: "L'Albatros", "Elévation", "L'invitation au voyage" and so on. We muttered them – piecemeal – in a low recitative duet.

> Mon esprit, tu te meus avec agilité.
> Et, comme un bon nageur qui se pâme dans l'onde,
> Tu sillonnes gaiement l'immensité profonde
> Avec une indicible et mâle volupté.

> Envole-toi bien loin de ces miasmes morbides:
> Va te purifier dans l'air supérieur,
> Et bois, comme une pure et divine liqueur,
> Le feu clair qui remplit les espaces limpides –

We muttered – talking on this march was forbidden – under our breath, our mouths half-closed, stepping over the frozen sleepers, trying not to stumble. The routine shouts of the guards, the barking of the escort dogs and the crunch of our footsteps all seeming somehow beyond the snowflakes and these verses.

The Rumanian had been an officer, a major, and I believe that he really had been a major, though soldiers in such situations often add a couple of stripes to their sleeve with pathetic self-assurance. The fact that he was an officer shone through in his aloof attitude and curt correctness. And yet he was the son of an academic, a professor of history whom I had heard of then but whose name now escapes me, and it was clearly this cultural family heritage that somewhat softened his stiff officer's bearing and made him seem more sympathetic, at least on that march for that one hour. But why have I begun to describe him in such detail? Ah yes, because in conversation with

that Rumanian I learnt a French word or, to be more exact, redis-
covered it. Words and situations are often interlinked in a peculiar
manner. My weak knowledge of French was characterized by the fact
that I frequently lacked the word for the most mundane objects, my
knowledge having been learnt in a bookish manner and not through
practice. A particularly weak side of my French is the slightly more
unusual words connected to those which are most common. And
when we paused from reciting Baudelaire or rather when we had got
through the Baudelaire, I do not quite remember if it was while he
was speaking about his family – did he not mention King Michael
himself in connection with his office? – he all of a sudden screwed up
his dark eyes and said:

"But what have we now become? The garbage of Europe!"

I have always had difficulties in reacting to a southern temperament.
The likes of us – or at least of myself – do not understand it entirely.
One never knows how thick the space is between outer shell and core.
Where theatricality ends and gravity begins. Is everything mere scenery
or does it all come straight from the heart? And for a split second I
weighed up what I should reply. Whether to answer: how do you mean,
garbage?! Perhaps it is just grains of a specific density picked out by
centrifugal force, etc . . . etc . . . ? No, my language knowledge was
simply not up to it and too childish to convey a cautious scepticism. Or
should I simply agree – whether or not it sounded cultivated for me to
do so, and say bluntly in any case: "Garbage, alas, garbage. And putre-
faction our most likely prospect – ?"

I do not quite remember, perhaps I allowed my gaze to roam in search
of an answer – over the alien earth, dappled with grey snow and black
soil as far as the eye could see and the low sky which was sprinkling a
little fresh snow like white ash onto our dark heap. And somewhere in
all this Baudelaire – And then suddenly I knew what I should reply –
But it had to be translated into French! All the necessary words were
there – apart from one, and that the most important of all: I had forgotten the French for "ashtray". I was obliged to explain: You know – a
vessel, into which you throw fag-ends – *les mégots* – I even knew the
word for fag-ends, but the one for ashtray escaped me.

"Eh bien, vous voulez dire – le cendrier – ?"

Exactly! I said.

"You know what we are? Fag-ends. In God's ashtray."

"In what way?"

"Those who have gone out have gone out. Those who still have a spark of life in them – those who haven't yet burnt out – if –"

He instantly grasped my meaning: "If God notices, he breathes into one and it starts burning again and he then gives it to someone who can get a puff out of it? Ha-ha-ha-haa. And you're hoping he's going to do so in your case too?"

What could I answer? I didn't want to look a fool. But I did want to be honest. Or perhaps I was willing my answer to come true –

"Hm – not exactly. But something like that."

Since that time the word *cendrier* has stuck in my memory. But by that time we had arrived at the siding behind the station, had walked along it and were being shoved into carriages. Me in one, the Rumanian in another.

A philosophically inclined fellow-prisoner once said, not on that occasion but during another helter-skelter deportation, that normal life must surely be a variant of prison life distorted by the magnifying glass of time: circumstances oblige and contacts undergo inevitability, some are moved to one end, others to another end of the horizon, some to one city, others to another. Here, the *starshina*, the warrant officer, bawls orders for some to enter one carriage, some a second, some one compartment, others another, some for one station, others a different one. The chop comes, of course, just as it does in life, only more abruptly and sharper. More lacerating, if you like, if you keep the arse of your soul too near the blade, as that fellow-prisoner once said.

The compartment into which I was ordered to climb was a normal "Stolypin" compartment with the yellow wood of a third-class compartment, now somewhat grey with wear, and with bars across the windows and door panes. Such barred carriage windows are indelibly printed on the consciousness of many people of my generation – I would even say that, if not through personal experience, then by way of postcards from Grandfather's time and from an illustration by a now forgotten artist in *A History of Russian Art*, which shows a barred window and behind it a pair of bearded men, a woman and a child who are attempting to throw crumbs of bread out to the pigeons busy pecking on the platform in the foreground. Pure sentimentalist naturalism. And, of course, a political protest against the spirit of the age and its soul-destroying carriages which His Grace Prime Minister Stolypin had begun to employ in 1905 – or perhaps they were already in use then but gained popularity at that time – which immortalized at least the name of the Prime Minister in common parlance until the epoch I am describing. And even, to a lesser extent, afterwards as well.

As is common knowledge, such a compartment was, in civilian use, intended for four persons. Under these special circumstances it would be used for – indeed, for how many? In order to accommodate as many as possible, an extra platform had been constructed between the ceiling and the upper bunks with a small opening to enable you to worm your way up and down and on which, by using a sardine technique, four or even five men could lie or rest on their elbows. The four remaining bunks were each to seat – how they managed to lie was their business – four men in a row, and this was no problem except that those on the second level had to let their feet dangle, which was no problem though you could not sit up straight – then there was room in each compartment for twenty-one men. And in that way, the little iron window-table would remain entirely free for the travellers to eat or play cards on – if the guards happened to be elsewhere and the players could manage to play silently or at most in a whisper.

I was slid into one of these compartments – the eighteenth man as it happened. And as no more were added, it was quite roomy in there: one free place on each level. The other seventeen, as far as I could gather, all Lithuanians and all of a decent sort. That is to say decent in the sense that none were *blatnois*, pickpockets, thieves, burglars or gangsters. So I did not have to worry about my reasonably respectable coat nor my medium-sized bundle. And as rumour had it, such worries were very real in such transports. But in other respects my travelling companions were a wretched lot. For they were wearing uniforms, presumably from the time of Lithuanian independence, from which all the insignia had been removed as well as the brass buttons which had been replaced by wooden ones. They were representative of what Estonians in a similar situation would look like, in their former Estonian uniforms – the Estonians having been former Omakaitse* officers, while these Lithuanians were ex-members of the LAF or TDA military units from the time of the German Occupation.

In the course of two days and one-and-a-half nights, I managed to communicate with these men to an adequate extent. They spoke Russian with a heavy Lithuanian accent, although their knowledge was,

---

* An Estonian military organization for the defence of an independent Estonia.

on average, better than mine. I had nonetheless already had a one-year intensive course in the language, albeit with poor learning materials. So that we did have a lingua franca. Besides, they asked me little and I asked them nothing at all. For I had developed a way of blending in with my surroundings which, although not possible to practise in a consistent manner, soon became an ideal towards which to strive: relating to any given situation as does an interested and observant tourist and outwardly blending with one's surroundings to the extent necessary at the time to avoid unpleasant tension, but not inwardly wanting to blend into the here-and-now of anyone or anything else. And so I outwardly felt quite at home in this somewhat cock-sure but harmless company and was prepared to travel along with them for a day or two more, a week or two as far as I was concerned, no matter how far, no matter for what reason, as it did not depend on me anyway. The rumour spread that we were on our way to the Petchora coalfield and at this slow pace (we were constantly uncoupled at stations and recoupled to the next train or the one after) the journey could last another day or two. And this period at least would be a reasonably secure one.

So it came as a most unpleasant surprise when I started out of my sleep in the middle of the night to hear: "Мирк, Лётр Иванович?! Где же он?! Здесь?! Ёб его мать! Быстро! С вещами!"* Thank God we were not sleeping in our pyjamas and that our things were not spread around a hotel room. I was in the corridor in ten seconds. I was not sure how they checked that I was who I was. Presumably against a photo which the head of the convoy had attached to his documents. The train nonetheless stood panting in the darkness and within two minutes I also stood doing the same – the train far away, now almost gone, now vanished completely, and all around me an absolute waste-land, complete snowy darkness and the stupefyingly pure frosty air.

I called out "Hello there!" lightly into the darkness to see if perhaps someone else had been dropped like myself. But not a soul. And if there had been, it would not have been clear by which logic such games were to be played here in the middle of nowhere. At any rate, there I stood quite alone – even the stars in the sky were absent and I thought to myself: nothing for it than to locate the rails with the toe

* "Mirk, Pyotr Ivanovich?! Where is he? Come on, you motherfucker! With your belongings!"

of my boot and start walking south-westwards. After two thousand kilometres I'll be home – (And I would like to add, for the sake of young people who are not expert in these matters and who wonder why I didn't try to escape, that such an action was a lost cause right from the start. The only way of escape would be along the railway itself which was the only way of any sort in these parts. And as the only buildings along the line were prison-camp huts and the guards' barracks, the kennels and exercising grounds of the guard dogs. And the private individuals, inasmuch as there were any out here at all, having themselves had a taste of the camps, were quite prepared to give up suspects at the drop of a hat, be it for the fear of further punishment or the temptation of the reward.)

Someone was obviously supposed to have come to fetch me. But there was no one there. This was a systematic failing such as occurred much less frequently in the army and especially in the prison-camp service than elsewhere in society. And, sure enough, I did not have to wait that long this time either. I had been standing there for several minutes, stretched, breathed deeply and realized from what stuffy carriage air laden with shag smoke and bodily odours I had come – when I began to make out a string of lights in the distance. And at the same time I noticed: among the string of lights one was making its way towards me.

A short while later a lantern approached, hissing. A leather glove was pushed in my face. The other glove dealt with my papers:

"фамилия! Имя? Отчество? Год рождения? Срок?*
I answered and they confirmed it was me they wanted.

"Лошли!"†

We began to walk along the line. The man with the lantern walking behind, of course, and me in front and not vice-versa. I could have made an attempt to ask what the name of the settlement was and the number of the prison camp to which we were going. From experience I know that it would not have proved impossible for my escort to tell me, alone as we were in the darkness. But it was just as likely – presumably more likely – that he would have snorted "Молчать!"‡ And And that would, however you look at it, have been too humiliating

---

* "Surname? Forename? Patronymic? Date of birth? Sentence?"
† "Quick march!"
‡ "Silence!"

to provoke. And so we walked the kilometre or so in silence, turned off the track and in a few hundred metres found ourselves at the gates to the camp.

In the check-in point under the watchtower sat three men in guards' uniforms with white sheepskin collars and red epaulettes around an electric lamp. The stove was roaring. The men's faces were red with night warmth and their eyes filled with sleep.

"A newcomer –? Oh damn. Lock him up in the transfer barrack until the morning. Then we'll see where he's to go."

But I had heard enough about transfer barracks or the places which could serve as such not at least to make an attempt. I said:

"Citizen Commandant – I am wearing more-or-less decent clothing. Are you so sure it will still be on my back, come morning, if you have me overnight in the transfer barrack?"

The wall-eyed red-faced guard was patently a sensible man. He muttered something and then said, though not to me but to my warder:

"All right. Let him spend the night in the sick bay. We'll sort the rest out in the morning." He cranked the phone and summoned the sick-bay orderly. He arrived within two minutes and took me along to where he was ordered.

I trudged along with this gnarled old orderly a couple of hundred yards across the camp along boarded snow footpaths and over two plank bridges with rococo balustrades. The empty snow-covered roads were well lit despite the sparsity of lamps and the whole camp had an absurd Christmas-card appearance about it.

The waiting room to the sick bay in a similar barrack to the rest was almost grand: the whitewashed brick stove was hot, the floor swept and there were cheesecloth curtains in front of the windows, in the corner narrow-footed flower boxes made from white planks with bright green asparagus plants in rows of pots. And against the whitewashed walls one or two wooden settees. The orderly pointed one of them out with his chin:

"You can kip there till six. At six comes the doctor."

"Why so early?"

"Work starts at seven. Before work begins, those who have reported sick have to be examined. So get yourself off the sofa by six."

I stretched myself out and the orderly turned off the light. The settee was short and could hardly be described as soft. But the air in

this spacious waiting room was, compared with that of cell and carriage of my recent sojourns, amazingly pure. And what was more: I
was sleeping for the first time in goodness knows how long in a dark
room. And so – despite the uncertainty of what lay in store for me
and the certainty that this could prove to be hell on earth if I had
bad luck, and even if I had good luck my stay would be no holiday
– I fell into a deep and restful sleep in that sick bay.

"Get up! Get up! The doctor's on his way!"

The servile zeal of the orderly did not bode well. Yet the doctor
himself had not yet put in an appearance. I still had ample time to
get up and wet my three-day growth of stubble in a bowl provided
by the orderly and wipe myself dry on a towel. Only then did the
doctor come in. He was of medium height and around thirty-five
years of age. A prisoner too, that went without saying. But an élite
prisoner. He was wearing a clean dark-blue padded jacket and a high-
collared black camp shirt around whose black upright collar peeped
a millimetre of snow-white vest. He had the ordinary, slightly bored
but not unfriendly face of someone well fed, clean-shaven cheeks and,
in accordance with the privileges enjoyed by men of his station, neatly
cut brown hair with a parting. I spoke first:

"I was sent to the sick bay to spend the night here –"

"Aha, you must have arrived in the night? Where have you just
come from? And where are you from?"

I explained. And at the same time I thought I detected in his brief
questions that selfsame Lithuanian accent which my *Darbo Apsauga**
men on the train had filled my ears with. And so it turned out to be:

"Aha, from Tartu? I'm from Kaunas."[†] He now shook my hand:
"Doctor Kačanauskas. Regret I've never been to Tartu. Have you ever
been to Kaunas?"

"Yes. Very briefly. To the Čiurlionis Museum[‡]. And the Opera to
hear *Birute*. But I've even as much as *stayed* in Klaipėda.[§] Two whole
summers."

"Oh, and when was that? And in what connection? But – do take

---

* (Lith.) Labour convoy.

† Tartu and Kaunas are the university towns of Estonia and Lithuania,
respectively.

‡ Mikolajus Čiurlionis (1875–1911) Lithuania's most significant composer and
painter.

§ Lithuanian port (formerly Memel).

a seat." He had hung his padded jacket up on a peg and was washing his hands in a bowl brought by the orderly and placed on a tripod. And I explained. How before the war my aunt and uncle had lived in Klaipėda. And how my uncle had represented some Dutch firm which sold ships' parts, ropes, paint, *et cetera*. And how I had stayed with them two summers running.

Doctor Kačanauskas washed his hands, dried them on the towel brought in by the orderly and came to sit by me:

"If you've stayed two summers in Klaipėda then you may have friends there?"

I thought for a while. Aunt Juuli and Uncle August no doubt had. They had lived there for over ten years before moving back to Tallinn the year before the war broke out. But me? I had sunbathed in the Juodkrantė Dunes from morning till night along with my cousin and had swum in the sea, lain on the beach reading books through sunglasses so that my eyes swam and our backs turned green. Friends? Ah yes, *one* person came to mind who visited Uncle August to dine on a couple of occasions:

"Well, there was for instance, Captain Bačenas – some pilot or other down at the port –"

"Captain Bačenas?" asked the doctor. "From Klaipėda? What did he look like –?"

"Well, how should I describe him? Taller than average. Stocky. Have you ever seen a portrait of Admiral Makarov?"

"I'm afraid not," the doctor had to admit.

I said: "Captain Bačenas had just the same kind of forked full beard –"

Doctor Kačanauskas burst into laughter and stood up: "Captain Bačenas with his full beard was a very good friend of my father's. Listen, let's go over to my bunker for a moment –"

We got up. I could see that the waiting room was filling up with five or six sickly figures – the first of today's batch of sick cases, presumably. The doctor addressed the orderly:

"Ivan Borisovich come and get the thermometers and distribute them –", and then, so that the patients could hear: "And keep an eye on them to make sure they don't fiddle their temperatures."

The three of us stepped into the doctor's tiny surgery. Two metres by three. A small white table. An instrument cabinet. Three white chairs. When the orderly had gone out with the thermometers the doctor asked me to sit down at his desk and himself took a seat behind it. He said with a smile, then growing more serious:

"Well, if Saint John Nepomuk* has arranged things so – look, here in the camp life is more or less bearable. Or it can become completely unbearable. In an hour in any case, the prisoner-overseer will find you and then you can end up doing all manner of things: make flower pots, fell trees, load planks, dig ditches – they get dug even at this time of year. And doing such work in November is no joke. Especially for those who are unaccustomed to such work. And I do not imagine that Estonian jurists are. You would, in any case, not be getting sufficient food rations for such work. And yet before the first letters from here reach home and the food packages reach us here six months can have gone by. Look. Such work can be avoided if you grease the palms of the *naryadchiks*.† With goods, money, whatever you can. But they are well-fed gents, mostly from the ranks of the criminal element. So you would hardly have anything to offer them. And even if you had, you would perhaps refuse to bribe them. But what I would like to say to you is this: as an Estonian you quite likely have a better means of finding acceptable work. You see, the central administration for a large area of prison camps is located here in the town of Knyazh-pogost. The administration runs a construction office. A dozen engineers, designers, draughtsmen, copyists. The deputy engineer who is in actual fact the boss is a compatriot of yours. Your *zemlyak*.‡ Yakov Pavlovich Kanter.§ A good chap. If he hands the necessary chit over to the head *naryadchik* on your behalf you will automatically be taken on there."

"But what will I do there? I'm no engineer, nor a builder, nor –"

"There are a hundred people at the office. There are all sorts –" said the doctor.

I said (to dampen my rising hopes and out of a certain measure of pride):

---

* Ján Nepomuk (1340–93), Czech martyr and Patron Saint of Bohemia. Kačanauskas comes from Catholic Lithuania, hence his keenness on saints.

† (Russ.) A prisoner who acts as foreman and is responsible for work quotas.

‡ (Russ.) A compatriot.

§ The Russified version of Jakob Kanter's name (cf Pyotr Ivanovich Mirk). Kanter, who is clearly Jewish, exemplifies Doctor Kačanauskas' comment that although Estonians are rather poor at looking after one another, Jews do so as a matter of course. A number of Russian Jews joined the KGB after World War II, presumably in gratitude for the expulsion of the Nazis by the Red Army, hence Mirk's initial caution.

"Well, my dear *zemlyaks* don't usually make grand gestures in such matters –"

And unexpectedly, Doctor Kačanauskas agreed with my doubts to an uncalled-for extent:

"In that, if you will excuse me, you are so right. I have observed that in matters of mutual assistance Estonians are unbelievably passive. Jews, for instance, are a hundred times more active. They'll help as a matter of course. I believe that even my own Lithuanians are ahead of you Estonians on that count. But allow me to add: the matter is more serious than you may have realized. For this reason: Comrade Kanter will be obliged to put you through a test. He is, let's face it – an Estonian pedant. But he does everything he considers he is able to do."

I said: "Doctor Kačanauskas, I would like to express my sincere thanks. And I promise that I will – consider –"

He said, almost angrily: "Listen here, Comrade Mirk, there's no time for *considering* around here. I suggest I send my orderly straight to Hut 27, right away. Kanter will be here in five minutes and then you will have made his acquaintance."

I said: "All right, if Saint John Nepomuk has arranged things so and will bless such nepotism –"

Five minutes later Jakob Kanter stepped into the doctor's room. He was a small broad-shouldered man of around fifty. Even more evidently an élite prisoner than the doctor. He had a noticeably large head, prematurely greying short hair, a longish reddish face, a tiny light-coloured and neatly trimmed moustache, a small mouth and strikingly blue eyes. The first impression he gave was of being an amiable and cultivated man but he was undoubtedly also what the doctor had said – a pedant.

The doctor introduced us and explained why he had called the Chief Engineer out even before work had started, and added:

"But now you must excuse me. I have to attend to my patients."

The doctor went out into the waiting room and closed the door to his office behind him.

"Well, –" said Comrade Kanter, "that is to say – what are you actually capable of doing?"

"Well now, I could draw up the regulations for the construction office – if someone could translate them into Russian. Or – I could write – for the office in general and the workers in particular – poems for special occasions. In unlimited quantities. Assuming again, of course, that someone translates them into Russian –"

I observed from Kanter's sour little smile that my little joke was not at all to his liking. So I said: "I can't really see that I can do anything which would be necessary in a construction office. Except for – perhaps I could acquire some necessary skill – some very basic one – quite quickly, I suppose."

"Can you read technical drawings?"

"At present, I would say – no. But if someone were to help me learn, then – I suppose I'd be able to in a week."

"I see . . ." said Kanter in a friendly fashion, but with some hesitation. "We have two chaps from Leningrad who can read blueprints rather well but they've been assigned forest work. Because in the office you have to be able to read fast and faultlessly –"

"That goes without saying," I wanted to say as I felt embarrassed and the feeling was increasing by the minute.

"Can you manage a technical drawer's pen and a compass?"

I said: "Only in a very rudimentary way. As much as I learnt at grammar school –" and at the same time I was thinking: why did this "very highly qualified engineer" as the doctor made him out to be, use the word "compass" instead of "pair of compasses"? And why such a clumsy expression as a "technical drawer's pen"? With the stress on *technical*? And immediately I had it: Kanter spoke perfect Estonian. Without an accent that is. And yet there was something about his intonation which did not quite ring true. And his use of "compass" gave me the clue, as did his way of stressing loan words: this man must be a Russian-born Estonian,[*] or an Estonian from Russia, at any rate. I asked:

"You yourself – you're not a graduate of the Tallinn Technical High School, are you?"

"No, I'm not. I was first a student at the Imperial Institute of Technology at Saint Petersburg. But then I graduated in Petrograd and sans Emperor."

---

[*] Communists who fled to Russia during Estonian independence (1920–40) returned to take up leading posts after the Communist takeover in 1944, such as First Secretaries Vaino and Käbin. Regarded with great suspicion and contempt by the average "home-grown" Estonian.

"And continued working in Russia –?" I added this in the first instance to avoid his asking me more about my skills. And I have to admit: to distance myself from him. A Russian-born Estonian was only a *zemlyak*, a compatriot of mine, in the year 1947 to a most problematical degree. Such *trusties* with their partly or wholly uncolloquial phrases, their unsure and distrustful eyes, who had, since the war, seeped into the university, the faculty, the sections and everyday life in general from executive committee and militia right down to local flat association level, had instilled in me a feeling which was as mixed as what must have been going on inside them themselves: pity and watchfulness. At any rate, Estonians and Russian-born Estonians had lived such different lives on our respective sides of the border, that our mutual alienation was an unbridgeable gap. On both sides of the border irrational things had been said and printed about the other side. In Estonia, hungry children were supposed to go about scavenging for food in dustbins. While in Russia, claimed the Estonian daily *Päevaleht*, in for instance 1937, the year of the great show trials, men who had been the vanguard of revolution only fifteen years previously were now infiltrators, traitors and foreign agents who with their own hands had mixed broken glass into the butter sold to the proletariat. Ten years previously nothing but such news items were to be found about Russia in our papers. And never a whisper of protest or denial from their side of the border, something which would have been quite natural in the circumstances. So you had to conclude: where there's smoke, there's fire. And this then led one to ask: *who* were mad there, the courts or those who appeared before them? And to answer without hesitation: the courts. For if the courts had been normal and the accused, therefore, mad, then the mass-executions of those accused would not have been able to take place. And Russia's Estonians lived right in the thick of this madness, in this oppressive atmosphere of mistrust which resulted from this madness, which Russia allowed especially to afflict the minorities on her western borders. So that people who were used to all this, seemed, according to my first impression, and soon *a priori*, more questioning, evasive, shifty-eyed and vague than others. Most of all if they tried (and as far as I could observe, they tried all the time) to verify whether what had been, and was still, occurring in their country was right and proper in itself; right and proper, that is, in the way that primitives use the expression, or right and proper according to less accessible, more inscrutable people, well, anyway, not always in that cosy petit-bourgeois sense of the expression, but in a nobler and more universal sense.

"Yes." said Comrade Kanter. "First I worked in Russia, then in Germany and then in Italy and then in Russia once again. Up to the year 1937. Does that say anything to you?"

I nodded: "Understood –" And the matter was indeed clear to me. Or at least the unclarity of the situation had become so. I did not go on to say: "Understood. Then you must obviously be a traitor and were no doubt an undercover agent or a spy for Germany or Italy or both." I merely grunted "Understood!" and left it at that. For in such a complicated case as this it was better to keep one's mouth shut. I made as if to rise from my seat and was about to say: "Comrade Kanter, I thank you for your kind concern for my welfare – but it is quite obvious that the two men working in the forest, who could perhaps find work in your office, have precedence over me. So be so good as to add my name to the list after theirs. And I will try and learn something in the meantime."

But Kanter beckoned me to sit down again and asked:

"Are you acquainted with technical script?"

"What do you mean 'acquainted with'?"

"Well, can you write technical texts in ink? Using standard script."

It was a strange moment. It was as if he simply couldn't bring himself to let me go. And I did not dare to reply: I can. And not simply because I could very well be proved there and then, within half-an-hour or the next day, to be a fraud.

"No, I can't."

"Hm –" He thought a little – I began to rise again from my seat. He asked: "Oh yes, you're from Tartu aren't you –?"

"Yes, I studied there, at least. And worked there too. For a short while. As long as I was allowed to. But I'm originally from Tallinn."

"I'm sorry, the doctor did introduce us but what was the name again?"

"Peeter Mirk."

"Mirk? From Tallinn?"

"That's right."

"And where in Tallinn did you live?"

Why was he asking this question? Had this man ever lived in Tallinn? Most unlikely. But I had no reason not to answer. I said:

"In Kalamaja. If that says anything to you. To the north-west of the centre. Vesker's machine-tool shop was out there. My father worked for Vesker's –"

Kanter looked at me with impish animation for a second or two:

"So you lived along by the foundry – on the right hand side of the small cross-street – in Vesker's workers' flats. You then lived in the lower flat on the left?"

I was speechless with amazement. Speechless for some time. Two lists of names intertwined in my imagination: clairvoyants and detectives – Swedenborg – Sherlock Holmes – Madame Blavatsky – the Witch of Aksi – and perhaps the weary face of Major Sidorov – if he had existed and been able to epitomize his colleagues . . . Where the hell could Kanter have known that from?!

He sat there savouring my consternation – for one whole minute it seemed – with the light smile of a magician on his lips, whereupon he explained:

"You see, it was like this – we decided in 1921, me and my wife at the time that is, – she's dead now – we decided to move from Petrograd to Estonia. In those days there was no question of being regarded as traitors to Russia for doing so. And from the Estonian point of view, we weren't really immigrants either, if you see what I mean. I was in fact born in Parnu.* I had also been allowed to leave my previous job and my papers were in order from the point of view of both countries. That was easy to arrange in those days. And there were only the two of us – we didn't have any children – but it then transpired that the theatre – my wife was a ballet dancer at the Maria Theatre – wouldn't let my wife go. Lopukhov† himself asked her to dance right up to the end of the season. So we decided that I would travel to Estonia, find a job in Tallinn, arrange a flat and move in and she would follow along later the next spring. I went to Tallinn. In the autumn of '21 I got a job at Vesker's factory. As an engineer. I worked there alongside your father. We serviced "OB" locomotives from the Russian Federation. But then it transpired in the spring of '22 that the theatre still wouldn't let my wife go. So I went back to

---

* Estonian seaside town, popular with liberal Russian and Jewish intelligentsia both between the wars and afterwards (Tarkovsky, Oistrakh, etc.).

† Fyodor Vassilievich Lopukhov (1886–1973), Russian ballet dancer and impresario.

Petrograd. But during the time I worked with your father, I was at your house several times, sometimes for reasons of work, at other times I played chess with your father. I remember you. You were one-and-a-half at the time. And so high." He showed how high with his hand – a little lower than the height of Doctor Kačanauskas' desk. Then he tapped the tips of his fingers against his rough black calico camp trousers: "You have sat on my knee – and quite a few times at that –"

I couldn't bring myself to say a thing. He continued: "But now I must hurry. At a quarter to seven we will be leaving with the convoy from the main gate. You will stay behind in the zone for now. I will leave a chit with your name on it with the chief *naryadchik*. I will be back at six. Look me up in Hut 27. I will have the necessary equipment for you with me. Paper. Pens. Ink. I am not allowed to have such things on camp premises. But I'll bring them along with me. You will practise. If you can't find anywhere else to do so, then here will do. I'll arrange it with the doctor. Get acquainted with the GOST techni-cal script as thoroughly as you are able. You have one evening, two nights and one day to do so. On Thursday morning we will leave for the office. Goodbye. And good luck. By the way, how is your father?"

"Dead."

"When?"

"Last year."

"Where?"

"In Mordva."*

"Oh, I see." He was silent a moment. "Well, once again, good luck. I hope that you get the hang of the script."

He smiled, a little guilty that he had to be so demanding with me, and left.

I breathed a sigh of relief and thought: he'll get his script, all right. And I also thought – and, you might say, am still thinking: this Earth does indeed contain a level at which such coincidences occur, confirming the existence of the Lord of the Ashtray.

Translated from the Estonian by Eric Dickens

---

* Autonomous republic. Home of a Finno-Ugrian people (like the Estonians) but also a region of Russian prison camps.

JOY WILLIAMS

Congress

Miriam was living with a man named Jack Dewayne who taught a
course in forensic anthropology at the state's university. It was the
only programme in the country that offered a certificate in forensic
anthropology as far as anyone knew and his students adored him. They
called themselves Deweenies and wore skull and crossbone T-shirts to
class. People were mad for Jack in this town. Once, in a grocery store,
where Miriam stood gazing into a bin of little limes, a woman came
up to her and said,

"Your Jack is a wonderful, wonderful man."

"Oh thanks," Miriam said.

"My son Ricky disappeared four years ago and some skeletal
remains were found at the beginning of this year. Scattered, broken,
lots of bones missing, not much to go on, a real jumble. The officials
told me they probably weren't Ricky's but your Jack told me they
were, and with compassion he showed me how he reached that conclusion." The woman waited. In her cart was a big bag of birdseed
and a bottle of vodka. "If it weren't for Jack, my Ricky's body would
probably be unnamed still," she said.

"Well thank you very much," Miriam said.

She never knew what to say to Jack's fans. As for them, they didn't
understand Miriam at all. Why her of all people? With his hunger for
life, Jack could have chosen better, they felt. Miriam lacked charm,
they felt. She was gloomy. Even Jack found her gloomy occasionally.

For breakfast, out in the garden, she would, at times, read Beckett.
Dew, radiant as angel spit, glittered on the petals of Jack's roses. The
garden was distinctive, the roses were fat and all had different names.
Jack was quite the gardener. Miriam thought she knew why he particularly favoured roses. The inside of a rose does not at all correspond
to its exterior beauty. If one tears off all the petals of the corolla, all

that remains is a sordid looking tuft. Roses would be right up Jack's alley all right.

"Here's something for you, Jack," Miriam said. "You'll appreciate this. Beckett described tears as 'liquefied brain'."

"God, Miriam," Jack said. "Why are you sharing that with me! You can be so creepy sometimes. Look at this day, it's a beautiful day! Stop pumping out the cesspit! Leave the cesspit alone!"

Then the phone would ring and Jack would begin his daily business of reconstructing the previous lives of hair and teeth when they had been possessed by someone. A detective a thousand miles away would send him a box of pitted bones and within days Jack would be saying,

"This is a white male between the ages of 25 and 30 who didn't do drugs and who was tall, healthy and trusting. Too trusting, clearly."

Or a hand would be found in the stomach of a shark hauled up by a party boat off the Gulf coast of Florida and Jack would be flown off to examine it. He would return deeply tanned and refreshed with a new crisp haircut, saying,

"The shark was most certainly attracted to the rings on this hand. This is a teen's hand. She was small, perhaps even a legal midget, and well nourished. She was a loner, adventurous and not well educated. The rings are worthless but appear to have been stolen. She would certainly have done herself a favour by passing up the temptation of those rings."

Miriam hated it when Jack was judgemental and Jack was judgemental a great deal. She herself stole upon occasion, sheets mostly. It was easy to steal sheets, for some reason. As a girl, she had wanted to be a witty, lively and irresistible woman, skilled in repartee and in arguments on controversial subjects, but it hadn't turned out that way. She had become a woman who was still waiting for her calling.

Jack had no idea that Miriam stole sheets and more. He liked Miriam. He liked her bones. She had fine bones and he loved tracing them at night beneath her warm, smooth skin, her jaw bone, collar bone, pelvic bone. It wasn't anything that consumed him, he just liked her was all – usually. And he liked his work. He liked wrapping things up and dealing with those who the missing had left behind. He was neither doctor nor priest, he was the forensic anthropologist and he alone could give these people peace. They wanted to know, they had to know. Was that tibia in the swamp Denny's? Denny, we long to claim you . . . Were those little bits and pieces they got when they swept the lake Lucile's even though she was supposed to be in Manhattan? She had told us she was going to be in Manhattan, there was never any talk about a lake . . . Bill had gone on a day hike years ago with his little white dog and now something had been found, found in a ravine at last . . . Pookie had toddled away from the Airstream on the 4th of July just as we were setting up the grille, she would be so much older now, a little girl instead of a baby and it would be so good just to know, if we could only know . . .

And Jack would give them his gift. He could give them the incontrovertible and the almost unspeakable news. That's her, that's them. No need to worry any more, it is finished, you are free. No one could help these people who were weary of waiting and sick of hope like Jack could.

Miriam found it somewhat puzzling. She herself had a fondness for people who vanished, though she had never known any personally. If she had a loved one who vanished, she would prefer to believe that they had fallen in love with distance, a great distance, she certainly wouldn't long to be told they were dead.

One day, one of Jack's students, an ardent hunter, a gangly blue-eyed boy named Carl who wore camouflage pants and a black shirt winter and summer presented Jack with four cured deer feet.

"I thought you'd like to make a lamp," Carl said.

Miriam was in the garden. She had taken to stealing distressed plants from nurseries and people's yards and planting them in an unused corner of the lot, far from Jack's roses. They remained distressed however, in shock, she felt.

"It would make a nice lamp," Carl said. "You can make all kinds of things. With a big buck's forelegs you can make an outdoor thermometer. Looks good with snowflakes on it."

"A lamp," Jack said. He appeared delighted. Jack got along well with his students. He didn't sleep with the girls and he treated the boys as equals. He put his hands around the tops of the deer feet and splayed them out some.

"You might want to fiddle around with the height," Carl said. "You can make great stuff with antlers too. Chandeliers, candelabras. You can use antlers to frame just about anything."

"We have lamps," Miriam said. She was holding a wan perennial she had liberated from a supermarket.

"Gosh, this appeals to me though, Miriam."

"I bet you'd be good at this sort of thing, sir," Carl said. "I did one once and it was very relaxing." He glanced at Miriam, squeezed his eyes almost shut, and smiled.

"It will be a novelty item all right," Jack said. "I think it will be fun."

"Maybe you'd like to go hunting sometime with me, sir," Carl said. "We could go bow hunting for mulies together."

"You should resist the urge to do this Jack, really," Miriam said. The thought of a lamp made of animal legs in her life and *turned on* caused a violent feeling of panic within her.

But Jack wanted to make a lamp. He needed another hobby he argued. Hobbies were healthy and he might even take Carl up on his bow hunting offer. Why didn't she get herself a hobby like cooking or baking he suggested. He finished the lamp in a weekend and set it upon an antique jelly cabinet in the sunroom. He had had a little trouble trimming the legs to the same height. But Miriam, expecting to be repulsed by the thing, was enthralled instead. It had a dark blue shade and a gold coloured cord and accepted a 60-watt bulb. A brighter bulb would be pushing it, Jack said. Miriam could not resist it. She often found herself sitting beside it, staring at it, the harsh brown hairs, the dainty pasterns, the polished black hooves, all gathered together, fastened together with a brass gimp band, in a space the size of a dinner plate. It was anarchy, the little lamp, its legs snugly bunched. It was whirl, it was hole, it was the first far drums. She sometimes worried that she would begin talking to it. This happened to some people, she knew, they felt they had to talk. She read that Luther Burbank spoke to cacti reassuringly when he wanted to create a spineless variety and that they stabbed him repeatedly – he had to pull thousands of them from his hands – but he didn't care. He continued to speak calmly and patiently, he never got mad, he persisted.

"Miriam," Jack said, "that is not meant to be a reading light. It's an accent light. You're going to ruin your eyes."

Miriam had once channelled her considerable imagination into sex which Jack had long appreciated but now it spilled everywhere and lay lightly on everything like water on a lake. It alarmed him a little. Perhaps, during semester break, they should take a trip together. To witness something strange with one another might be just the ticket.

At the same time, he felt unaccountably nervous about travelling with Miriam.

The days were radiant but it was almost fall and a daytime coolness reached out and touched everything. Miriam's restlessness was gone. It was Jack who was restless.

"I'm going to take up bow hunting, Miriam," he said. "Carl seems to think I'd be a natural at it."

Miriam did not object to this as she might once have done. Nevertheless, she could not keep herself from waiting anxiously beside the lamp for Jack's return from his excursions with Carl. She was in a peculiar sort of readiness, and not for anything in particular either. For weeks Jack went hunting and for weeks he did not mind that he did not return with a former animal.

"It's the expectation and the challenge. That's what counts," he said. He and Carl would stand in the kitchen, sharing a little whisky. Carl's skin was clean as a baby's and he smelled cleanly if somewhat aberrantly of cold cream and celery. "The season's young, sir," Carl said.

But eventually Jack's lack of success began to vex him. Miriam and the lamp continued to wait solemnly for his return but he always returned empty-handed. He grew irritable. Sometimes he would forget to wash off his camouflage paint, and he slept poorly. Then one late afternoon when Jack was out in the woods he fell asleep in his stand and toppled out of a tree, critically wounding himself with his own arrow which passed through his eye and into his head like a knife thrust into a cantaloupe. A large portion of his brain lost its rosy hue and turned grey as a rat's coat. A month later the result of the incident was this. He could walk with difficulty and move one arm. He had some vision out of his remaining eye and he could hear but not speak. He emerged from rehab with a face expressionless as a frosted cake. He was something that had suffered a premature burial, something accounted for but not present. Miriam was certain that he was aware of the morbid irony in this.

The lamp was a great comfort to Miriam in the weeks following the accident. Carl was of less comfort. Whenever she saw him in the hospital's halls, he was wailing and grinding his teeth. But the crooked, dainty, deer-foot lamp was calm. They spent most nights together quietly reading. The lamp had eclectic reading tastes. It would cast its light on anything actually. It liked the stories of Poe and tales about brave and morally superior wolves in the Arctic. The night before Jack was to return home, they read a little book in which animals offered their prayers to God – the mouse, the bear, the turtle and so on – and this is perhaps where the lamp and Miriam had their first disagreement. Miriam liked the little verses. But the lamp felt that though the author clearly meant well, the prayers were cloying, and confused thought with existence. The lamp had witnessed a smattering of Kierkegaard and felt strongly that thought should never be confused with existence. Being in such a condition of peculiar and altered existence itself, the lamp felt some things unequivocally. Miriam often wanted to think about that other life, when the part knew the whole, when the legs ran and rested and moved through woods, washed by flowers, but the lamp did not want to reflect upon those times.

After their heated discussion about Kierkegaard they glanced at another book in which they learned that the great naturalist Thoreau passed serenely from this life uttering the word *moose*. Knowing this about Thoreau and the moose made them feel better. Life couldn't be all accident, it had to be fate and possibility too.

Jack came back and Carl moved in with them. He had sold everything he owned except his big Chevy truck and wanted only to nurse Jack for the rest of his life. Jack's good eye often teared and he indicated both discomfort and agreement with a whistling hiss. Even so, he didn't seem all that glad to see Miriam. As for herself, she felt that she had driven to a grave and gotten out of the car but left the engine running. Carl slept for a time in Jack's study but one night when Miriam couldn't sleep and was sitting in the living room with the lamp, she saw Carl go into their room and shut the door. And that became the arrangement. Carl stayed with Jack day and night.

One of the first things Carl wanted to do was to take a trip. He believed that the doleful visits from the other students tired Jack and that the familiar house and grounds didn't stimulate him properly. Miriam didn't think highly of Carl's ideas but this one didn't seem too bad. She was ready to leave. After all, Jack had already left in his fashion and it seemed pointless to stay in his house. They all three would sit together in the big roomy cab on the wide cherry-red custom seat of Carl's truck and tour the Southwest. The only thing she didn't like was that the lamp would have to travel in the back with the luggage.

"Nothing's going to happen to it," Carl said. "Look at dogs. Dogs ride around in the backs of trucks all the time. They love it."

"Thousands of dogs die each year from being pitched out of the backs of pick-ups," Miriam said.

Jack remained in the room with them while they debated the statistical probability of this. Even though he was gaunt and his head was scarred, he tended to resemble, if left to his own devices, a large white appliance. But Carl was always buying him things and making small alterations to his appearance. This day he was wearing pressed khakis, a crisp madras shirt, big black glasses and a black Stetson hat. Carl was young and guilty and crazy in love. He patted Jack's wrists as he talked, he didn't want to upset him.

Finally, complaining that he had never seen a dog fall out of a pick-up truck, Carl agreed to buy a shell and enclose the back. He packed two small bags for himself and Jack while Miriam got a cardboard carton and arranged her clothes around the lamp. Her plan was to unplug whatever lamp was in whatever motel room they stayed in and plug in the deer foot lamp. Clearly, this would be the high point of each day for it.

They took to the road that night and didn't stop driving until daylight disclosed that the landscape had changed considerably. There was a great deal of broken glass sparkling and huge cacti everywhere. Organ pipe, saguaro, barrel cactus and prickly pear. Strange and stern shapes, far stiller than trees, less friendly and willing to serve. They seemed to be waiting for further transition, another awesome shift of the earth's plates, an enormous occurrence. The sun bathed each spine, it sharpened the smashed bottles and threw itself through the large delicate ears of car-crushed jackrabbits. They saw few people and no animals except dead ones. The land was vast and still and there seemed to be considerable resentment towards the non-human creatures who struggled to inhabit it. Dead coyotes and hawks were nailed to fence posts and the road was hammered with the remains of lizards and snakes. Miriam was glad that the lamp was covered and did not have to suffer these sights.

The first night they stopped at a small motel which was six rooms strung out along the road and attached to a Chinese restaurant and lounge. Miriam ordered moo goo gai pan for dinner, something she had not had since she was a child, and an orange soda, but the dish was gummy and grey and garnished with parsley and the soda was warm. Carl fed Jack some select tidbits from an appetizer platter with a pair of chopsticks. After they ate, Miriam wandered into the lounge, but there was only a cat vigorously cleaning itself who stared at her with its legs splayed over its head. She picked up a few worn paperback books from the exchange table in the office and went back to her room. Through the walls she could hear Carl singing to Jack as he ran the bathwater. He would shampoo Jack's hair, he would scrub his nails and talk about the future . . . Miriam turned on the lamp and examined one of the books. It concerned desert plants but many of the pages were missing and someone had spilled wine on the pictures. She did learn, however, that cacti are descended from roses. They were late arrivals, adaptors, part of a new climate. She felt like that, felt very much a late arrival, it was her personality. And she had adapted readily to being in love, and then adapted to not being in love anymore. And the new climate was . . . well . . . this situation. She put the book about cacti down.

The other book was about hunting zebras in Africa. I shot him right up his big fat fanny, the writer wrote. She had read this before she knew what she was doing and felt terrible about it, but the lamp held steady until she finally turned it off and got into bed.

The next day they drove. They stopped at mineral springs and hot springs and ghost towns. They stopped on an Indian reservation and Carl bought Jack coloured sand in a bottle. They stopped at a Dairy Queen and Miriam drove while Carl spooned blueberry blizzard into Jack's mouth. They admired the desert, the peculiar growths, the odd pale colours. They passed through a canyon of large, solitary boulders. There was a sign threatening fine and imprisonment for defacing the rocks but the boulders were covered with paint, spelling out people's names mostly. The shapes of the rocks resembled nothing but the words made them look like toilet doors in a truck stop. On the other side of the canyon was a small town. There were two museums there, a brick hotel, a gas station and a large bar called The Horny Toad. Miriam had the feeling that the truck had stopped running.

"Truck's stopped," Carl said.

They coasted to the side of the road and Carl fiddled with the ignition.

"Alternator's shot, I bet," he said. He took Jack's sunglasses off, wiped them with a handkerchief and carefully hooked them back over

Jack's ears. He was thinking, Miriam thought. Underneath her elbow, the metal of the door was heating up.

"You check into the motel," Carl said. "Jack and I will walk down to the garage." Miriam looked at him. "He likes garages," Carl said.

Carl helped her get their luggage from the back and carried it into the hotel's lobby. She arranged for two unadjoining rooms. They were the last rooms left, even though the hotel and town appeared deserted. The museums were closed and everyone was at the bar, the manager told her. One of the museums had only a petrified wedding cake and a petrified cat in it. It also had some rocks and old clothes. It was typical and not worth going into, the manager confided. But people came from far and wide to see the other museum and speak to the taxidermist on duty. He was surprised that they had come here without having the museum as their destination. The taxidermist was a genius. He couldn't make an animal look dead if he wanted to.

"He can even do reptiles and combine them in artistic and instructive groups," the manager said.

"This museum is full of dead animals?" Miriam said.

"Sure," the manager said. "It's a wildlife museum."

Miriam's room was in the back of the hotel. It was over the kitchen and smelled somewhat wetly, like the inside of a lunch box, but it wasn't unpleasant. She rearranged the furniture, plugged in the lamp and gazed out the single window at the bar, a long, dark structure that seemed, the longer she stared at it, to be almost heaving with the muffled sound of voices. That was The Horny Toad. She decided to go there.

Miriam had always felt that she was the kind of person who somehow quenched in the least exacting stranger any desire for conversation with her. This, however, was not the case at The Toad. People turned to her immediately and began to speak. They had bright, restless faces, seemed starved for affection, and were in full conversational mode. There were a number of children present. Everyone seemed wildly stimulated. A young woman with lank thinning hair touched Miriam with a small dry hand.

"I'm Carolyn Dickman and I'm an ex-agoraphobic," she said. "Can I buy you a drink?"

"Yes," Miriam said, startled. People were waving, smiling.

"I used to be so afraid of losing control," Carolyn said. "I was afraid of going insane, embarrassing myself. I was afraid of getting sick or doing something frightening or dying . . . it's hard to believe, isn't it?"

She went off to the bar, saying she would return with gimlets. Miriam was immediately joined by an elderly couple wearing jeans, satin shirts, and large identical concha belts. Their names were Vern and Irene. They had spent all day at the museum and were happy and tired.

"My favourite is the javelina family," Irene said. "Those babies were adorable."

"Ugly animals," Vern said. "Bizarre. But they've always been Irene's favourite."

"Not last year," Irene said. "Last year it was the bears, I think. Vern says that Life is just one thing but it takes different forms to amuse itself."

"That's what I say, but I don't believe it," Vern said, winking broadly at Miriam.

"Vern likes the ground squirrels."

Vern agreed. "Isn't much of a display but I like what I hear about them. That state of torpor thing. When the going gets rough, boom, right into a state of torpor. They don't need anything. A single breath every three minutes."

Irene didn't seem as fascinated as her husband about the state of torpor. "Have you gone yet, dear?" she asked Miriam. "Have you asked the taxidermist your question?"

"No, I haven't," Miriam said. She accepted a glass from Carolyn who had returned with a tray of drinks. "I'm Carolyn Dickman," Carolyn said to the old couple, "and I'm an ex-agoraphobic."

"He doesn't answer everybody," Vern said.

"He answers the children sometimes but they don't know what they're saying," Irene said fretfully. "I think children should be allowed only in the petting zoo."

A gaunt, grave boy named Alec arrived. He identified himself as a tree hugger. He was with a girl named Argon.

"When I got old enough to know sort of what I wanted," Argon said, "I decided I wanted either a tree hugger or a car guy. I'd narrowed it down to that. At my first demonstration, I lay in the road with some other people in a park where they were going to bulldoze two-hundred-year-old trees for a picnic area. We had attracted quite a crowd of onlooking picnickers. When the cops came and carried me off, a little girl said, 'Why are they taking away the pretty one, Mommy?' and I was hooked. I just loved demonstrating after that, always hoping to overhear those words again. But I never did."

"We all get older, dear," Irene said.

"Car guys are kind of interesting," Argon said. "They can be really hypnotic but only when they're talking about cars actually."

"Choose well for thy choice is brief but endless," Vern said. He spoke heartily but he looked a little bewildered.

Some time later, Alec was still in the midst of a long story about Indian environmentalists in the Himalayas. The tree-hugging movement started long ago, Alec had been telling them, when the Maharaja of Jodhpur wanted to cut down trees for yet another palace and a woman named Amrita Devi resisted his axemen by hugging a tree and uttering the now well known couplet, "a chopped head is cheaper than a felled tree", before she was dismembered. Then her three daughters took her place and they were dismembered too. Then 359 additional villagers were dismembered before the Maharaja called it off.

"And it really worked," Alec said, gnawing on his thumbnail. "That whole area is full of militant conservationists now. They have a fair there every year." He gnawed furiously at his nail. "And on the supposed spot where the first lady died, no grass grows. Not a single blade. They've got it cordoned off." He struggled for a moment with a piece of separated nail between his teeth, at last freed it, examined it for a moment, then flicked it to the floor.

"You know Alec," Argon said. "I've never liked that story. It just misses the mark as far as I'm concerned." She turned to Miriam. "Tree huggers tend sometimes not to have both feet on the ground. I want to be a spiritual and ecological warrior but I want both feet on the ground too."

Miriam looked at the white curving nail on the dirty floor. Jack wouldn't have had much to go on with that. Even Jack. Who were these people? They were all so desperate . . . You couldn't attribute their behaviour to alcohol alone . . .

Other people gathered around the table, all talking about their experiences in the museum, all expressing awe at the exhibits, the wolves, the mountain lions, the wading birds, the herds of elk, and the exotics, particularly the exotics. They had come from far away to see this. Many of them returned, year after year.

"It's impossible to leave the place unmoved," a woman said. "Impossible."

"My favourite is the wood ibis on a stump in a lonely swamp," Carolyn said. "It couldn't be more properly delineated." She spoke cautiously.

"That's a gorgeous specimen all right. Not too many of those left," someone said.

". . . so much better than a zoo. Zoos are so depressing. I hear the animals are committing suicide in Detroit. Hurling themselves into moats and drowning . . ."

"I don't think other cities have that problem so much. Just Detroit."

"Even so. Zoos . . ."

"Oh absolutely, this is so much nicer."

"Shoot to kill but not to mangle," Vern said.

"A lot of hunters just can't get that part down," Irene said. "And then they think they can bring those creatures here! To him!"

"I have my questions all prepared for tomorrow," Argon said. "I'm going to ask him about the eyes. Where do you get the eyes, I'm going to ask."

"Those children got there ahead of you on that one, I'm afraid," Irene said. "Some little goldilocks in a baseball hat."

"Oh no!" Argon exclaimed. "What did he say?"

"He said he got the eyes from a supply house."

"I'm sure he would have expressed it differently to me," Argon said.

Alec, gnawing on his other thumb, looked helplessly at her.

"I just hate that," somebody said. "Someone else gets to ask your question, you'll never get to the bottom of it."

"Excuse me," Miriam said quietly to Irene, "but why are you all here?"

"We're here with those we love because something big is going to happen here we think," Irene said. "We want to be here for it. Then we'll have been here."

"You never know," Vern said. "Next year at this time, we might all have ridden over the skyline."

"But we're not ready to ride over the skyline yet," Irene said, patting his hand.

The lights in The Toad flickered, went out, then came back on again more weakly.

"Well, it's closing time," several people said at once.

They all filed out into the night. Many were staying in campers and tents pitched around the museum, the others were staying in the hotel.

". . . I wouldn't want to pass my days in Detroit either," a voice said.

"I was using terror as an analgesic," Carolyn was explaining to no one as far as Miriam could see. "And now I'm not."

"You say you want to participate in life," Argon was yelling at Alec, "but you sit there like a clot. You're just a big clot of something is all. Your problem is your centre is on the periphery, that's your problem."

Back in the room, Miriam sat with the lamp for some time. The legs were dusty so she wiped them down with a damp towel. She was thinking of getting different shades for it. Shade of the week. Even if she slurred her words when she thought, the lamp was able to follow her. There were tenses that human speech had yet to discover and the lamp was able to incorporate these in its understanding as well. Miriam was excited about going to the museum in the morning. She planned on being there the moment the doors opened. The lamp had no interest in seeing the taxidermist. It was beyond that. They read a short sad story about a brown dog whose faith in his master proved to be terribly misplaced, and spent a rather fitful night.

The next morning, Miriam joined Jack and Carl in their room for breakfast. Carl greeted her politely, he always seemed surprised to see her. "Oh hello! . . ." he'd say.

"We've just finished brushing our teeth," Carl said. Jack's glasses were off and he regarded Miriam skittishly out of his good eye. Miriam poured the coffee while Carl buttered the toast and Jack peeled the backing off band-aids and stuck them on things. He preferred children's adhesive bandages with space ships and cartoon characters on them to the flesh-coloured ones. He plastered some on Miriam's hands.

"He likes you!" Carl exclaimed.

They drank their coffee in silence. A fan whined in the room.

"Truck should be ready today," Carl said.

"Have you ever been in love before?" Miriam asked him.

"No," Carl said.

"Well, you're handling it very well, I think."

"No problem," Carl said.

Miriam held her cup. She pretended there was one more sip in it when there wasn't.

"Why don't we all go to the museum," she said. "That's what people do when they're here."

"I've heard about that," Carl said. "And I would say that a museum like that, and the people who run it, well it's deeply into denial on every level. That's what I'd say. And Jack here, all his life he was the great verifier, weren't you, Jack, and still are by golly." Jack cleared his throat and Carl gazed at him happily. "We don't want to go into a place like that," Carl said.

Miriam felt ashamed and determined. She didn't feel anything. "I'll go over there for an hour or two," she said.

There were many people in line ahead of her, although she didn't see any of her acquaintances of the night before. The museum was massive with wide cement columns and curving walls of tinted glass. Dimly, she could make out static, shaggy arrangements within. The first room she entered was a replica of a basketball player's den in California. There were 1500 wolf muzzles on the wall. A small bronze tablet said that Wilt Chamberlain had bought a whole year's worth of wolves from an Alaskan bounty hunter. It said he wanted the room to have an unequivocally masculine look. Miriam heard one man say hoarsely to another, "He got that by God . . ." The next few rooms were reproductions of big game hunters' studies and were full of heads and horns and antlers. In the restaurant, a group of giraffes were arranged behind the tables as though in the act of chewing grass, the large lashed eyes in their angular Victorian faces content. In the petting area, children toddled among the animals, pulling their tails and pretending to shake their paws. There was a wolf, a white rhino, a lion light as a feather. Miriam stepped quickly, past flocks and herds and prides of creatures, to stand in a glaring space before a polar bear and two cubs.

"Say 'hi' to the polar bear," a man said to his child.

"Hi!" the child said.

"She's protecting her new-born cubs, that's why she's snarling like that," the man said.

"It's dead," Miriam remarked. "The whole little family."

"Hi, polar bear," the child crooned, "hi, hi, hi."

"What's the matter with you," the father demanded of Miriam. "People like you make me sick."

Miriam threw out her hand and slapped his jaw. He dropped the child's hand and she slapped him again even harder. Something yellow flew from his nostril. He must have had a cold, Miriam thought as she hurried from the room.

She wandered among the crowds. The museum was lit dimly and flute music played. The effect was that of a funeral parlour or a dignified cocktail lounge. All the animals were arranged in a state of extreme and hopeless awareness. Wings raised, jaws open, hindquarters bunched. All recaptured from death to appear at the brink of departure.

"They're glorious, aren't they," a woman exclaimed. "It makes you think anything's possible in this world, doesn't it. Anything."

"Tasteful," someone said.

"None of these animals died a natural death though," a pale young man said. "That's what troubles me a little."

"These are trophy animals," his companion said. "It would be unnatural for them to die a natural death. It would be disgusting. It would be like Marilyn Monroe or something. James Dean, for example."

"It troubled me just a little. I'm all right now."

"That's not the way things work, honey," his companion said.

Miriam threaded her way past a line of people waiting to see the taxidermist. He was seated in a glass room. Beside him was a locked, smaller room, filled with skins and false bodies. There were all kinds of shapes, white and smooth.

The taxidermist sat behind a desk on which there were various tools – scissors and forceps, callipers and stuffing rods. A tiny brilliantly coloured bird lay on a blotter. Behind the taxidermist was a large nonhuman shape upon which progress seemed to have slowed. It looked as though it had been in this stage of the process for a long time. The taxidermist wasn't working on it. He was listening to a question that was being asked.

"I'm a poet," a man with yellow hair and a shovel-shaped face said, "and I recently accompanied two ornithologists into the jungles of Peru to discover heretofore unknown birds. I found the process of finding, collecting, identifying, examining and skinning hundreds of specimens for use in taxonomic studies tedious. I became disappointed. In other words, I found the labour of turning rare birds into specimens mundane. Isn't it mundane?"

The taxidermist spoke. His voice was loud and seemed to possess a lot of chilled space around it. It was like an astronaut's voice.

"You're mundane," the taxidermist said.

He stood up and fixed his eyes on Miriam. He waved and gestured to her. The gesture indicated that he wanted her to come around to the side of the glass room. He pulled down a long black shade upon which were the words, THE TAXIDERMIST WILL BE RIGHT BACK.

"I'm thrilled to see you!" the taxidermist exclaimed. He wore a jumpsuit with a wide, hand-painted tie loosely knotted. Miriam peered at the tie. Buffalo were scattered about a winter landscape bleeding brightly onto the snow.

"This is from my ecological collection," the taxidermist said. "Man's relationship to nature . . . You know, I saw and heard everything back there. There are monitors and microphones all over this place. I like a woman with spirit. I find that beliefs about reality affect people's actions to an enormous degree, don't you? Have you read Marguerite Porete's *Mirror of Simple Annihilated Souls?*"

Miriam shook her head. It sounded like something the lamp would like. She would try to get it.

"Really? I'm surprised. Famous broad. She was burned at the stake but an enormous crowd was converted to her favour after witnessing her attitude towards death."

"What was her attitude?" Miriam said.

"I don't know exactly. Thirteenth century. The records are muzzy. I guess she went out without a lot of racket about it. Women have been trying to figure out how to be strong for a long while. It's harder for women to find ways than a man is my belief. Not crying about stuff isn't enough. What they're doing these days is abandoning their babies. They perceive that this is strength and they're going for it. The drill goes like this. They keep the whole nine months secret, pop out the newborn and leave it in a shopping cart outside a hospital or church. It happened even here. We get them all passing through here, believe me."

Miriam said nothing. Back in the room, the lamp was hovered over *Moby Dick*. It would be deeply involved in it by now. It would be slamming down Melville like water. The shapeless maw of the undifferentiating sea! God as indifferent, insentient Being, composed of an

infinitude of deaths! Nature . . . gliding . . . bewitching . . . majestic
. . . capable of universal catastrophe! . . . The lamp was eating it up.

"Do you know how long I've been here?" the taxidermist said.
"Too long. But I bought some class into this place. The guy before
me, he had no idea, zero, none. A few ratty displays. Medallions were
his speciality. Things have to look dead on a medallion, that's the
whole point. But when I finished with something it looked alive. You
could almost hear it breathe. But of course it wasn't breathing. Ha!
It was best when I was working on it, that's when it really existed,
but when I stopped . . . Uhhh," he said. "I've been here for years and
I've gone as far as I can go. I've reached my oubliette, do you know
what I'm saying?"

"I do," Miriam said.

"Oh," he said. "I'm crazy about that word oubliette, that word says
it all."

"It's true," she said.

"So you'll stay!" the taxidermist said. "You'll take over!"

"I couldn't possibly," Miriam said.

"But you must, you must. Look, it's mostly questions."

"I don't know anything about questions," Miriam said.

"The only thing you have to know about them is that you can
answer them anyway you want. For example, a question you'll get a
lot is, 'What's the saddest thing you've ever seen?' Sometimes I say *It
was a large dead beetle I found once in the jungle. On its back there was
what seemed to be a painted mask intended to frighten its enemies*. But I
don't say that all the time. Sometimes I say, *Misgiving on a child's face*,
but I hate myself for dishing out that one. You've got to be flexible.
You'll go nuts if you don't change the answers . . . It's all got to be
too much for me though, keeping this town going. And so much of
what I learn is discouraging. Do you know what travellers want in a
room? They don't want to be frightened or humbled or mystified.
The women want big bathrooms with enough light to put on
make-up. The men want longer phone cords. These are the desires of
today's travellers."

"I'll think about it," Miriam said. But actually she was thinking
about the lamp. The odd thing was she had never been in love with
an animal. She had just skipped that cross-species eroticism and gone
right beyond it to altered parts. There was something wrong with
that she thought. It was hopeless. Well, love was hopeless . . .

"It's usually not this crowded," the taxidermist confessed. "For example, tomorrow might be a slow day."

"All right," Miriam said.

"There might be no one actually. That's the way it is sometimes."

"I see," said Miriam.

"Of course you have all the animals . . ." He made a gesture toward all the pretty death. "I find I make up a lot of stories."

"And what do you do with all these stories?" Miriam asked.

"That's the problem, isn't it, what to do with them."

It was almost noon and there was still a long line of people waiting to get into the museum. Miriam passed them on her way out.

"I've been back five times," a bald woman was saying to her friend. "I think you'll find it's almost a quasi-religious experience."

"Oh, I think everything should be like that," her friend said. "Do you think he's going to know the name of the horse that crushed Cole Porter's legs?"

"I don't see why not, we've come all this way, but I've never understood why you're so interested in knowing that."

"You know that I know all his lyrics."

"But that's really it. That's going to be your question?"

"Yes," the bald woman's little friend said, "I've given it a lot of thought and that's what I want to know. The name of that awful awful horse that caused Cole so much pain."

Carl's big truck was no longer at the garage. Miriam gazed around her for awhile but the truck did not resume its appearance and probably, as far as she was concerned, never would. For most people, and apparently Carl and Jack were two of them, a breakdown meant that it was just a matter of time before they were back on the road again. She walked over to the hotel and up the stairs to their room. The door was open and the beds were stripped. The pillows without their pretty covers looked like flayed things. They were a puzzle to Miriam, it was as though she couldn't remember anything. Their only possible function might be to turn into something else.

What would she say tomorrow when she assumed her post? What would she say in response? The living aren't here to be loved and entertained. Maybe that's what she'd tell them. The living aren't here to be comforted.

She went down the corridor and opened the door quietly to her own room. She looked at the lamp. The lamp looked back, looked at her as though it had no idea who she was. Miriam knew that look. She'd always felt it was full of promise. Nothing could happen anywhere was the truth of it. And the lamp was burning with this. Burning!

GIUSEPPE TOMASI DI LAMPEDUSA

Joy and the Law

When he boarded the bus he got in everyone's way.

There was his briefcase crammed with other people's papers, the enormous parcel bulging out under his left arm, his plush grey scarf, his umbrella on the point of flying open: everything conspired to obstruct his showing his return ticket. He was obliged to rest the great package on the conductor's ledge, provoking an avalanche of small change; he tried bending down to pick up all this insubstantial coinage, rousing those behind him to cries of protest – they were desperate in case his dilly-dallying left them with their coat-tails caught in the automatic doors. He managed to insert himself into the line of strap-hangers; he was slight of build, but what with his paraphernalia he had all the corpulence of a nun bundled up in seven habits. As the bus skated through the slush amid the dreary welter of traffic, the sheer awkwardness of his bulk sent a wave of disgruntlement from one end of the vehicle to the other: he trod on toes and got his own trodden on, he occasioned remonstrations, and when he even overheard, behind his back, three syllables alluding to his presumed conjugal infelicities, honour required him to turn his head, and he liked to imagine that his lacklustre eyes were charged with menace.

Meanwhile they were travelling through streets of rustic baroque frontages that concealed a hinterland whose squalor was at all events exposed at every corner. The ochre lights of eighty-year-old shops slid by.

On reaching his stop he rang the bell, alighted, tripped over his umbrella and finally found himself in sole possession of his square metre of dislocated pavement; he hastened to check that he had his plastic wallet. And he was free to relish his own happiness.

Contained inside the wallet were thirty-seven thousand two hundred and forty-five lire, his Christmas bonus (comprising an extra month's pay) remitted to him an hour ago – in other words the removal of several thorns: that of the landlord, all the more insistent because his was a controlled rent and he had two quarters' owing; that of the most punctual collector of the instalments on his wife's "chinchilla" jacket ("It suits you far better than a full-length coat, darling; it makes you look more svelte"); that of the black looks from the fishmonger and the greengrocer. Those four high-denomination notes also disposed of the worries over the next light bill, the anxious glances at the children's shoes, the nervous scrutiny of the fluttering flames on the bottled gas. The notes did not represent opulence – far from it! – but they promised a respite from worry, and that is the true joy of the poor. A couple of thousand would, moreover, survive for a moment to be expended in the splendour of the Christmas dinner.

But he had received plenty of Christmas bonuses in his time, and the rose-tinted euphoria that now buoyed him up was not to be attributed to the fleeting exhilaration that *they* elicited. Pink of hue, indeed, like the wrapping on the gentle burden that was bringing an ache to his left arm. It stemmed, in fact, from the seven-kilo *panettone* he had brought home from the office. Not that he was mad about that mixture (however highly guaranteed, nay, however dubious) of flour, sugar, powdered egg and raisins. On the contrary, deep down, he did not care for it. But seven kilos'-worth of luxury all at one go! an abundance at once circumscribed and boundless for a household whose sustenance generally arrived by the hundred grammes and half litres! A high-class product in a larder dedicated to the labels of third-rate goods! What a pleasure for Maria! What a lark for the children, who would spend a fortnight on the trails of that unexplored El Dorado, an afternoon snack!

These, however, were the joys of others, material joys comprised of vanilla essence and coloured cardboard, in other words, *panettone*. His private happiness was quite different, it was a spiritual joy, compounded of pride and tenderness; yessirs, a spiritual joy.

When, a little earlier, the Managing Director had handed out the pay envelopes and Christmas greetings with the supercilious bonhomie of the old party boss that he was, he had added that the seven-kilo *panettone*, sent in to the office as a gift from the Big-Time Production Company, would be allotted to the most deserving employee, and so he asked his dear colleagues if they would democratically (that was his word) designate the fortunate man there and then.

Meanwhile there sat the *panettone*, in the middle of the desk, inert, hermetically sealed, ("cumbered with portent" as the same official would have put it twenty years earlier) in its cloth lining. The colleagues muttered and sniggered; then they all of them, led by the Managing Director, had shouted his name. A great satisfaction, an assurance of the continuation of his employment, in a word, a triumph. And nothing had succeeded in shaking that tonic sensation, neither the three hundred lire he had been obliged to fork out in the bar downstairs, in the doubly livid light of the stormy sunset and the low-wattage neon, when he had stood his friends coffee, nor the weight of the booty, nor the scurrilous words overheard on the bus; nothing, not even when there flashed in the depths of his mind the notion that his fellows had all been engaged in an act of disdainful pity for his indigence. He was, in truth, too poor to permit the weed of vanity to sprout where it had no business.

He made his way home along a street to whose decrepitude the air-raids, fifteen years earlier, had put the finishing touches. He reached the spectral piazza at the end of which crouched his ghostly dwelling.

But he gave the hall-porter Cosimo a cheery greeting, though the man despised him in the knowledge that the bookkeeper earned even less than he did. Nine steps, three steps, nine steps up to Mr Bigshot's floor. Pooh! What if he did drive a *millecento* – his wife was an old trollop and ugly too. Nine steps, three steps, whoops!, nine steps up to Dr Thingummy's residence. Worse yet! A bone idle son who was crazy about motorcycles; besides, his waiting-room was always empty. Nine steps, three steps, nine steps: his own apartment. Here lived a man who was well liked, honest, highly regarded, his merits rewarded, a peerless accountant.

He opened the door, stepped into the tiny entrance hall permeated with the odour of sautéed onion; on a chest no bigger than a hamper he deposited the dead weight of the parcel, the briefcase pregnant with other people's concerns, the cumbersome muffler. His voice piped up: "Maria! Come quickly! Come and see what I've got!"

His wife came out of the kitchen in a housecoat soiled from the pots and pans; her little hands, reddened from rinsing the dishes, rested on her belly deformed from child-bearing. The runny-nosed infants crowded, chirruping, about the pink phenomenon but dared not touch it.

"Well done! And your pay, have you brought it? I don't have so much as a lira left."

"Here it is, darling; I'm keeping back only the small change, two hundred and forty-five lire. But take a look at this abundance!"

Maria used to be adorable and until a few years ago she had the liveliest little face, lit up by a mischievous pair of eyes. Now the rows with shopkeepers had coarsened her voice, the unwholesome fare had ruined her complexion, the incessant scrutiny of a future of looming fog and reefs had dowsed the sparkle in her eyes. All that survived in her was a saintly spirit and therefore inflexible and devoid of tenderness, a deep goodness constrained to find expression in rebukes and prohibitions. There was also a tenacious if chastened pride of caste, because her uncle was a leading hatter in Via Indipendenza and she disdained the origins (quite, quite other) of her Girolamo whom she still adored as one dotes on a stupid but lovable child.

Her glance slid indifferently over the decorative box. "That's good. Tomorrow we'll send it to Avvocato Risma. We owe him a favour."

A couple of years ago the lawyer had entrusted him with a complex job of bookkeeping and, in addition to paying him for it, he had invited them both to dinner in his apartment, all abstract art and tubular-steel furniture, during which the accountant had been in agony with the new shoes he had bought especially. And now, thanks to this lawyer who did not lack for anything, his Maria, his Andrea, his Saverio, their little Giuseppina, he himself, had to sacrifice the one and only vein of abundance they had struck in all those years!

He dashed into the kitchen, seized a knife and lunged to cut the gilded string gracefully tied round the package by some industrious Milanese factory-girl. But a raw red hand tapped him wearily on the shoulder: "Girolamo, don't be a baby. You know we have to return Risma's favour."

It was The Law speaking, The Law handed down by irreproachable hatters.

"But darling, this is a reward, it is evidence of merit, an acknowledgement of standing!"

"Never mind. They're a fine lot, those colleagues of yours and their delicate feelings! It's charity, Girò, nothing more than charity." She called him by her old affectionate nickname, and smiled at him with eyes in which none but he could detect the erstwhile charms.

"Tomorrow you can buy another *panettone*, a little one, that'll do

for us; and four of those pink corkscrew candles on display at Standa;*
that'll make it quite festive."

So the next day he bought an anonymous *panettone*, not four but
two of those amazing candles and, through an agency, sent the
Phenomenon to Avvocato Risma, which cost him a further two hundred lire.

After Christmas, furthermore, he was obliged to buy a third *panettone*, and bring it, sliced up for disguise, to his colleagues who had
been teasing him for not giving them so much as a crumb of the
original prize.

As for the original *panettone*, a pall of mist descended upon it.

He went to the "Lightning" agency to complain. The despatch note
was offhandedly shown to him – the lawyer's domestic signature on
it was upside down. After Twelfth Night, however, a visiting card
arrived "with heartiest thanks and good wishes".

Honour was satisfied.

Translated from the Italian by Guido Waldman

* A chainstore for thrifty shoppers, similar to Woolworth

EVGENY POPOV

I Await a Love that's True

In our village, Vesna, there lived a guy called Vaska Metus, and he had a wife.

"So what?" you'll say, "A lot of people live in this village, and almost all of them have got wives."

But he really hated his wife and would have liked to get rid of her.

"So what!" you'll say again. "A lot of people really hate their wives and would like to get rid of them."

But look. Listen to this. There are lots and lots of people like that, but Metus upped and brought home a second wife while his first was still alive and kicking.

He brought her in and left her in the hallway. And he himself went right inside the hut.

Sitting there at home were his, so to speak, actual wife Galka and Metus's old mother Makarina Savelevna, who considered her son a fool, despite the fact that he provided her with food and drink, and clothed her in print frocks.

The women were cracking sunflower seeds.

There was music and singing on the radio. The wall clock was ticking. The pussy cat was purring, and his relatives pounced on Vaska, telling him he was a drunk.

"Where you been loafing about, yer bastard?!"

"Where?" said Metus, repeating the question, and told them where.

The women started running round the kitchen, thinking that Vaska was now going to set about them.

But he didn't start hitting them, on the contrary, he sat down at the kitchen table, covered with oil-cloth, and said in faltering tones:

"G-glina! I've got to discuss a very important question with you."

"Question, question! What question! What you on about? You'd better lie down, Vasenka, and we'll have a talk tomorrow," replied

Galina, in a voice full of tears and evidently braced for one of Vaska's beatings.

"Sit down, sit down, woman!" repeated Vasily sternly and imperiously, and he began to sing:

"I await a love that's true,
One that's great, that's huge!

Understand?"

"No, I don't understand," answered Vaska's wife Galina, who sold groceries at a stall at the Livestock Processing Plant.

"Well you soon will. I'll explain everything to you," promised Vasily.

And he explained to Galina that she could pack her bags and clear off back home or wherever else she wanted, seeing as not only did he not love her, not only did he not see in her his ideal, or for that matter any ideal at all, but that he even had a new claimant to her position.

"So that's all there is to it. Great. Easy come, easy go."

Vaska came out with this proverb of unknown origin and thought that that was, as they say, the end of the affair.

But oh no it wasn't.

"Oy-yoy-yoy! Oy, I wish I'd never been born!" howled Galina. "You . . . you . . . you and me are husband and wife! Vasenka!"

Shouting. Crying.

"You and me were never husband and wife. You're telling lies. We shacked up together, that's what happened, we shacked up together, and now I'm giving you a divorce," said Vasily, explaining the formal aspect of the question.

He went on explaining and explaining, meanwhile opening the door into the little hallway, where his newly intended had secreted herself, and shouting:

"Come on. Come in 'ere!"

His newly intended turned out to be not bad at all, and in the darkness of the hallway even looked something of a beauty. Seeing this, Galina started howling even louder, and the hallway beauty entered the house.

She looked daggers at Galina, and then looked into the corner where the icon was hanging, and then plonked herself down at Makarina Savelevna's feet.

"Forgive me, Mama! Forgive us! You too, Vasily, get down, get down!" she said, sobbing and beating her breast.

They all wept and cried. Even Metus let slip a tear. But, truth to tell, he didn't get down on his knees. He embraced his old ex-"shacked-up" wife, gave her a farewell kiss, and started to push her out the door.

They all wept and cried, only his old mother maintained complete calm.

"You're a fool," she said to her son.

"Why?" said the latter, taking offence.

"A fool. A fool. Down, Vasya. Down!" said his new wife in agreement, beating her head on the floor.

And that's how they started their new life. They lived very well. It was only on the first night that the vexations, as described above, which accompanied the changeovers and re-arrangements, manifested themselves. Afterwards, everything sorted itself out: Galina went off back home to the other end of the village, where her parents lived. She went off, and soon afterwards, according to rumours, she got married to a soldier from a military construction battalion who was billeted in their hut. The soldier had promised to marry her as soon as his term of active service was completed. Whenever she met Metus she pointedly refused to look at him.

The new young Metus couple got off to a surprisingly good and harmonious start, despite the fact that Valka, as the newly intended was called, was a bit pock-marked. She had had smallpox as a child, and the smallpox had left pock marks on her face.

"Smallpox is no big deal," Vasily would tell his mother heatedly, excitedly. "Plenty of people look as if someone's been digging holes in their moosh."

And Makarina Savelevna's reasoned response to this was always:

"You're a fool and always will be."

"Just you see what a hard worker she is," boasted Vaska.

And his wife Valka really did turn out to be hard working. She got a sucking pig and a heifer and she fed them very well on slops and left-overs which she brought from the canteen. She worked in the canteen. She did the washing up there.

She fed them, watered them, cared for them, and the sucking pig and the heifer grew as if they'd been reared on vitamins.

She even found time to look after Vaska and Makarina Savelevna too. The long and the short of it was, she took the household into her own hands. Sometimes Vasily didn't even have any idea as to what was going on. What there was in the house, or what there wasn't. And neither did Makarina Savelevna. But Valka knew.

They lived very well. It was harmonious, and it was good, and every now and then Vasily would sing that old song of his:

"I await a love that's true, one that's great, that's huge . . ."

"You oughtn't to sing like that, Vasenka, or you'll put the mockers on our happiness," said his wife, flatteringly pressing herself to the mighty chest of her unlawfully wedded husband.

"I'm only singing. Singing, that's all," replied Vasily stubbornly. "I sing because life is varied and it can be anything and everything. You and me could split up ve-ery easily. Like ships at sea."

"Now, now," said his wife in fear.

"Yes. I sing. Anything and everything is possible. I ought to tell you that you're not at all my ideal."

And lo and behold – he turned out to be right.

Because one fine day along came a guy into the yard and ordered him to hand over the sucking pig and the heifer, since "Valentina Ivanovna sold them thar animals to me through the solicitor."

And the guy started shoving a piece of paper with a crested stamp on it under all their noses.

"Well take a look at this, will you?" said Metus, making the guy an appropriate gesture, and then he dashed headlong round to where his wife worked at the canteen, and there it came to light that his alleged wife had already given in her notice.

"And we don't know where she's gone," chortled her workmates, bold as brass.

Don't know. And no one knew at first. He had to hand over the heifer and the sucking pig, because there's no arguing with a crested stamp – you could come a cropper, and the next time the guy came round he brought a policeman with him. There were no flies on this guy, by the way. He had a house – a railwayman's box and he'd decided to set up home there. He told Metus that perhaps he even understood him, but seeing as the money had already been paid, there was nothing he could do to help.

So they had to be handed over. And only afterwards was the swindle discovered, namely that Valka had been in cahoots with the railwayman. It came to light that they had come to an agreement ages ago, and had only been waiting, apparently, for the heifer to grow up a bit. Now they began to live under one roof, in the box, and thus Vasya's love came to an end and was smashed like a glass bauble.

All this drove Metus round the bend and he said to his mama:

"There, you see, Mama."

And in reply the old woman said to him only:

"It's all because you're a fool."

"I await a love that's true . . ." sang Metus and then started planting potatoes in the field, seeing as it was spring. He planted out ten whole perches of potatoes, and almost a whole sackful in the vegetable garden.

Apart from that, he wanted to take legal proceedings against his ex-wife Valentina Ivanovna, on the grounds that she had stolen all his livestock from him, but she had a change of heart, got scared and agreed to give him 125 roubles as an out of court settlement.

Metus used this sum of money to buy himself a motorbike. The motorbike was very old and all sort of rusty, but it possessed one important feature: the pillion was a smart, black, soft, beautiful, sprung saddle from off of a BMW brought back from the war.

Soon there were passengers too, because Metus got married again. How he got married this time is neither here nor there, and maybe it's not even important. All that can be said is that his last wife was no worse than the first two. She wasn't pock-marked or squint-eyed, but just looked a little bit like a mop.

Well, Metus just carried on living in his own sweet way. Completely devoid of passion he sang his "I await a love that's true".

Well then. August came round, the month when the yellow leaves fall and the air turns blue, when migratory birds start to head for home, when the potatoes are earthed up and you have to give a thought as to how to gather them in and where to get hold of a truck to bring in the crop from the field.

On the truck they got was a soldier from the construction battalion, Rafail by name, a person of Eastern origin.

On one occasion, they, Rafail and Metus, went back to Metus's place and started drinking and talking business.

They drank, and his wife didn't interfere because she wasn't at home, and the old woman kept quiet because she couldn't care less.

They drank and talked business, and then Metus started complaining that his motorbike was all rusty and squeaked a lot.

"And the exhaust pipe's bent," he said, resentfully.

"The rings, the pistons, the battery, they'll all have to be replaced, but then you watch her go!" said Rafail, scything the air with his open hand.

> "The truck won't go.
> The starter's bust,
> From the cab climbs the driver,
> All grime and dust,"

sang Metus.

And they had another drink.

"The rings, the pistons, the exhaust – we can get all that," said Rafail.

"Where from?" asked Metus in astonishment. "There ain't any anywhere."

"Oh-ho-ho!" said the man of Eastern origin, making a wry face. "There's a countryman of mine in town, and he's got rings and pistons and mistons, and we can clean it and sheen it – he's got everything."

"You're lucky then," said Metus in admiration. "You people have fellow countrymen everywhere."

And he immediately set to work.

"Mama," he said officiously. "Tell my wife that she's not to upset herself, we're just going into town for some spare parts."

Mama kept quiet.

"It's all for your benefit. One tries, one tries," explained Vasily, pulling the family savings of forty roubles out of the chest of drawers. "We'll be back by tonight."

"We're going in the truck," explained Private Rafail.

And off they went. But they didn't come back by nightfall.

They didn't come back next morning either.

Then his new slip of a wife said to old Makarina:

"Mama, maybe the traffic cops have got them."

"No, daughter, the traffic cops can't get them, because Rafail is in the army. Only the military police can get them, and then if they did, they would let Vaska go, because he's a civilian," answered the wise old woman.

And she added:

"They're off on the bottle somewhere, the parasites."

And sure enough, they'd been on the bottle, and a lot more besides.

Private Rafail made his way back to them towards evening. Made his way back under his own steam to be precise, not in the truck. He was holding a guitar with a fine red cord in his hands, and he addressed Makarina Savelevna directly, saying:

"That's all there is to it, ma. Don't weep, don't sob, but your son's in prison and they're going to throw the book at him."

And he told a terrible story of how, once again, Metus's "I await a love that's true" had let him down.

. . . Of course they hadn't found any spare parts, because the wife of his fellow countryman, a fat old cow, told them that he'd gone off somewhere.

"Well, where could he have gone to? Why should he go anywhere?" said the friends, dubiously.

"How should I know?" said the old cow, and wouldn't let them in the house.

So then they thought they'd wait for him, and went off to the park of culture and rest, where a wind orchestra was playing, where lectures about Mars and astronauts were being given, and also where they sold tumblers of rosé port.

They were in a trellised summer house, overgrown with ivy.

"I await a love that's true," sang Metus promptly and shook Rafail by the shoulder, who opened one eye and mumbled:

"Ah! Get off, man. Let me have a rest."

And he lay his head on the table.

Then Metus went out on to the nice gravelled path through the park, and started walking along, admiring the culture that surrounded him, and also the rest.

And suddenly – yes, it really was suddenly and not somehow or other – straight out of the blue, he saw the one whom he'd apparently been waiting for all his life.

"I await a love that's true," he sang once more, as he went up to the woman.

"Really?" she enquired hoarsely, sporting a bruise under her eye, beautiful black hair, ear-rings, and painted lips with a cigarette between them. There was a ladder in her stocking, but she was as utterly fair and graceful as a fallow deer. "Really?" the woman asked again. "You're not taking the piss, are you?"

"Stop bitching, I love you. Ooh, you're so nice," said Metus, putting his arms round her.

"Oh, get on with you!" said the woman, bursting out laughing just as she'd burst out bitching. "I fancy you. I fancy you, but have you got any cash?"

"Yes, I have," said the simple-hearted Metus. "There you are."

And he showed the woman a ten-rouble note.

"Oh! There's a good boy!" said the woman, feeling quite herself, and she sang out:

> "'Come on, ol' girl,' says he,
> 'Buy a bottle of booze for me,
> If you don't buy booze for me,
> I'll find another ol' girl,' says he.

Hee-hee-hee."

"One that's great, that's huge," sang Metus in response to her.

Then they drank the booze in the same summer house overgrown with ivy, where Rafail had by now finished his rest and was chatting with some people, making frenzied gestures with his hands. He congratulated Metus, lasciviously smacked his lips, took a look at the lady and drank to their health.

Then he stayed behind in the summer house, while they went swaying off along the nice paths, arms around each other, smoking and, by their appearance, providing amusement for the young people resting there.

And time passed. And night fell over the earth, sowing the dark sky with a fine sprinkling of stars, and the moon shone. It shone and shone, and it shone on the ingenuous festival of love being celebrated by Vasily Metus and the black-haired citizen there in the centre of the park, in the bushes, right behind the plaster-cast statue of the hart.

Then, you see, a policeman showed up. Obviously, the park attendant had told him. The policeman disturbed them. He came up and discovered the love birds, pulled Metus off her, set him on his feet, and somewhat equanimously gave him the following advice:

"Look 'ere mate, you'd better just clear off out of it nice and quiet like."

And to the citizen he said:

"And if I catch you 'ere again, Tanya, you'll 'ave yer 'ead shaved, yer tart."

"I wasn't doing nothing," whined Tanya.

Now Metus ought to have heeded the voice of an experienced man, gone and found Rafail, and cleared off out of it, cleared off out of it hell for leather.

But, fool that he was, he upped and started yelling at the policeman, charged at him like a bull, and let him have it in the head with a love-smitten fist.

The policeman blew his whistle, Metus took another swipe. Rafail came over when he heard the whistle and restrained Metus from any further ill-considered acts.

But no matter how he cajoled, no matter how he pleaded with the policeman, no matter how many mountains of Eastern gold currency he promised him, the policeman was immovable, and Metus was taken away.

"He felt very insulted," explained Rafail. "And well, I wonder, wouldn't you, ma, if someone started punching your head in, while you were carrying out your official duties, and just offering a bit of good advice."

The old woman burst into tears and said:

"I always said he was a fool. Do you think they'll stick him in the nuthouse rather than prison?"

"I don't know. I don't know. Better get some rusks baked for him. What else can you do?"

And Rafail went off, adding in anticipation and by way of a joke:

"Don't cry, Mama, or I won't send you any dried apricots."

And so he went off somewhere with his guitar. He didn't even say anything about his truck, where they'd put it for him.

Don't cry, he says, but how can you help it? Eh?

And the old woman cried. She cried, but was already getting together the first food parcel: potatoes, gherkins, rusks.

"What do you think, Maria, will they let him have gherkins?" she asked his slip of a wife.

But she was turned to stone. When she heard what had happened, first of all she turned all red, then she turned to stone and turned speechless.

She was speechless for a few days, and then she spat, and with awesome strength set about carting hay and firewood for the houses and digging the potatoes.

Then she made a trip into town and got herself taken on by a recruiter to go and work on the island of Shikotan gutting fish. She didn't go to the trial.

"I'm sorry, Mama," she said, bowing to the old woman. "I'll send you a bit whenever I can, but I can't live with Vaska, because he's a parasite."

"He's a fool," said the old woman.

By this time everyone knew all about what had happened. There was a trial. And Vaska got eighteen months. But they promised him that if he behaved himself he could be freed "halfway through" or sent off to "do compulsory community work at a chemicals plant or somewhere".

"Now just you see, there'll be an amnesty of some sort," people said to Makarina Savelevna to comfort her.

So now Vaska is behind barbed wire. His wives are here and there. Rafail was demobbed and went away.

Vaska was given eighteen months, and no one knows what he is going to do when he comes out. He'll probably start by getting shacked up again.

But for the present no one needs him. Is that the way it is apparently? Who needs him? He hasn't got a wife. Rafail has gone away. Is that the way it is apparently?

No, that's not the way it is.

For old Mama Makarina Savelevna is silently and stubbornly waiting for her fool, whom she gave birth to, brought up, bathed in a tub where he said his first "googy-googy" baby words, nursed him, bought him an ABC book and gave him the strap for getting bad marks at school.

She is waiting, hoping for the money to come from the distant island of Shikotan, for the dried apricots and for the Lord God.

She is waiting, living on potatoes, pickled cucumbers, beetroot, cabbage and mushrooms – in a word, on everything that you don't need to pay a penny piece for and which grows free of charge on the landlords' native land.

Translated from the Russian by Robert Porter

JULIAN MAZOR

The Munster Final

While a light rain fell, a forty-five-year-old American sat behind the wheel of a white Ford Escort parked on the main street of Ennistymon, a town in the west of Ireland. He was listening to the radio. A voice announced that there would be a reunion of the Tenth Infantry Batallion that had served in the Emergency. The weather forecast followed, rain and occasional sunny spells over the entire nation.

As he lit a cigarette, a slight tremor played about his mouth and the corner of his left eye. Inhaling deeply, he let out a fine stream of smoke which passed out the car window and faded into a background of low sombre buildings and cloudy sky. Then he leaned forward and rested his head against the steering wheel. "Cheer up, Harry," he said, but he was a depressed personality, serving in an emergency of his own.

He was waiting for a woman with whom he had been living for two years. Her name was Ardis, and she was buying provisions in a local market for their rented cottage farther north in County Clare. Having come over only the day before on the ferry from Swansea to Cork, they were on their way to the cottage for the first time.

A month before Ardis had given him a warning. After their week in Ireland, he either married her or they went their separate ways.

Pressing two bags of groceries against the car with her body, she used her free hand to open the rear door, then placed the bags in the back seat. Then she stood up and raised her face to the light rain, rubbing her eyes with the backs of her fingers. She was an attractive woman, pink and ruddy in the moist air, but she appeared vulnerable and uncertain, with small lines at the corners of her eyes. She was thirty two.

Standing for some time by the rear fender, she avoided looking at him, pulling aimlessly at a stray wisp of auburn hair. Finally, she took a deep breath and walked over to him, turning up the collar of her raincoat.

"Why don't we take a walk, Harry. It might do us good," she said. She had hoped to sound cheerful but felt embarrassed by a slight stridency in her voice. Humiliated by her helpless desire to please him and by what she saw in herself as dishonesty and emotional confusion, she hated him at that moment as much as she hated herself.

He let out a small groan and got out of the car.

As they walked along the main street, Ardis observed that she had never seen so many bars in one little town.

"We might as well have a drink," Harry said. It was about four o'clock in the afternoon.

They descended a narrow iron stairway and entered a dim room. An elderly bird-like woman was seated at a table near the door, talking to a man whose hands were folded by his glass.

"Well, come right in," the woman said, smiling and rising from the table. She led them to a dark wooden bar on the other side of the room.

Harry had a little trouble getting up on the stool.

"He has a back problem," Ardis said.

"Oh, the poor man. Would you care to sit at a table then?"

"No, this is fine," Harry said.

He had a shot of Jamieson's and a glass of water on the side. The old woman put down a draught Guinness for Ardis.

"May health and joy go with you," the woman said.

"Thank you," Ardis said. "May it go with all here."

Harry raised his glass in a salutary gesture and drank some whisky, then water as a chaser.

"I can't get over all the bars in Ennistymon. It's amazing," Ardis said.

The old woman smiled.

"Yes, there are twenty-three here now. But in my father's time, there were forty-three. And there were coopers, five blacksmiths – a different place altogether," she said, without regret. "Well, may all change be for the better."

"God bless you," Harry said, and he had another drink before they started on the road again.

"Are you all right?" Ardis said, as they drove along.

Harry nodded, but he was so numb with exhaustion that he could scarcely keep awake, and he wondered if it was the whiskey that had made him tired, though it never had before. It might be hypoglycemia, he thought, the low blood sugar syndrome that he had read about recently. At times he seemed to have all the symptoms, the hunger and nervousness, profuse sweating, alternate pallor and flushing of the face, and vertigo. He thought he was having a little vertigo at that very moment.

They began the final leg of their drive through the grey limestone hills of the Burren. Meandering through the twisting turns of Corkscrew Hill, they descended with a view of the bay into Ballyvaughan.

It was about seven in the evening, but there was still plenty of summer light, though the sky had clouded up again.

"How lovely," Ardis said, genuinely moved.

It was her first time in Ireland, but Harry had been there seven years before with his wife and young son. They had lived for a year in County Galway on a small inheritance from his aunt. His marriage had ended in divorce a few years after their return to America. He had been resigned to its ending, but leaving his son was the saddest experience he had ever known, and he had not gotten over it, nor did he think he ever would.

As for his future with Ardis, or without her, he was unable to clear up the doubts in his own mind. It wasn't that he didn't care for her. He was very fond of her, but the idea of settling down and starting over with a new wife unnerved him and oppressed him almost to the point of illness. After all he had been through, he no longer believed in the possibility of conjugal happiness; and the last thing he wanted at this time of his life was to get involved in a doomed marriage. He really liked her. He knew that she was a good person, and that she loved him more than he deserved. But he felt depressed, and he often told himself that it was Ardis and her sorrowful nature that depressed him, though he knew the painful truth: that he, not her nature, was the cause of her sadness, and what made him unhappy was his awareness of what he had done to her. If she could only smile occasionally from the heart; if she could only manage, even after all he had put her through, to show a little gaiety and light-heartedness and cheer him up somehow, then perhaps he might feel more inclined to marry her; but as it was she stood before him as a living accusation. When he was with her, he often felt the urge to get away for good, but no sooner had he decided to leave than he would begin to miss her, and he would remain, tentative and double-minded and on the verge of leaving again. He was confused. He knew it. What he needed was more time to work things out.

"But you've had two years," she had told him.

It was true. He felt that he was ruining her life. And in spite of his recent talent for flight and evasion and self-apology and tricky rationalization, he was obsessed with his own guilt.

In her desire to please him and make him happy, and to have him love her, she had lived at first in a state of hope and exhilaration. It was only later, after things had gone wrong between them, after Harry through panic and guilt over the question of marriage had become unreasonable, hostile and critical of her slightest fault, it was only then that she had become a discouraged and unhappy person. Though she knew what a poor impression her unhappiness made on him, and tried in spite of everything to be cheerful and pleasant, her heart wasn't in it; she was shaken by the seriousness of her predicament, that time was passing, that she was getting older with nothing to show for her life. She hated to lose him, and loved him still; but the strain had become too much for her, and she had given him, sorrowfully and with regret, her ultimatum.

Did he love her? God, what was love? he thought. It was an illness from which you always recovered in time. Did he love her? He really couldn't say. Perhaps he did. But then, was it good for the duration? Perhaps he loved her today but he wouldn't tomorrow. Yet, whatever the truth, he didn't want to entirely lose her. It would be nice to see her regularly, to see her happy and pleasant, the way she used to be when they were just living together without talk of marriage and commitment. If she could only be reasonable and kind and largehearted about his difficulty, and not obsessed with security, which was only an illusion; for he felt that life was brief and uncertain and that you had to take it on the wing. And how much time did he have left, anyway? he thought. Not much. He wasn't that well. No, he didn't have time for that sad convention called marriage. But the thing is, he was very fond of her, he thought, and he wanted to get close to her, though not too close. He wished to be her friend and lover but at the same time not get too involved with her in ordinary life, not at least until he had worked things out in his own mind. Yes, he had to make up his mind, he thought. He had to make up his mind. In truth, he did not know what he wanted, saw no solution, and he hoped for a miracle.

"She lives on the main street," Ardis said, as they passed a small hotel. "There, Harry, the house with the red shutters." Ardis got out of the car and knocked on the door of the house where the caretaker lived. A thin woman in her fifties opened the door and peered out.

"Who is it you want now?"

"Deirdre O'Callahan, please."

"About the cottage, is it?"

"That's right," Ardis said.

"Deirdre, it's the Americans," the woman yelled inside the house.

"I'm coming now," a voice rang out, and then a small pretty woman with reddish hair came to the door.

"How do you do?" she said, fastening the belt of her raincoat and holding out her hand. "The McNeills wrote that you were coming, but I expected you yesterday."

"We moved slowly," Ardis said. "I hope it didn't inconvenience you."

"Not at all, but when you weren't here at half-eleven, I began to wonder," she said. She was about twenty-five, lightly freckled and with blue eyes. Harry admired her at once, thinking that she had a gravity and calmness seldom found in American women of her age.

"Well, if you'll follow me out, I'll take you to the cottage. It's just a few miles from here," she said.

She started up the engine of her car, a small brown Morris Minor, and they followed her farther east along the coast road.

In a little while, they turned off into a side lane that went part way up a hill. A white cottage with a red slate roof was built on its slope, and it looked out on Galway Bay.

Deirdre pointed to the hills behind them.

"You're on the Burren. All the hills along the coast here are part of the Burren. You can climb up and find lovely wild flowers, but you mustn't uproot them. They were brought here by the glacier," she said. She nodded toward the cottage.

"Well, please make yourselves at home while I prepare the tea. Scones I made earlier, and they need only to be warmed."

They sat down at an oval table by a window that looked out on a mist over the water. The scones were on the table with a plate of butter and a jar of rhubarb preserves. A turf fire burned in the grate.

"It was so nice of you to do this," Ardis said, smiling.

"Oh, it was nothing at all," Deirdre said. "Well, what are your plans now? Do you plan to tour about?"

"Harry has been to Ireland before. He's going to show me some of it."

"Ah, that's good. There are Norman castles nearby and an old stone fort, and there are the megalithic tombs and the Cave of Allwee, and the Burren itself. But there's one other thing that you might enjoy while you're here, and that's the Munster Final. It's for the hurling championship of the province, and County Clare is in it this year, against Cork. Clare has not won in my lifetime, not since 1932, not in forty-five years, so you might be interested in seeing that. But I ought to tell you, it's a long drive to Thurles. It's in County Tipperary."

"When is it?" Ardis said.

"On Sunday."

"Do you think we could go, Harry?"

"Sure, why not," he said. He had always loved the sporting life.

After the tea, they looked about the cottage. There were four rooms in all, two small bedrooms and a large sitting room with a fire place that burned turf, since there was no wood available. Located near the front door was a small kitchen which included a metal sink, a refrigerator that had one compartment and was built low to the floor, and a gas stove. The cottage was without a telephone or a television, but there was a radio in good condition in the main bedroom.

As they walked Deirdre to her car, she stopped on the porch and raised the lid of a wooden box. "Your turf's in here, for burning in the grate," she said. "If you need me for anything, please come by the house. Somebody's usually there, and I'll get your message. Well, goodbye then. I'll bring you lettuce from time to time, and tomatoes. My uncle has a vegetable garden."

"Was that your mother at the door?" Ardis said.

"Oh, no, it was the mother of my husband."

"We hope to meet him and have you both to dinner while we're here."

"That's kind of you, but my husband and I are separated. He lives in Dublin now."

Later, in the dusk, Harry and Ardis sat on the porch and watched the sky and water. The mist had cleared away, and the lights of Galway sparkled on the far shore. About a half mile towards the water, there was a farm that bordered an inlet. The farm buildings and a martello tower on a small peninsula beyond were in silhouette.

"It's so peaceful and lovely," Ardis said.

"It is," he said, feeling oppressed.

In the morning, they went down to the farm near the water to buy some fresh eggs. Walking down from their cottage, they crossed a field, then climbed a low stone wall, following a path through another field until they came to a stone farmhouse. Ardis knocked on the door, and a small woman with grey hair and wearing wire-rimmed glasses looked out the window. Harry said that they were Americans living in the McNeill house, and that if possible they would like to buy some eggs from her.

"So it's eggs you want," she said.

She invited them inside and put fresh eggs in a paper bag for them. When Harry tried to pay her, she said, "It's all right. I don't want any money today. You can pay me next time." The kitchen had white rough plaster walls, and there was an open hearth with a hanging black pot above an iron grate. On the far wall was a picture of Jesus of the Sacred Heart.

It was the O'Ryan farm.

They walked outside with Mrs O'Ryan. Several sheep were in the pasture. Mr O'Ryan waved his cap at them from a distant field as they walked to the barn. Inside, the O'Ryan's son, a twelve-year-old boy, was milking a cow. Ardis asked him if he was going to fill the bucket with milk.

"Oh, no, it takes two milkings to fill a pail," the boy said, smiling. "But I'll fill it in the evening."

"God bless you," Harry said.

That afternoon, they drove along the coast road until they came to a ruin by the water. It was from there that Ardis wished to climb one of the hills of the Burren, and Harry had agreed to try. It was the least he could do for her, he thought. Parking the car near the ruin, they walked across the road to the hill called Cappanwalla. It was slightly over a thousand feet high.

With Ardis leading the way, they began to climb. It was cool and cloudy, with the threat of rain.

The lower part of the hill was primarily underbrush, briars, grass and lichen. Farther up, they climbed two stone walls and made their way over rocky limestone with large fissures. Harry found that the physical exertion was making him out of breath and irritable. He watched her far ahead of him, moving through a slope of wild flowers, yellow and purple ones, thyme and bluebells. She turned and waved and shouted encouragement.

Harry climbed slowly to the area of wild flowers, and then stopped and rested, breathing in the fragrance.

Near the top, she held out her hand for him and pulled him up. Stepping on cracked, flaking limestone slabs that were full of erosion holes, they climbed higher to a summit of green vegetation.

From there they could see the Aran Islands, Galway, the twelve bens of Connemara, and stone walls on green land.

Harry was still out of breath, and his heart rate seemed abnormally rapid to him.

She saw that he was tired, and she put her arms round him. "Harry, maybe this was too much for you. I'm sorry."

"No, I'm fine. I'm really all right," he said. He sat down on the ground and lit a cigarette.

She knelt beside him.

"Harry, please listen to me now. I can't just let the days pass without saying what's on my mind. This is our last chance. If we don't get married, I think it will be a tragic mistake. Years from now you'll regret it very much." He groaned and shook his head, not so much out of disagreement but that he found the whole subject distasteful. "Harry, I love you, and I know that deep down you really love me, too. I know that or I wouldn't still be here. But this is our last time together, and I find it very sad, very poignant. You're a very intelligent person, but you're so troubled by this that your mind isn't even working. I think if we got married, you'd find that we'd be good for each other. And we'd be happy. I honestly believe that. I'm quite convinced of it, Harry. But you have to show a little courage."

"Ardis, I haven't resolved it yet," he said.

"You haven't resolved it yet? What does that mean?" she said. "What do you mean, you haven't resolved it?"

"I have doubts. I need more time."

"Harry, you've had worlds of time, you know that. We have only a few days left. And more time wouldn't resolve your doubts. It would just deepen your confusion. Everyone has doubts. In the final analysis, you just have to take a chance." Some white gulls flew low over the water. He could see some men in a small fishing boat. "I'm not pleading my case, Harry. Not exactly. I'm just trying to appeal to your intelligence."

"Ardis —" he said, unable to say more, and he shook his head and made a small wave of his hand.

Looking stricken, she stood up and walked away from him.

He took a deep breath and shook his head. He knew that he had been a lot braver the first time he considered marriage, but then he had been ignorant of all the things that could go wrong, even between two people with the best will in the world.

"Well, I'm going," she said, and she began to go down the side of the hill with great single-mindedness.

She was going to leave him, she was really going to leave him this time, he thought, as he rose to his feet; and he felt heartsick already at the prospect of separation; but there was nothing he could do about it.

The descent was hard on his knees. He tore his pants on the briars, and his legs began to bleed. He felt sort of an aura, a prelude to a spasm in his lower back. It was a relief to get down on the road and back in the car again. The physical comfort that he felt more than compensated for her silence and his mental anguish.

When they got back to the cottage at about five in the afternoon, Harry went right to bed and didn't leave it until the next day.

On the following morning as they entered County Galway and Harry saw the familiar terrain he remembered from seven years before, he thought of his former wife and his son and of all the changes that had taken place. He was so moved that he could hardly speak.

He and Ardis were on their way to Galway city to play tennis and do the laundry. Not too far past Oranmore, Harry slowed down and parked outside a grocery store.

"I knew the owners," he said.

It was the store that he and Wanda had patronized, and the proprietors, John and Kate McBride, had become friends of theirs.

Harry saw Kate in the rear of the store. She was behind the counter, reading the paper and drinking a cup of tea. Aside from having gained a little weight, he did not think she had changed much.

Ardis remained up front while he walked back.

"Hello, Kate," he said.

She looked mystified, frowned, then her face broke into a wide grin.

"Oh, no, it can't be. It's Harry," she said, coming out from behind the counter. She put an arm round him and squeezed his shoulder. "Well, I never thought I'd see you again. The other day John remarked how people you're fond of disappear and you don't see them until the next world. He'll be sorry he missed you. He went to Roscommon to see his sick mother." She looked up front and saw Ardis and said in a low voice, "Oh, you've got a new one."

Harry explained that he and Wanda had been divorced for almost four years.

"Divorced? You and Wanda? Well, I hope you're happy now," she said, with a note of reproval in her voice. "And how is Wanda – and dear little Walter?"

"I think Wanda's all right. She married again. As for Walter, he's not so little anymore. He's nine years old."

She looked towards a back room.

"Megan, come here," she said. A willowy girl with brown hair and green eyes came out. She was about ten.

"Look who's here. It's Harry – the American. Do you remember him? It's little Walter's da. You remember Walter, don't you?"

"Yes, I remember him," she said, smiling shyly.

"I can't believe it. The kids have changed, and we've remained exactly the same," Harry said.

Kate laughed.

"Of course, you look younger. Are you back for long, Harry?"

"Only for a week. We're at a cottage near Ballyvaughan."

Harry waved to Ardis. She came back, and he introduced them.

"So, you married Harry. Well, good luck to you. You'll need it," Kate said. "Tell her I'm only joking, Harry."

Harry smiled. He thought of explaining to Kate that they weren't married, that they only lived together, but he felt the news would have been a shock to her moral system, as Ireland had not yet caught up with much of the western world.

"It's good being back in Galway," he said.

"It's here you should stay, not Clare. Down there all they think of is the Munster Final. Well, good for them, but Cork's going to win," she said. "Are you going to it, Harry?"

"We might."

"And do you know about hurling then?"

"Very little," he said.

She looked at Ardis.

"Well, ignorance never stood in his way," she said. "One thing about Harry is that he always enjoys himself."

He had to smile. The Harry she described had long since departed.

"It's been very nice meeting you," Ardis said, as they were leaving.

"Take good care of him. He needs all the help he can get," she said, smiling. "Goodbye, Harry, come back and see us before you leave."

"God bless you," Harry said, as he put his arms round her. He felt very moved at seeing her again.

They passed the greyhound track and continued on into Eyre Square. After showing Ardis the square and the cathedral and the River Corib, he drove along the beach front and turned right on the road to the Galway Tennis Club.

With its brown wall and wooden gate, it was the way he had remembered it when he had last walked through with Wanda and young Walter. The grass courts appeared on the right, but instead of being deserted as they usually were at that late morning hour, there were players on all of them. A tournament was in progress.

Harry and Ardis stood outside the small clubhouse, where a number of players speaking German and French were sitting round a few small tables, drinking Coca-Cola.

"It was an entirely different atmosphere seven years ago," Harry said. "All the players in the tournament were Irish, and mainly from this part of Ireland. A Dublin player was considered exotic. And the tournament itself was not played in the morning or afternoon, but, as I recall, in the twilight."

"A Celtic twilight," Ardis said. "You sound so disappointed, Harry."

"Do I?" he said.

He ordinarily liked an international flavour but not there. The truth was that he regretted all the changes that he saw. He had grown conservative and preferred to live in the past that he knew and remembered, in that time when he was light-hearted and alert and winning, not leaden with fear and confusion. He embarrassed himself now, and the past was very appealing to him.

Harry had hoped to get a guest membership, as he had done when he was last in Ireland, so that they might play for an hour or two. But the club was not available for private play until the end of the tournament. They decided to leave.

On the way out, he saw one of the old men he remembered who had maintained the courts.

"Hello, Frank, do you remember me?" he said, extending his hand. "I'm Harry, the American who came here seven years ago. I gave you a lift to Salthill a few times. We had a drink together before your kidney surgery."

The man's eyes strained for recognition.

"Oh, yes, I remember you," he said, polite and bewildered; and Harry knew that he had been forgotten.

"Well, it's good seeing you, Frank," he said.

The man nodded earnestly.

"And it's good seeing you, and may you have a good day now."

They drove back to Eyre Square and parked the car. Harry took the bag of laundry from the back seat.

"I'll take care of this. Why don't you look around, Ardis," he said.

He pointed out the streets he thought she would find interesting and mentioned some old book stores that she might enjoy.

They arranged to meet in an hour and a half at the square, by the statue of the storyteller, Padraic O'Connaire.

"This is awful for you," she said.

"I've seen Galway many times. I don't mind," he said. Actually, he preferred it, he was so depressed.

Carrying the bag of laundry, he walked to a washeteria on the top of Prospect Hill. From a nearby construction site came noise of generators and jackhammers. A mist of fine dust hovered over the street. He found it hard to breathe.

He went inside and put the clothes into a machine, and, after adding soap from a dispenser, started it up. He sat down on a chair against the wall and picked up a day-old newspaper from the floor and began reading the front page stories of violence and death in the north, of bombings and assassination, of murder, of random and accidental killing, of the death of innocent bystanders. Wanting to be cheered up, he turned to the sporting news. He was about to read a story on the Munster Final when he felt suddenly tired; he put the paper down and looked at a blue wall on the far side of the street, and though he tried not to think of anything, he began to think of Ardis. It occurred to him that no matter what decision he arrived at concerning marriage, it would be the wrong one. It was true that he didn't want to marry her, but at the same time he feared the loneliness of their separation. As he sat there with a vision of himself growing old alone, sitting in bars for the sake of conversation and human warmth, he tried as he had often done in the past to imagine himself married to Ardis, settling down in the small routines of domestic life. He imagined himself, for example, going regularly to Schenectady, NY, to visit her family. The thought depressed and frightened him, and he became light-headed and faint. He was too old, too nervous, he told himself, to go through all that again.

An old woman came through the door with her laundry in a plastic bag. She was in no hurry to get on with the wash, and she sat down and smoked a cigarette before putting her clothes in a machine.

Harry put his wet clothes in a Loadstar dryer, and then he sat down beside her.

"How are you?" he said.

"Not well at all, but I'm not complaining."

Harry nodded sympathetically.

"Well, who's going to win the Munster Final?" he said.

"Cork. Clare doesn't deserve to win. The people there are daft, and I won't be sad when they lose at Thurles. I'll raise my glass to the side from Cork."

She stood up and sighed, and put her clothes in a washer.

Harry looked through the window of his dryer and watched the clothes go limp as the cycle ended. He folded the laundry on a table and then placed it in his bag.

"Well, goodbye and good luck," he said, waving to the woman.

"We all get what we deserve. Luck doesn't enter into it," she said.

Outside, it was warm for Ireland, and the air in the narrow street was heavy with fumes and dust.

He had about half an hour before meeting Ardis again, and after he walked back to the square and put the laundry in the trunk of the car, he sat down on a bench near the statue.

Feeling tired, his back bothering him, he watched the traffic move around the centre of the city. Exhaust fumes irritated his throat and nasal passages. He went into a paroxysm of coughing, which lasted for nearly a minute. A feeling of weakness came over him. He wiped his face with a handkerchief, and he thought that he felt worse than he had in a long time.

A man and woman in their twenties walked by, laughing.

"I don't believe you, Conor. You're too outrageous," the young woman said.

"I don't care. What do I care?" he said, and he began to laugh harder than before. She took his arm and pressed it affectionately to her side.

Harry found the contrast between them and himself unspeakably painful. God, to be young again, he thought, and he continued to envy them long after he couldn't see them anymore.

A little later, Ardis arrived, with a few small parcels. He was not glad to see her.

"I found some sailing prints and some wonderful maps of the region," she said, smiling. "I had a lovely time, Harry. But I missed you." He nodded. It seemed to him that she was only pretending to be happy in order to please him, that she was being insincere. He would have preferred an open declaration on her part of sorrow or blame, not this false good humour with its depressing unreality. It was genuine feeling that he needed, and he only wished that she was capable of it. Was that too much to ask? he wondered. And he felt a lingering suspicion, always with him, that he was being unfair to her again.

During lunch at the Great Northern Hotel, Harry was reticent and shamefacedly polite. Afterwards, during a long silence, he watched her write postcards to her parents and sister and a favourite aunt, and he was touched by her real affection for her family.

Later they drove to the waterfront and strolled along it, passing through the Spanish Arch, and looking at the ships and small boats in the harbour.

"Harry, thanks for showing me Galway," she said, with a remoteness and formality that nearly broke his heart. It was as though she were already fading from his life, and he had a feeling of grief.

On the way home, a man in the road shouted something unintelligible, and then he shouted again. "Clare will win!" He smiled and waved, and Harry waved back and drove on.

Back at the cottage, they ate a supper of poached eggs, potatoes, salad and wine; and then, feeling tired, with the sky filled with orange light, they turned in early, as they were going to the Munster Final in the morning.

Ardis went right to sleep, but Harry couldn't fall asleep for some time. He lay in bed and listened to the radio, to a programme called 'Across the Water'. It was dedicated to staying in touch with the Irish who had gone to England. These transplanted Irish men and women living in Irish enclaves across the Irish Sea spoke of their present life in London or Liverpool or in some other English city, with an air of homesickness for the towns they had left behind. It seemed, Harry thought, that life everywhere was longing and regret.

He heard a programme about prison life in Ireland, about the deprivations experienced in prison, of the loss of privacy of the prisoner, of the disappearance of identity, the loss of power over his own life, of the loss of hope. The speaker said that there were many ramifications of the loss of freedom, but the main one was the effect on the personality of the prisoner. Freedom was necessary for personal development. A man must make mistakes in order to learn. And this was also to be considered. The prisoner was deprived of sensory life. All the stimuli needed to feed his identity and personality were denied him. Total deprivation occurred in solitary confinement. It was almost impossible under those conditions to retain the personality intact, for we needed continuous stimulation to remain ourselves. Problems served to identify us. Prison life was an anaesthetic. There was an awareness that one was less than a person, less than a human being. A prisoner is forced into a routine, and he ends up in a numbed condition, out of touch with his deepest feelings, his spontaneity gone. A former prisoner told of his experience after his release. "I couldn't bring myself to go back to the prison, though I had promised to bring things to my friends still inside, to do errands for them and to stay in touch. I felt guilty of a kind of betrayal, but I couldn't go back for the place had such a terrible effect on me."

They left for the Munster Final in the morning. It was Sunday. After the rain of the previous night, the sky was a clear rich blue, the air was fresh with the smell of grass and hay and wild flowers. Wet fields sparkled in the sunlight.

At Ennis they filled the car with gasoline, and then followed the main road to Limerick. They came upon a great procession of cars filled with Clare fans on the way to Thurles. Blue and yellow streamers were flying from many of the cars. On the slow ride to County Tipperary, they passed children on walls and by the road waving Clare colours. In the towns, people stood in doorways and leaned out windows, shouting, "Up Clare" and "Beat Cork".

"Up Clare," Ardis yelled out of the car window. She was genuinely excited. "I love it, Harry. I love it."

He felt a pleasant excitement himself, the false spring of the sporting life.

They parked the car on a grass field about a mile from Semple Stadium, and walked along the road with the crowd. On the way, some celebrants from Cork carrying a red and white banner and raucously singing surged past them.

Semple Stadium was brownish and old. At the ticket window, Harry purchased two general admission tickets. The reserved seating had been sold out for hours.

Inside the stadium, a preliminary match was in progress between two junior teams from Cork and Limerick. Finding no vacant seats in the unreserved sections, they looked for the standing room area. They were pushed along with the crowd, amidst much jostling, laughter, shouting and confusion.

A young man put his hand on the shoulder of an old priest and said, "If you're on your own, Father, you might come along with us."

Over the public address system, there was an announcement, "A little girl four years old by the name of Jane Hayes has been lost."

Harry and Ardis finally ended up standing behind a barrier at ground level in back of one of the goals. Large men pushed in from all sides, and the crowd roared as the teams came on the field.

"What a crush," Ardis said, ducking her head slightly.

They struggled for a position behind the barrier. Harry received an elbow in his ribs and Ardis was knocked sideways. He put his arm round her and led her away.

"Rough country lads," he said.

A deep masculine roar rose into the air, as they made their way to a small ground just outside the stadium, still within the main enclosure. People were picnicking there, sitting on lightweight folding chairs or half sprawling upon blankets on the grass. The excited voice of the commentator, reporting the introduction of the teams, came over a number of portable radios. When the game commenced, the crowd noise came over the radio and from the stadium itself, and at times the cheering nearly drowned out the voice on the radio.

It was sunny and pleasantly warm. They sat down on the grass. Harry read the programme and listened to the radio, and Ardis turned her face to the sun.

After a while, Harry went back inside the stadium with the hope of seeing some of the match. Returning to the barrier behind the goal, he managed to wedge his way in among the crowd of men. He stood on his toes and caught fleeting glimpses of the players swinging their hurling sticks, sending the small hard ball with a sharp crack in long high arcs through the air. He had no knowledge of hurling. He only knew that if the ball went under the horizontal bar of the goal it was one point; and if it went above the bar and between the uprights, it was three.

He stayed there for a good part of the first half.

When he joined Ardis outside, she was seated cross-legged on the grass, reading the programme.

"Listen to this, Harry. It says that the hurling stick is called a hurley. It's made of ash – that's the only wood suitable," she said. "I quote, 'No other timber has the same strength and elasticity to withstand the most severe strain and sudden shock which the hurley is subjected to on our fields of play.'" She smiled up at him. He genuinely hoped that she was having a nice time. For a few minutes, he imagined again the sorrow of their coming separation, and he hoped that she would remember some day how they had enjoyed themselves at the Munster Final, and think of him with affection.

They stayed out on the grounds, listening to the radio and taking the sun. Harry went inside the stadium a few more times to get the feeling of the crowd.

The match was nearly over, with Cork leading Clare by a small margin, when they came out on to the road. They hoped to avoid the traffic and get an early start home. As they started up the road, a huge cheer rose from the stadium, and shortly after the cheers died down, people came through the gates and on to the road.

A thin, angular man, with the blue and yellow colours of Clare hanging from his coat pocket, moved quickly past them.

"Who won?" Ardis said, smiling at him.

He stopped and glared at her.

"Go to bloody hell," he said, and then he turned and walked rapidly away.

"What's wrong with him?" Ardis said, her feelings hurt. "I thought it was only a game."

Harry shook his head.

"No, that's the whole point. It's more than a game to him. Much more than that," he said.

"He was rude to me – and for no reason."

"It's true that he was rude but not without a reason," Harry said. "I think it was the way you asked the question that upset him. You weren't deeply involved. He picked that up right away. You came at him from an unserious level, and it bothered him."

"Oh, I see. It was my fault that he was rude."

"I didn't say it was your fault," he said, feeling guilty. "It wasn't anybody's fault." Why was he so helplessly critical? he thought. Why did he hurt her at every opportunity? Was it simply because she had a talent for irritating him? Or did he have some special problem of his own? As they walked along, he wondered if he was a difficult person, or simply a person with difficulties; and the more he thought about it, the more confused, uncertain and hopeless he became.

They moved slowly with the crowd. Cork partisans waving red and white colours and shouting, "Up Cork", moved with wild hilarity up the road. The Clare flags and streamers were put away, or carried at some angle of defeat.

On the road to Limerick, Harry turned on the radio just in time for a special bulletin. "The ticket office of Semple Stadium at Thurles was robbed during the second half of the Munster Final by three armed men. The men were judged between eighteen and twenty-one years old. They warned the officials not to move. The sum taken was estimated to be about 24,000 punt." The weather forecast followed. Long spells of sunshine.

"And we never knew it," Harry said.

He looked over at her. She was slumped sideways in her seat, leaning against the door. Her mouth was slightly open, and she appeared drained and remote. It wasn't his fault, he thought. God knows, he had never promised to marry her.

Harry made a wrong turn in Limerick, and it took him twenty minutes to find his way again.

They were on their way to Doolin in County Clare. Earlier he'd promised Ardis that he'd take her to hear folk singing at one of the pubs there. The folk singing was a local tradition, a woman from Kinvarra had told them, that took place every Sunday and was "particularly attractive to Americans". He had never been to Doolin, and, until recently, had known it only as a place where a boat could be taken to the Aran Islands.

At about seven in the evening, they went into McGann's Pub and sat down at a small table and ordered draught Guinness. The room was crowded. A young man with a guitar was singing an Irish folk song. Some older men at a table across the room noisily interrupted him by singing a song of their own.

"Will you not show me the courtesy? Is that too much to ask of you?" he said.

After he finished, another man sang and played the guitar. His voice was thin and sincere, and his song was in Gaelic. There was relative quiet for a time, and some of the older patrons appeared contemplative. Then the room became noisy again. A man stood up and played an accordion and danced a jig. The waiters passed back and forth with large glasses of dark stout and lighter shades of ale. The young man with the guitar who had sung first played and sang again, and he was once more interrupted by the group of older men at the table across the room.

"For God's sake, be quiet now," he shouted.

A few of the older men laughed, and he resumed his singing, with a quaver in his voice that had not been there earlier.

Harry got up and went to the lavatory. On the way back to his table, he passed by the table of the older men, and they looked up at him.

"And who are you then?" one of them said, with a touch of belligerence. The man's face was ruddy, and he was missing some of his upper front teeth.

Harry nodded and smiled at him and was about to walk on, when the man said, "Where did you get that cap now? It looks like an old one."

"It was my father's. He gave it to me years ago," Harry said.

"Oh, it was your father's. Do you know the song, 'Me Father's Hat'?" He began to sing it, and though it was in English, Harry couldn't understand all of the words.

"That's an old cap," one of the other men said. "There were caps like that during the Easter Rising."

"Sit down and join us in a pint," the man missing the front teeth said.

"I should probably get back," he said, nodding towards his table across the room.

"Oh, she'll wait for you. Sit down, lad."

Some of the men made room for Harry, and he pulled up a chair and sat down at the table.

"What would you have?" the ruddy man said.

Harry hesitated, thinking of his glass of Guinness.

"Give him a pint of Smithwick light," the man said to the waiter. "And the same all round."

A man at another table stood up and began to dance to the sounds of a fiddle, and then he stopped abruptly, as though he had pulled a muscle in his side, and sat down again.

Filled glasses were put down.

"My name's Thomas," the ruddy-faced man said. "All at this table are from Corofin or nearby. This is Matt and Colum and Martin – and this is Joe. Joe has been living in New York." The man called Joe nodded. He was a thin, gaunt, elderly man. "Joe has come back to live for good in Ireland, not just for visits in the summer," Thomas said.

"New York is no longer a good place for an Irishman," Joe said. "I've come to live on my brother's farm. The social security will come each month."

Harry introduced himself.

"And you're an American yourself, by your accent," Thomas said.

"Yes, I am."

Harry finished the pint of Smithwick, and before he could leave, another pint was put down in its place; and though he said that he had to be going, the men insisted that he remain.

"You must show us the courtesy and finish your pint," Thomas said.

Harry looked over at Ardis. She regarded him with a look of suffering, and he felt that he was neglecting her.

After he finished his pint, he said, "Let me buy this round."

"Oh, you can't do that. It isn't right. Not in McGann's," Thomas said. He ordered the same all round, and then said, "And what have you been doing in Ireland?"

Harry said that he had not been doing much of anything, but on that day they had been to the Munster Final.

"The man was there. He was at Thurles," Thomas announced to the others. He looked at Harry and shook his head. "It's a bloody shame how the referee threw the Clare lad out of the game – and he had got eight stitches in his face, and yet *he* was called guilty!"

"And did you hear about the robbery? They got away with the whole bloody take," Colum said.

"No doubt they were Clare men," Matt said.

"If it was one, I'd say it was a Clare man, but since it took three, they are from Galway," Colum said.

"And the game itself, that was a robbery!" Thomas said.

"We don't want to talk about the bloody game," Martin said. "To hell with County Cork."

"Speaking of Cork, here comes Desmond," Thomas said. "He's from Cork but is here visiting his wife's family. Of course, he's glad of the result."

"Oh, I don't care at all," Desmond said. He was a slightly-built, affable man, and he carried a small dog.

Harry made room for him, and Desmond sat down. Thomas introduced them.

"Jesus, he brought the mutt again," Colum said. "That dog can't get enough to drink."

Desmond laughed, and he ordered a pint of ale.

He told Harry that he was a coach driver, and that his profession took him all over Ireland.

"What I like most about all of the travelling is observing the differences in people," he said. "The people in Cork, for example, are more homely than the people in Dublin, who are more cosmopolitan. Of course, it's only my opinion."

"And what about the people here?" Thomas said.

"Oh, the people here are very odd, particularly the ones from Corofin," Desmond said.

The men laughed.

After he finished his ale, he said that he had to get back to his wife and her family. He shook hands with Harry, then stood up with his puppy.

"Goodbye to all here and good luck. Wave your paw at them, Sonny," Desmond said, and then he left.

Harry looked across the room at Ardis. She appeared embarrassed and confused, and she seemed to question him with her eyes, which seemed to say, "How can you go to such lengths to be unpleasant to me?" Although he felt guilty, he was unable to move.

"Have another one, Harry," Thomas said, and a glass of Smithwick was placed next to an empty glass which was then removed.

A man sang "Spencer Hill". Then he said something in Gaelic and slumped down in his chair.

"Did you hear this one?" Thomas said, nodding at Harry. "A priest was giving a sermon about whisky. 'Drink kills,' he said, and he illustrated the point by taking a live worm out of a small box he was carrying in his pocket, and then he drowned the worm in a glass of whisky. Then the priest poured some whisky in another glass and drank it down, and a man who was watching this said, 'But, Father, if drink kills, then why are you drinking that whisky?' and the priest said, 'I've got worms, man, and I've already demonstrated that whisky kills them.'" Thomas slammed a hand down on the table and threw his head back and laughed.

"He had worms, you see," he said.

"What I want to know, is drink more dangerous than music?" Colum said. "This priest said to me that it was music that makes the first assault, for it breaks down the nervous system, and then any craziness can enter."

Thomas shook his head.

"Craziness doesn't enter in such a case. It was there all the time. The music is just an innocent bystander." He turned to Harry. "And speaking of music, I played a tin whistle long ago, but now the lads get paid for it, and it isn't the same. A man from here recently came home with a packet of money for playing Irish music. It wasn't like that in my day, when it was played for fun and played for nothing."

He paused. "Well, Harry, you're not quite done, and here's another."
A pint of Smithwick was put down before him.

"Oh, no, I couldn't," Harry said.

"Did you hear that, Colum? Harry said he couldn't," Matt
said.

"Drink it or you'll get sick," Colum said. He laughed and put a
hand on Joe's shoulder. Joe looked pale and old, and his eyes were
tired.

"Well, you'll not see New York again," Colum said.

"He'll not miss it," Martin said. "It's not a good place for an
Irishman."

"Was it ever?" Colum said.

"Oh, yes, a long time ago," Joe said.

"What I want to know, is Ireland a good place for an Irishman?"
Thomas said. "The north is a bloody disaster, and in Dublin there
are gang rapes in Phoenix Park, and Galway city, well, that's become
a poor sad place. The courtesy's gone. The people don't even say
'sorry' when they jostle you on the street but push you aside without
a word. It's money on their brains, not kindness."

"It's the Common Market," Colum said.

"Well, here's to prosperity, at least," Martin said, raising his
glass.

"The saddest thing of all is the younger generation," Thomas said.
"They show no respect for anything."

"And what about you, Thomas?" Colum said. "What do you show
respect for?"

"I'm a courteous man," Thomas said.

Colum smiled and turned to Harry.

"He was a wild boy, and now he envies the younger lads, that he
can't be wild like them."

"He's still wild, but he's slow and can't keep up with them," Martin
said.

Thomas laughed.

"Oh, God, what lies they say about me," he said.

Harry finished his ale as Ardis walked over. He was surprised to
see her. He stood up and introduced her to the other men.

"You thought Harry had run away, but he had just gone across the
room," Thomas said. "Some go across the water, and you never hear
from them again."

Ardis smiled.

"She has a beautiful smile, Harry," Thomas said. "You had better not go far from her."

"I won't," Harry said. He shook hands with all the men at the table. "I wish I could repay your kindness," he said.

"Oh, we'll meet again," Thomas said.

"Yes, in heaven," Colum said.

It was late twilight, and a breeze with the smell of the sea passed through the town.

They got in the car, and Harry started up the engine. The car began to move down the road.

"Harry, the car is weaving."

"Don't worry," he said, but he felt light-headed and drowsy, and he had a hard time judging the road.

He pulled over and slumped forward with his head on the wheel. "I'll be all right in a minute," he said. "I know a good restaurant in Kinvarra."

"You'd better rest first, or we'll never get there," she said. She shook her head and sighed. Her feelings were still hurt from the way he had abandoned her in the pub.

Harry slumped down in the seat and half dozed, with the radio playing. A commentator was speaking of Gaelic football, of the time when Galway won the Connacht Final by beating Mayo, who had won in 1931. Galway and Mayo had met in nine Connacht Finals. Bobby Baker was one of the great heroes of Gaelic football. And Montclair and Jerry O'Malley were other Connacht players worthy of remembering.

He fell asleep to the sound of their names and slept for half an hour. He was all right when he woke up, except for a feeling of melancholy and a stiffness in his lower back.

The twilight was turning to dusk.

After they came round a curve, Harry saw in the distance, on the slope of a hill, an old trailer and a dilapidated car. In front of the trailer, a big pot was sitting over some dead coals. Suddenly, as the car approached, a man began to run down the side of the hill, frantically waving his arms. A teen-aged boy was with him.

"You better not stop. They're tinkers," Ardis said.

"Maybe they're in real trouble," he said. He went past them, then stopped and backed up the car.

He had always felt a little sorry for the tinkers, Ireland's itinerant population; but he felt uneasy in their presence.

The man wore a shabby pin-striped coat over a white T-shirt. He was smiling abjectly and carrying a piece of hose. Beside him stood a husky, slightly-stooped boy of about fourteen with a large metal bucket.

"My wife is sick. Can you spare some petrol?" the tinker said.

"What's wrong with your wife?"

"An ailment."

"I'll take her to the hospital," Harry said.

"No, the doctor is coming."

"If he's coming, then why do you need the gas?"

"To give to him for having used up his own. It's the least I can do since I have no money to pay."

"Well," Harry said.

"Harry, this is absurd," Ardis whispered.

He got out of the car.

"All right, I can give you a little," he said.

"May God keep you," the tinker said. "My boy will siphon some of your petrol." He made a sign to his son who walked over with the bucket, quickly removed the cap, and then blew into the hose, dropping one end into the tank and the other into the bucket. Harry could hear the gas begin to flow onto the bottom.

He tried to watch the siphoning, but the man moved between him and the boy.

"Would you have fags then? For my nerves," the tinker said.

Harry gave him what was left of a pack of cigarettes.

The tinker's son removed the hose from the gas tank and started to walk away with the bucket. Harry noticed that it was filled to the brim.

"Good lord, he filled the whole bucket!" he said.

"No, the bucket was partly filled when he started," the tinker said, backing away and smiling.

"Then why didn't you give *that* gas to the doctor?"

"Oh, it wasn't nearly enough. He's coming a great distance."

"Look, the bucket wasn't filled when he started. I heard the gas hit the metal bottom."

"Did you hear that then?"

The boy hesitated. His father shouted at him and struck him hard on the shoulder. Looking frightened and tilting to one side, he carried the bucket up the hill.

The tinker slowly backed up the slope.

"You have plenty left in your tank. May God bless you for your kindness," he said.

Harry stood by the car, feeling sick and light-headed; and then he got in and started up the engine and began driving down the road.

"What was that all about?" Ardis said.

He didn't say anything.

"I'll tell you what it was all about. You let him take advantage of you, to punish yourself."

He felt warm with anger, but he tried to be measured.

"Look, I know I was a bit of a fool. But my basic impulse was to be fair, to do the right thing," he said.

She laughed with sudden hysteria.

"The right thing? You don't know anything about that. Look what you're doing to me."

He excitedly raised one hand from the steering wheel.

"God, can't you ever be pleasant? You're so damned depressing," he said.

"I'm depressing? And what about you, Harry? You're the depressed personality of our time."

Harry raised a hand and waved it wildly.

"Well, you've depressed me," he said. "You never let up from morning to night, with your sighs and sadness and your litany of complaints. I'm really sick of you, Ardis."

Her eyes began to blink rapidly, then her mouth trembled.

"I can think of plenty that's wrong with you, too, Harry," she said. She shook her head, and her breath caught in her throat, and she gasped. Then she took a deep shuddering breath and tried to let the air out slowly. She wanted to be calm and retain what was left of her dignity. "You're selfish and arrogant and blind," she said in a tremulous voice. "You're an emotional invalid, a hypochondriac. I don't know why I ever loved you, Harry. But I really hate you now."

"I'm glad," he said.

She began to sob.

It was all over, he thought, feeling suddenly weary. It was finally obvious to him that there was not even a glimmer of hope for them, that they would separate, and the sooner the better. It was a relief, in a way, he thought.

Then the car lost power and the engine died. As he got out to look under the hood, he realized what was wrong.

"We're out of gas," he said.

Ardis leaned forward against the dashboard and continued sobbing. He looked at her through the car window.

"I'm going to Kinvarra for gas," he said. She looked up briefly, her face distorted and wet with tears, and then buried her face in her arms again.

Kinvarra was nearly two miles away. In the dusky light, Harry walked past fields with small herds of grazing sheep. What was wrong with him? he thought. He was getting old, nothing pleased him, and he displeased everyone. It was a hopeless situation.

A car passed, the first car he had seen. He forgot to hail the driver, then decided to walk all the way to Kinvarra.

The sky was filled with stars. It was one of the clearest nights he had ever known in Ireland, and one of the more beautiful days. He thought he would always remember it as the day he finally finished with Ardis, on the day of the Munster Final.

A breeze came out of the fields and chilled him. He had a headache and began to feel sick. After he had walked about half a mile, he decided to stop and rest. Feeling dizzy and slightly nauseous, he sat down on a stone wall. She was making him ill, he thought. It was bad to live in such an atmosphere, and it was making him sick and tired and old before his time, and he couldn't take it anymore. It wasn't right that he should feel such guilt and distress, he thought. He wasn't a bad person, not compared to all the really bad people in the world. He didn't deserve to be the target of her rancour and bitterness and her disappointment in life, and of his own tormenting conscience. He began to feel sicker, more nauseous; and there was now a mild pressure in his chest.

He looked beyond the wall to a field with a haycock. The grey light seemed to waver and bend, and he thought there was something wrong with his eyes. Some crows flew up in the sky. Part of him seemed to rise with them, and the sense of motion increased his nausea and vertigo. As he rose to his feet, he felt a sharp pain in his chest and a heavy pressure on his shoulders which forced him to sit down by a ditch on the side of the road. He broke into a sweat. His chest began to tighten, and the ground seemed to rise and then drop away from him. Holding on to the side of the ditch, he tried to smile and relax. "Cheer up, Harry," he said, but he was badly frightened, for it occurred to him that he was dying. "Oh, no, I've got to get gas. Ardis is waiting for me," he thought.

In order to calm himself, he lay down on his back and attempted to meditate. At first, he tried to concentrate on his uneven breathing, and then he closed his eyes and imagined a vacant white screen from which he tried to remove, as they appeared, all unpleasant impressions.

His breathing became laboured and his heartbeat rapid and irregular. Along with fear and intense disappointment, he experienced hurt feelings. It wasn't fair, he thought. It wasn't right. He rose to all fours, then collapsed on his side, sliding down the bank of the ditch. The ditch appeared like an open grave to him. Frightened, he staggered to his feet and climbed the stone wall, then went reeling into the pasture, ran for twenty yards, and fell.

He lay face downward on his arm, his cap beside him, and lost consciousness.

He dreamed that he was leaving his body and that he began to rise slowly into the air. Looking down he saw himself in the field, his head resting on his arm. As he continued rising, the details of the landscape grew smaller, and the whole region stretched out before him. He could see their white Ford Escort to the west and the town of Kinvarra farther to the east and small moon-lit lakes and fields and little houses and the winding road. Rising higher, he felt an unbelievable gladness that he was in a new realm, that his suffering was over. He could see the western coast of Ireland and the Atlantic Ocean, and then he found himself suspended above pale clouds, no longer rising. He reached upwards to go higher, but he began to go down, descending slowly to the west of Ireland, to County Clare, to the small field by the road to Kinvarra, until, hovering over his body, he said, "Oh, no," for he wanted to rise again, and he entered into himself.

Harry opened his eyes and looked helplessly around him. He got to his knees as another wave of pain and nausea swept over him, and he threw up in the field all the ale he had drunk in the pub at Doolin, and everything else.

He lay back and looked up at the night sky. The stars shone down in a vast profusion of benevolent light. A breeze passed over his face and body. He felt better. The nausea and pain were gone, and he could breathe easily again. He was very moved that he was still alive. He sat up and laughed. A flock of birds flew over him. Sheep bleated in the pasture. "I'm all right. It was indigestion," he shouted in the direction of the haycock.

It was then that he realized that he had decided to marry her. The more he thought about it, the more his conscience felt at peace; and this produced in him a sensation of light-headedness. Yes, he loved her, he thought. He had always loved her, and he would be kind to her now. He wouldn't have to leave her and never see her again and add that mistake to all the others he had known, and it would have been the worst mistake of all, he thought.

He looked forward to her happy surprise when he asked her to marry him over the wine at dinner. It made him glad to think that for once he would be the bearer of good news. In his mind's eye, he saw her looking nervous and confused at the change that had come over him, and then he asked her to marry him. "I don't believe you, Harry. Are you serious?" she said, and began to cry and asked through tears if it was true. "Yes, it's true, Ardis," he said, and he put his arms round her.

Harry rose to his feet and walked to the stone wall and climbed over it to the road, and then he began walking toward Kinvarra. The tightness and contractions of his body had eased; the stoop had gone from his shoulders. He swung his arms and moved with a confident and easy gait, his head erect. He was not himself. But after he had walked a mile, he became hesitant and uncertain, and he slowed down and stopped. "What do I think I'm doing? Am I out of my mind? I'm not ready. I need more time," he said. It seemed for a moment that he would not begin walking again.

But he continued on through moonlight and shadow, feeling a troubled happiness and wishing life were clearer; and as he approached the outskirts of Kinvarra and walked on into the town, where he discovered that its lone gas station was closed, he knew in his joyous and fearful heart that he would become again a married man.

JAVIER MARIAS

An Epigram of Loyalty*

FOR MONTSE MATEU

Mr James Laurence looked up. He had just that morning rearranged
the window display of the bookshop of which he was manager,
Bertram Rota Ltd, Long Acre, Covent Garden, one of the most
prestigious and discriminating second-hand bookshops in London.
He preferred not to overcrowd the window, displaying, at the most,
ten carefully chosen books or manuscripts, each one of which was
extremely valuable. They were the sort of editions guaranteed to
attract his usual clientele which consisted exclusively of distinguished
gentlemen and the occasional elegant lady bibliophile. That morning,
with some pride, he had placed in the window works such as *Salmagundi* by William Faulkner, never reprinted after that first 1932 edition (of 525 numbered copies) and the first edition of *Jacob's Room*
by Virginia Woolf, priced at £2,000. Although he himself set the
prices according to the state of the market, he could still never get
used to the fact that a book could be worth so much money. But
those books were nothing compared with Beckett's novel, *Watt*, typed
and corrected by the author himself and priced at £50,000. He had
had his doubts about putting such a valuable item in the window,
but in the end, he had decided to go ahead. It was a source of great
satisfaction to him and, after all, he would be there all morning and
all afternoon, stationed at his desk, keeping guard over the window.
Nonetheless, he felt uneasy and looked up from his desk whenever
he noticed someone, some figure, standing on the other side of the
glass. He even looked up when people walked past. This time, how-

---

* Although this episode from the life of the writer John Gawsworth is a new and
independent text, I should point out that only readers of my novel *Todas las almas*
(1989 [*All Souls*: 1992]) will be in possession of all the facts necessary to understand
it fully. J.M.

ever, he kept his head raised, for before him, at the window, was an unkempt-looking beggar. His hair was rather long and he sported a few days' growth of reddish beard. He was well-built and had a large, apparently broken nose. His clothes, like those of any mendicant, were shabby and of some indefinable colour. In his right hand he held a half-empty bottle of beer; but he was not drinking, that is, he did not from time to time raise the bottle to his lips, rather he was utterly absorbed, staring into the window of Bertram Rota. Mr Laurence wondered what he could be looking at. At Camus? One of the books on display was a copy of *La Chute* dedicated by the author himself and open at the appropriate page. But *La Chute* was on the right-hand side, next to the typescript of *Watt* and the beggar was looking to the left. On that side Laurence had placed *Salmagundi* and the second 1839 edition of *Oliver Twist*, priced at £300. Dickens was possibly of more interest to the beggar than Faulkner. He might have read Dickens at school, but not Faulkner, for the man was at least sixty years old, possibly more.

Mr Laurence looked down for a moment, believing (though without really thinking it) that perhaps that would make the beggar disappear. He looked up again immediately and, to his surprise, found that the man had in fact gone, there was no one there. He got up and, standing slightly on tiptoe, checked that everything in the window was still in order. Perhaps he should remove *Watt*, all £50,000 of it, or perhaps display only the first few pages. He returned to his seat and for a couple of minutes gave all his attention to the new catalogue he was compiling, but again he noticed a change in the light (someone was blocking the light coming from the street) and he felt obliged to look up. The beggar was back, bottle in hand (the beer would be completely flat by now), this time accompanied by two other beggars, each more ragged than the other. One was a young black man wearing green mittens and, in one ear, a single earring; the other, the same age as the first man, had a domed head that made the jockey's cap with which he tried to cover it seem even smaller; the cap (purple and white, although the purple had faded and the white was now yellow) was covered with large, greasy stains. The beggar with the reddish beard was urging them to draw nearer and when he had persuaded them to do so, all three of them stared in through the window, again at the left-hand side of the display, and the first beggar kept pointing at something with one grimy finger. He did so with pride, for afterwards, he would turn to his companions, first to the black man and then to the jockey, with obvious satisfaction. Was it *Salmagundi* or Dickens they were looking at? There was another item there too, a curious document consisting of an eight-page pamphlet which, in the previous catalogue, Laurence had entitled *An Epigram of Loyalty*. It contained three poems by Dylan Thomas never published elsewhere. Laurence opened a drawer and took out the catalogue in which it had first appeared, the 250th since the founding of Rota, and rapidly re-read the description: "Printed privately for the members of the Court of the Kingdom of Redonda, [1953]." Seventeen years ago. "Thirty commemorative copies, each numbered by John Gawsworth himself. Very rare. These three poems, not listed in Rolph's bibliography of Thomas, are statements of the poet's 'loyalty' to John Gawsworth, Juan I, King of Redonda, who, in 1947, named Thomas 'Duke of Gweno'. £500." Five hundred pounds, not bad for a few printed pages, thought Laurence. Perhaps that was what the beggars were looking at. He noticed that the one with the beard was now pointing at himself, tapping his chest with his forefinger. The others were also pointing, but in the way one points one's finger at someone else, at a person deserving of ridicule. Now the three of them were talking and arguing. Though Laurence could hear nothing of what they said, he was beginning to feel worried. Why had they chosen to stand for so long outside *his* shop window of all places? Sales at Rota did not depend on passing trade, but their disquieting presence there would certainly scare off any potential distinguished customers (only distinguished people bought books at Rota). He couldn't get rid of them though, they weren't breaking any law, they were simply looking at a window full of old books. But that particular window contained the typescript of *Watt*, and *Watt* was worth £50,000.

Laurence stood up and went over to them, still keeping to his side of the window. Perhaps they would go away if they saw him watching them from inside. He crossed his arms and fixed them with his blue eyes. He knew that one glance from those cold, blue, unfriendly eyes had often proved an effective deterrent in the past, one which he intended to deploy now to intimidate those three beggars. But the beggars were still embroiled in their argument, taking not the slightest notice of him, or else his presence, closer now, remained a matter of complete indifference to them. Now and then, the first beggar would again point at the window and Laurence was certain now that the focus of his interest was the *Epigram*. Laurence could stand it no longer. He opened the door and addressed them from the threshold:

"Can I be of any assistance?"

The beggar with the beard looked Laurence up and down, as if he were an intruder. He was considerably taller than Laurence, indeed, despite his years and his wretched appearance, he was very solidly built. The man could easily have knocked him to the ground, thought Laurence, or else the other two could have held him down whilst the first beggar grabbed and made off with the *Epigram* or, worse still, with the typescript of *Watt* worth £50,000. He regretted having opened the door. He was exposing himself to attack.

"Yes, yes, you can," said the beggar after a pause of a few seconds. "Tell my two friends here who the King of Redonda was. You must know." Laurence looked at him, perplexed. Hardly anyone knew anything about the King of Redonda, only a handful of bibliophiles and scholars, people of great learning, experts. He saw no reason, however, not to reply. "His name was John Gawsworth, although in fact his real name was Armstrong. Quite by chance, he inherited the title of King of Redonda or Redundo, an uninhabited island in the Antilles, of which he never actually took possession. He did, however, set about creating an aristocracy, bestowing a few fictitious titles on friends, like this one given to the poet Dylan Thomas," explained Laurence, indicating the pamphlet to his left. "He was only a very minor writer. Why are you interested in him?"

"You see, isn't that what I told you? How else could I possibly know all that?" said the tall beggar, turning to the other two. Then to Laurence he said: "How much are you selling the *Epigram* for?"

"I'm not sure you could afford it," said Laurence in paternalistic tones, feigning hesitancy. "It's worth £500."

The jockey with the domed cranium jibed: "Yeah, £500 that won't be coming your way. Why don't you give us a few of your other books and we can sell them all to this gentleman?"

"Shut up, you idiot, I'm telling you the truth. That pamphlet was mine once and the loyalty expressed in it was dedicated to me." And turning to Laurence again, the man with the beard added: "Do you know what became of John Gawsworth?"

Laurence was growing weary of the conversation.

"I don't actually. I think he died. He's an obscure figure." And Laurence looked at the typescript of *Watt*, fortunately still there (no one inside the shop, none of the other employees, had stolen it whilst he, like a fool, was standing at the door with these three beggars).

"No, sir, there you're wrong," said the beggar. "You're right about him being a minor writer and an obscure figure, but he isn't dead. Though these two fellows here won't believe me, *I* am John Gawsworth. I am the King of Redonda."

"Oh, come now," said Laurence impatiently. "Stop cluttering up the pavement and move away from this window. You're drunk, the lot of you, and if you fell, you could break it and injure yourselves. Be off with you." And with a rapid movement he slipped back into the shop and bolted the door.

He returned to his desk and sat down. The beggar was looking at him coldly now from the other side of the glass. He seemed offended. He was angry. His brown eyes were genuinely cool, unfriendly, intimidating, more so than Laurence's own cool, intimidating blue eyes. The other two beggars were laughing and jostling the tall beggar as if to say: "Come on, let's go" (though Laurence could hear nothing). The first beggar, however, remained quite still, as if rooted to the pavement, staring at Laurence coldly, threateningly. Laurence could not hold his gaze. He looked down and tried to immerse himself once more in the compilation of the next catalogue, the 251st since the founding of Rota, the discriminating bookshop of which he was manager. That way perhaps he'll disappear again, he thought. If I don't look at him, don't see him, he'll disappear, the way he did the last time. Although, of course, then he came back.

He kept his eyes lowered until he noticed a change in the light. Only then did he dare look up to see that the window was clear. He stood up and went over to check the display again. On the pavement lay a shattered beer bottle. But there, safe and sound, awaiting their distinguished bibliophile purchasers, were *Salmagundi*, £350, *Oliver Twist*, £300, *La Chute*, £600, *Jacob's Room*, £2,000, *An Epigram of Loyalty*, £500, and *Watt*, £50,000. He gave a sigh of relief, picked up the typescript of *Watt* and clasped it to him. It had been typed by Beckett himself, who had never trusted anyone else with the task. Perhaps he should withdraw it from display, it was after all worth £50,000. He carried it back to his desk to consider the matter and there, for a moment, allowed himself an absurd thought. A copy of *An Epigram of Loyalty* bearing John Gawsworth's signature would be worth twice as much. A thousand pounds, he thought.

Laurence looked up, but the window was still empty.

Translated from the Spanish by Margaret Jull Costa

RAIJA SIEKKINEN

A Small Lie

The white cat had started to hate her.

Only half a year ago, Marja remembered, it had been playing with the hems of her robe, while she had passed the morning reading and drinking coffee. Right now it was staring relentlessly at her from the bookcase where it was ensconced: out of reach, she thought. Its stare was green and mean. At night it attacked her ankles; it lurked in the crevices of the apartment and when it heard her approaching steps it leapt past her, screaming, and crossed the room to the curtains or the table. The curtains fell, books crashed to the floor, the cat stared with its eyes opened wide, the pupils like narrow slits. She would lock the cat into the other room for the night, hear it mew and feel the door with its paws; she fell asleep only after the cat had calmed down. When she approached it during the day, stroked it and called its name, it looked at her, motionless, as if it had seen and known everything, and then she withdrew her hand, backed off, started behaving as if there wasn't even a cat in the apartment.

"What's happened to it," she thought; and she wondered what to do with the cat, as if it were some object, without looking at it or trying to approach it anymore.

When the eviction notice came, she again started thinking about the cat and what to do with it: have it put to sleep or take it along.

When she was preparing for the move she remembered all the other moves: specially the last one, the one after the divorce. She remembered the books that she had given away or sold, and the records and the clothes that she had thrown away, and then the things that her husband had taken, as if she were handling them now, and not those things that she had bought herself, so beautiful and still so new that you could not see a scratch on them. The knives, the spoons, the forks; the coffee cups, the tea cups; the clear stemware that had not been used a single time; as she was packing them she remembered the cup with the glaze cracked near the rim, grey with dirt, a fine hairline crack, and the dent on the side of the pot, and a feeling of defeat seemed to be oozing from those things, but whether it came from the old ones or from these new ones, that she did not know. But she remembered the day they went to court: how sleet had been coming down, how she had been sitting there watching the big globs of wet snow that stuck to the window and how it had melted and run down as water as soon as it touched the glass, and how new sleet had constantly melted into the water. There had been a map of prisoner transports on the court bulletin board; all the prisons in the country had been there, and the railroads, and the cities, through which the railroads went, all of them on a white background, and otherwise the map had been empty as if nothing else had existed except for prisons and the trains that went to them. She still remembered the route, and the blue vinyl sofa and the hole in it, and the foam rubber filling that could be seen through that hole, and the sleet.

The feeling of disgust had lasted for days. She had cleaned, aired the place, washed clothes, filled the trash container at the back of the house with things that would get carried away in the early morning hours by old men and women, and by children during the day.

One day in the spring, she recalled, two doves had come in through the open window. She had heard their thumps against the windows: as if someone had been kicking a ball inside. The bird droppings had stained the walls, the floors, feathers had flown in the air, and the rustling of wings had filled the air. She had fled to the bathroom, sat on the rim of the tub, through the closed door she had heard the bangs, the pounding on the glass, and everything had felt ruined, impossible to repair, even after the janitor had gotten the birds out and she had cleaned up their stains and gathered up the feathers. A new and beautiful life; a clean life; in those days she began to look for a new apartment where all this would be possible.

She was spending a last few days in the apartment that she had come to one year ago. The windows divided the view into small squares. The afternoon sun, and the lights from the cars at night, were reflected through the crown glass differently each time: as if through water. The reflections were visible on the walls for only a moment, and their appearance brought a sense of sadness over their brevity. She walked around in the apartment without knowing what else she should do. The kitchen floor had a board that always creaked;

the water pipes gurgled in the wall when someone turned on the faucet in the next-door apartment, the toilet tank hissed. She noticed all of this, and at the same time she noticed that she had got so used to the noises that she had not really heard them for a long time.

The cat spent these last days trying to avoid her, but was still constantly close by. Every now and then she met its omniscient stare.

She had postponed the move until the last moment as if she had expected the eviction notice to be cancelled. She slept poorly, and when she woke up at night she thought about the first nights that she had spent in this house.

She remembered how she had hoped that she would grow to resemble her house after she had moved there. The house stood at the edge of the park and it was different from any other house. Looking through the windows, you could see the colours of the rainbow reflected on their surface: like oil on water. A lace-like wooden trim framed the eaves and the windows. In one end of the house was a tower, it stood empty, its diamond-shaped windows broken: birds flew in and out of them. She had stayed awake listening to the rustling above her, and to the wind in the trees of the park which, in the middle of the city, was like the sound from another world and the birds waking up in the park in the early morning. There had seemed to be a clear line separating her previous life and this new one, and life in this beautiful, century-old house was just the way it should be. She had started thinking about her previous self as a stranger, whose doings seemed somewhat puzzling.

But the new flat was going to be in an apartment house, a two-room apartment, and new; the sounds that would be heard there would be the sounds of neighbours, not of the house, trees and birds. When she tried to imagine the cat in this new house and apartment, she always thought of that very same white porcelain cat that she had seen on some old maid's window-sill, with a red silk ribbon around its neck.

One night she woke up, and the cat was next to her. The door had remained open, the cat was purring the way it used to purr as a kitten. She stretched out her hand to stroke it, and then withdrew before she had touched it. The cat stretched its paws towards her, was

tenderly clawing the blanket. It was the same movement that it used
to make when sucking its mother's milk. Even though her feet were
sticking out from under the blanket, the cat did not go after them. It
arched its neck toward her cheek, and she lay stiff, frightened, without
moving.

As a kitten it had slept under her blanket. She had carried it around
on her shoulder, searched for it with a flashlight in the back yard and
in the corners of the cellar. It had grown: it had started spending the
nights outside. She remembered the first time she had woken up to
the screaming of the cats: as if some deranged women had been yelling
in the back yard. In the morning there had been blood on the snow.
Night after night you could hear the whines of the tomcats, a rising
and falling sound, seemingly endless, and after that the thumps of the
fighting cats against the walls as they tumbled down the stairs,
entangled in each other. There were tufts of hair on the ground, the
cat's ear got torn. Later, when it started to sleep indoors again, she
shooed it away from her bed, locked it into the other room. The cat
tried to return to its old ways, she prevented it: she was not going
to forget. And thinking of this she remembered the sounds of the
elevator, the sounds of the newspaper boy's footsteps on the empty
streets, and then finally the first buses of the morning.

"You should have had it neutered," said the women where she
worked as they took their coffee break in the small, windowless smoking room of the library, where coffee breaks from all the bygone years
appeared as yellowish, foul-smelling stains on the walls. They were
divorced women, all of them: while they were smoking they talked
about other people's marriages and about their husbands' new ones,
and in all of these there seemed to be all kinds of faults: divorce was
only a question of time.

"I guess you could still have it neutered?"

"Not anymore 'cause it's fully grown."

"Have it put to sleep," someone said. "Get a new kitten and have
it neutered."

The cat started licking itself. In the dark you could hear the smack-
ing of its tongue against its coat. Marja withdrew further, against the
wall, dozed off and woke up again. For a little while, through her
sleep, the purring of the cat had sounded like the buzzing of a fly in
her ear, and she had been back in the country, in the house of her
mother-in-law, had been sitting at the end of the bench in the big

family room with an unopened book in her lap, been looking at the
deepening blue line of the forest beyond the empty stretch of road,
feeling pressured and sad. She was wide awake now: for a brief
moment in her sleep she had understood her mother-in-law, this
woman who had aged early, who had been left alone and whose hands
were swollen from cold water, bluish red, and whose face seemed
moulded by years of crying. But no, she thought, remembering words
and looks, and then she remembered the flies that had always woken
her up there in the early morning, and the irritation she felt in the
hot closed-off room, and the morning light.

She pushed the cat further away. Its eyes were half closed, but you
could see them gleaming. Its fur was very soft. The purring came
from somewhere deep within its throat, the tip of its nose was wet
and cool. Its every touch felt all over her skin like the scraping of
fingernails against the school blackboard used to feel, or the way paper
felt against her fingertips after a long day in the library.

Marja got up. Sitting at her empty desk and looking out into the
morning, where the shapes and colours of trees and houses were
beginning to emerge, she felt as if she had come close to something
dangerous, as if she had barely avoided it. She remembered how, just
for a moment, she had understood her mother-in-law, and in the light
of that understanding she realized how futile much of what she had
done would seem and how life would be out of kilter, each piece
slightly out of place, like a chess board that is jolted in the middle of
a game so that the pieces move. Outside, in front of her, contours
were beginning to emerge. The tangled branches of the bush, the
leaves of the birch, each one separately, were rising up as if out of a
haze. Slowly, and one at a time, she was remembering things from
her life, and when she went to bed after the sun had already come
up, the cat no longer bothered her: she had made her decision.

After she had driven her car to the back of the house and turned
off the engine and applied the handbrake, Marja continued to sit in
the car. Through the windscreen she saw the grey cement wall, and
above it the brick wall that continued up through the branches of the
trees, and through the side window she saw asphalt, then black soil,
with grass seeds scattered over it, and some saplings; some of them
would grow into trees, others would die. Next to her was the empty
cat basket. She reached inside and tapped her fingernails on its surface.
On the way here, and for no apparent reason, she had thought of

something that happened many years ago, nothing important at all: still she could not forget it. It had been a question of where she had been; she had said that she had been to the bank when she had actually been to the pharmacy. She smiled. It was an insignificant thing, meaningless. But then she began to remember other similar incidents, just small inaccuracies really: still, something about them had started to bother her.

She withdrew her hand from the basket, closed the lid, put the basket on the back seat: she could use it for shopping, it was good handiwork made by the blind.

She rolled up the window, closed the other front door from the inside, took the keys out of the ignition. Still, she could not get going. In the grey plaster of the wall there was a thin, vertical crack. She stared at it, lit a cigarette, leaned her head against the seat back. Did that crack reach far into the foundations of the house, she wondered, or was it just on the surface of the plaster: and all the time, something was bothering her.

"Is it fleas or worms or diarrhoea, or what's the trouble," she remembered the vet having asked.

"No, it needs to be put to sleep."

"Oh, put to sleep, that's what it is."

"It's got some sort of character fault," she had explained; and she remembered how the vet had been scratching the cat under its chin and how the cat had laid down on the examination table very peacefully.

"So that's what this one's got, some sort of character fault," the vet had said, examining the cat while she was telling him of the trouble it was causing, glancing at her from time to time.

"And then I'm moving into an apartment house."

"And it's hard to find a new home for the cat, isn't it, who would want a grown-up cat, a kitten is really the best."

"That's right," she had answered before she could think. And she remembered how she stood in the doorway and saw how the vet held the cat by the scruff of the neck and gave it an injection and then moved over to his desk to write out the bill.

"I'll take care of that, you don't need to stay and wait," the vet had said, and she had paid and walked out carrying the empty basket. On the treatment table lay the white cat, its legs straight, looking at last like that porcelain cat that she always remembered.

And in the car, on the way here, she had recalled some small lie, then some other ones, all of them for no reason.

She looked at the house. The apartment still smelled of paint, everything was new and clean like in a hospital. She had already run into the other inhabitants of the building: old women, who lived in the same kind of two-room apartments as she did, and who lived alone. They smiled their thin smiles at her, quickly sizing her up with their precise, cold stares. Now that she was sitting in the car and saw the brick wall, and the asphalt, and the soil with its saplings planted at regular intervals, she knew that she was safe now, in this house and among those women, one of them: that she would like it here, in this house and apartment; that very soon she would call it home.

Translated from the Finnish by Stina Katchadourian

LUIGI PIRANDELLO

The Fly

Breathless, crushed for breath, no sooner plumb below the village but
– Up here! This way! Follow me! Quick! Quick! – they saved priceless
time scrambling hands-and-knees up the shaly limestone bluff – for
their hobnailed boots – God in heaven! – how they slipped and they
slithered!

No sooner breasted the rise, beetroot in the face, than the women
thronging and chattering around the wash-trough at the gateway to
the village all turned agape. "Now then, aren't those the two Tortorici
lads? Poor devils! Why the mad scurry?"

The younger of the two, Neli by name and at the end of his tether,
paused a moment to catch his breath and give the women some
answer. But Saro grabbed him by the arm and hauled him on.

"It's our cousin Giurlannu Zarù!" shouted Neli over his shoulder,
flailing a sign of the Cross in the air.

The women burst into wailings of grief and horror. One of them
bawled "Who did it?"

"Nobody at all! 'Twas an act of God!" shouted Neli from a distance.
And the lads veered away and dashed to the scrap of a square where
the doctor lived.

This worthy doctor, Sidoro Lopìccolo, unkempt, hawking and coughing, ten days' stubble at least on his flabby jowls, with bloated, bleary
eyes, was drifting from room to room, shuffling in his slippers and
bearing in his arms an ailing, waxen-hued invalid girl, some nine years
of age and all skin and bone.

His wife on her sickbed these last eleven months, six offspring
round and about the house besides the girl in his arms (his eldest!),
all of them betattered, unwashed, running wild; the entire house

topsy-turvy – a midden! Shards of crockery, scraps of peel, piles of garbage on the floor, rickety chairs, springless sofas, beds unmade since heaven knows when, the blankets in shreds because the boys had the time of their lives pillow-fighting over the beds – the little darlings!

Sole thing intact, in the room that had once been the sitting-room, an enlarged photograph hanging on the wall: the portrait of the man himself, Dr Sidoro Lopìccolo, when still a young man and freshly qualified – smart and spruce and smiling.

Before this portrait passed he now, shuffling. He bared his teeth to it in an ingratiating smile. He bowed low, and with outstretched arms proffered his sickly child.

"Sisiné, take a look at this!"

Sisiné, you see, had been his mother's pet name for him – his mother who had expected such great things of him as the mainstay, yea the figurehead, of the family.

"*Sisiné!!*"

He whisked around on the two peasant-lads like a rabid dog – "*Whadyerwant!*"

Saro Tortorici spoke up, cap in hand and still breathing hard.

"Doctor, sir, there's a poor fellow . . . our cousin . . . he's dying . . ."

"He's got all the luck! Let the bells peal out!" bellowed the doctor.

"No no, sir! He's dying, your honour, all of a sudden and no one knows of what! Down there in the farmsteads of Montelusa, in a stable."

Lopìccolo fell back a pace. "At *Montelusa!*" he shrieked in his fury. (That was a good seven miles down the road. And *what* a road . . .)

"For the love of God get a move on," implored Tortorici. "He's gone the colour of a lump of liver, and so swelled up it's a fright to look at. Come along, for pity's sake!"

"What d'you mean? On foot?" screeched the doctor. "Ten miles on foot! Are you out of your minds? The mule! I must have the mule! Is she there waiting?"

"I'll be off and get her," cried Saro. "I'll get the loan of her . . ."

"In the meanwhile," said Neli, "I'll step over to the barber's and get a shave."

The doctor wheeled on him and looked daggers.

"It's Sunday, sir," said Neli apologetically, with a smile of bewilderment. "I'm engaged to be married . . ."

"Oh it's that what you are is it?" sneered the doctor, utterly beside himself with rage. "Then take this one here!"

And so saying he thrust his sick daughter into the young man's arms. Thereupon, one after another, all the rest of the brood now clinging to him by the trouser legs, and flung them with fury at the kneecaps of the young man Neli. "Take this one! And this! And this for good measure! Damn it all! Damn it all! Damn it!"

He turned his back on them and made to walk off, but he turned again, took the sick girl back into his arms and bawled at the two lads:

"Get a move on! Fetch the mule! I'll be with you at once!"

The grin returned to Neli's face as he followed his brother down the stairs. Twenty years old, he was; his fiancée Luzza, sixteen – and a rosebud! Only seven children? That's not many! He had twelve in mind. And to nourish them all the help he'd need would be this one pair of arms, but brawny with it, his gift from God. To work away and sing away, always in good spirits, everything shipshape. Not for nothing did they call him *Liolà* – the poet! And, knowing himself to be loved by one and all for his kindness of heart and unfailing good humour, he beamed upon the very air he breathed. The sun had not yet managed to wrinkle his skin or parch the gold blond of the curls which so many women were inclined to envy him, women who flushed and blushed if he were to look at them in that certain way with those clear bright eyes of his.

But more deeply than the misfortune of his cousin Zarù, what really and truly smote him that day was the displeasure in which he would be held by his Luzza, who had for six days been yearning for Sunday to spend a little time with him. But could he, in all conscience, shirk that act of Christian charity? Poor Giurlannu! He, too, engaged to be married. What a calamity, right out of the blue! There he'd been, Zarù, beating down the almonds on the Lopes estate at Montelusa. The morning before, the Saturday, it had smelt like rain, though there seemed no imminent danger of it. However, towards midday Lopes says: "Within the hour the skies will shower. Boys, I wouldn't fancy the almonds left on the ground in the rain." And he ordered the women at work on the gathering to get on up to the storehouse and start shelling.

"And you," he says, turning to the men beating the almonds to the ground, Neli and Saro Tortorici among them, "if you feel so inclined go up and shell along with the women."

Whereupon Giurlannu Zarù: "Ready and willing," says he, "but will I get my regular 25 soldi for the whole day?"

"You will not," says Lopes. "Half-day at your usual wage and the rest at half a lira, like the women."

The rotten little bully! No reason why the men shouldn't work a full day and earn a full day's wage. It wasn't raining, nor in fact did it rain for the rest of the day, nor during the night.

"Half a lira, like the women?" says Giurlannu Zarù. "I wear breeches! Pay me that half-day at the rate of twenty-five soldi and I'll be on my way."

But he didn't leave. He stayed on until evening waiting for his cousins, who had accepted the deal to shell almonds at half a lira, along with the women. At a certain point, however, weary of sitting idly looking on, he betook himself to a nearby stable to lie down for a nap, enjoining the drudges to wake him when it was time to go home.

They'd been beating the trees for a day and a half and the yield was scanty. The women suggested shelling the lot of them that same evening, working late and staying on to sleep the rest of the night, rising before dawn to get back to the village next morning. And so they did. Lopes served up boiled broad beans and a couple of flasks of wine. At midnight, the shelling finished, they all of them, men and women alike, flopped down to sleep on the threshing-floor, under the stars, where what straw remained was as sodden with dew as if it really had rained.

"*Liolà, give us a song!*"

And he, Neli, all at once began to sing, as the moon glided in and out of a dense tangle of black and white cloudlets – and the moon was the round round face of his Luzza, wreathed with smiles or with frowns, according to the sad, or the gladsome, peregrinations of love.

Giurlannu Zarù had not budged from the stable. Before dawn Saro went down to wake him up and found him there, bloated and puce in the face and scathed with the fever.

All this Neli Tortorici recounted there at the barber's, and the latter, in a moment of distraction, nicked him with the razor. A tiny cut near the chin, scarcely visible, come on now! Neli had no time even to notice it, because in the shop doorway Luzza had appeared with her mother and Mita Lumìa, Giurlannu Zarù's poor betrothed, howling and crying her eyes out in desperation.

It took heaven and earth to convince the poor girl that she could not go all the way to Montelusa to abide by her fiancé. She would see him by nightfall, as soon as they had fetched him back as best they could. At this point Saro appeared, bawling that the doctor was already in the saddle and could wait no longer. Neli drew Luzza aside and begged her to be patient: he'd be back before dark and would tell her lots of wonderful things.

Wonderful things indeed are even such things as these – for two young people engaged to be married, small things spoken while holding hands, and gazing into each other's eyes.

Villainous, vile road! Steeps that caused Dr Lopìccolo to stare death in the face, for all that Saro and Neli, one on each side, had the mule by the halter.

From the heights you could scan the whole vast sway of the landscape of plains and flowing valleys, olive groves and almond orchards, cornfields now yellow with stubble, here and there black from the burning-off. In the distance lay an acidulous blue sea. Mulberries, carobs, cypresses and olives flaunted their various shades of green, as ever; the crowns of the almonds had already thinned out.

All around, within the broad swath of the horizon, there whispered a suspicion of the wind. But the heat was gruelling; the sun went splitting the stones. Every so often, from over the prickly-pear hedges came the shrill cry of a woodlark or the raucous voice of a magpie, which caused the doctor's mule to prick up her ears, and the doctor grumbled "Mouldy old mule, you mouldy old mule!"

Not to lose sight of those ears he neglected to notice the sun glaring in his eyes, and he left the big green-lined peasant umbrella lain open across his shoulder.

"Don't be afraid, your honour," the brothers urged him. "We are here with you."

The doctor, in all likelihood, was not afraid. But he had his children in mind. For the sake of those seven poor little brats he had to watch his skin.

In order to calm him the lads began talk about the poor harvests: the wheat scanty, scanty the broad beans, scanty the barley. As for the almonds, everyone knows they don't always set, so the trees are laden one year and not the next. And as for the olives the less said the better! The chill mist had nipped them in the bud. Nor was there hope of making up for it with the grapes – every vineyard in the district had the blight.

"Cold comfort!" put in the doctor from time to time, with a shake of the head. "Cold comfort!"

After two hours of journeying all conversation was at an end. The road ran straight as a die for a fair stretch, but on the deep layer of whitish dust the only chatter now was between the four hooves of the mule and the hobnailed boots of the two peasants. Liolà at a certain point started to sing, listless and low. He soon gave up. They met not a soul, for all the peasants, it being a Sunday, were up in the village, some for Church, some for shopping, others simply for a bit of a rest. Maybe down there at Montelusa no one had stayed by the side of Giurlannu Zarù, and he was dying alone, if indeed he was still alive at all.

Alone, in fact, they found him, in the foul musty stable, stretched out on the low wall as Saro and Neli Tortorici had left him, his face bruised, huge, changed beyond all recognition. And the croak in his throat.

Through the barred window near the manger streamed the sun, striking on features that no longer looked human: the nose obliterated by the swelling, the lips black and horribly bloated. And from those lips issued the rattle, like an angry growl. Among his black and almost negroid curls a fragment of straw glittered in the sunlight.

The three of them stopped in their tracks and gazed down, arrested by the horror of the sight. The mule pawed the cobblestones. Saro Tortorici moved to the side of the dying man and called on him tenderly.

"Giurlà, Giurlà, we've brought the doctor."

Neli led the mule over and tied her to the manger where, there on the wall, was what might have seemed the shadow of another animal, the outline of the donkey whose home that stable was, printed there by dint of constant rubbing.

Giurlannu Zarù, at a second call, ceased to croak. He forced open his darkening, bloodshot eyes, filled with terror. He parted his ghastly lips and groaned from the fire within him, "I'm . . . dying."

"No, no!" Saro in his anguish hastened to assure him. "The doctor's here. We brought him ourselves. Can you see him?"

"Take me to the village," begged Zarù, with immense effort, unable to bring his lips together. "Oh, God help me!"

"Yes, yes, we've got the mule here," replied Saro at once.

"But even in our arms, Giurlà," said Neli, hurrying up and bending over him. "I'll carry you myself. Don't lose heart!"

Hearing Neli's voice Giurlannu Zarù turned his head, studied him for a moment with those bloodshot eyes of his as if at first he didn't recognize him, then moved an arm and hooked onto his belt.

"You, lad, you?"

"It's me, yes, so cheer up! Are you crying, now? Don't cry Giurlà, don't cry. It's nothing . . ."

And he laid a hand on that chest heaving with sobs that could find no means of escape. Choking, at a certain point Zarù shook his head in impotent rage then raised one hand, got a grip on the back of Neli's neck and pulled him down towards him:

"Together . . . we . . . were going to be married . . ."

"And married together we will be, have no fear!" said Neli, removing the hand that clasped his neck.

Meanwhile the doctor was scrutinizing the dying man. No doubt about it: a case of anthrax.

"Tell me, do you remember being bitten by some insect?"

Zarù shook his head. No.

"An *insect*?" queried Saro.

As best he could the doctor explained the disease to those two unlettered yokels. Some farm animal in the neighbourhood must have died of anthrax. Upon the carcass, cast into the depths of some gully, goodness knows how many insects might have alighted. One of which had taken wing and inoculated the disease into Zarù in that very stable.

While the doctor spoke Zarù turned his face to the wall.

No one knew it, but death in the meantime was still present, so tiny as to be barely perceptible, even had anyone heeded it.

A fly, there on the wall, apparently motionless. But, on closer inspection, now it poked out its minute proboscis and pumped with it, now rapidly cleaned its two frail forelegs, rubbing them together as if in glee.

It caught Zarù's eye. He observed it intently.

A fly.

Maybe it was that one, maybe another. Who could know? Yes now, hearing what the doctor was saying, he seemed to remember . . . Yes, the day before, when he had lain down there to sleep, waiting for his cousins to finish shelling Lopes's almonds, he had been pestered by a fly. Could this be the one?

He saw it all of a sudden buzz away, and he shifted his gaze to follow it.

Aha! it had alighted on Neli's cheek. Down from the cheek, light as could be, in two short bursts it scurried onto his chin and to the nick left by the razor. And there it clung, ravenous.

Giurlannu Zarù lay eyeing it for some time, absorbed and thoughtful. Then, wheezing with effort, in a sepulchral voice he asked: "Could it have been a fly?"

"A fly? Why not?" replied the doctor.

Giurlannu Zarù said nothing more. He set about watching the fly which Neli, stunned by the doctor's words, did not brush away. He, Zarù, was no longer paying attention to the doctor, but was pleased that by his talk he was so absorbing Neli's attention as to make him stand stock-still, all unaware of the botherance of the fly on his cheek. O let it be the same one! Then, then indeed, together they would be wed! A sullen envy, a fierce visceral jealousy had seized him against that young cousin of his, so handsome and so flourishing, for whom still full of promises was the life which he, in a trice! was being deprived of.

All of a sudden Neli, finally feeling a bite, raised a hand, brushed away the fly and began to press his fingers against his chin, where the razor had nicked him. He glanced at Zarù, whose eyes were fixed on him, and was horrorstruck to see that the latter had spread his horrendous lips in a hideous grin. For a short space they looked each other in the eye. Then, almost in spite of himself, Zarù said:

"The fly."

Neli failed to hear the words and bent his ear closer: "What's that?"

"The fly," repeated the other.

"What fly? Where?" asked Neli in panic, turning to the doctor.

"There . . . where you're scratching . . . I'm sure of it," muttered Zarù.

Neli showed the doctor the little wound on his chin: "What've I got. It's itching me."

Frowning, the doctor took a look at it. Then, as if in need of a better light, led him outside the stable. Saro followed.

What then? Giurlannu Zarù waited, he waited a long time, in a state of anguish that stirred his very bowels. Outside he heard a muffled babble of voices. Suddenly Saro burst into the stable, seized the mule and without so much as turning to look at him rushed out moaning, "Ah, my little Neli, my little Neli!"

So it was true, then! So they meant to leave him there like a dog. He tried hoisting himself up on one elbow, he cried twice over "Saro, Saro!"

Silence. No one. He failed to stay propped on his elbow. He fell back and began grubbing and snuffling around him like a pig for a while, so as not to hear the silence of the open spaces, which terrified him. Of a sudden it occurred to him that he had dreamt the whole thing, that he'd had that nightmare in his fever. But when he turned over towards the wall he saw the fly, there once more.

Behold it . . .

Now poking out its minute proboscis and pumping with it, now rapidly cleaning its two frail forelegs, rubbing them together as if in glee.

Translated from the Italian by Patrick Creagh

LUIGI PIRANDELLO

Bosom Friends

Gigi Mear, wearing an Inverness cape that morning (after forty, dammit, you take the north wind seriously!), his scarf drawn up and folded meticulously under his nose, and wearing a pair of heavy English gloves – Gigi Mear, well-nourished, smooth and rubicund, was waiting on the Lungotevere de' Melini for the tram to Porta Pia, destined to take him, as on every other day, to Via Pastrengo and the Court of Accounts, where he was employed.

By birth a noble count, but now alas with neither cash nor county to his name, he had in the innocence of his youth evinced to his father his resolve to enter that government office, under the naïve impression that it was the Court of *Counts*, which all noble counts had a right to enter.

We all of us know that when we are waiting for trams they never come. They have a tendency to stop half-way along the route for lack of current, or opt for crashing into a cart or even crushing some poor devil to death . . . A great convenience they are, none the less – by and large.

That day the north wind was blowing indeed, icy and slicing, and Gigi Mear stamped his feet as he gazed at the ruffled water of the river, which also seemed to suffer from the cold, poor thing, down there strait-jacketed between the drab, intractable walls of the new embankment.

In God's good time, *ding-dong, ding-dong*, here at last was the tram. And Gigi Mear was preparing to leap on without troubling it to stop when, from the newly-constructed bridge, the Ponte Cavour, he heard some person hailing him loudly: "Gigìn! Gigìn!"

And he beheld a man running towards him flailing his arms in semaphore fashion. The tram moved on. In recompense Gigi Mear had the consolation of finding himself in the arms of a stranger: his bosom friend, to judge from the violence with which he felt himself kissed *there! there!* on the silk scarf which swathed his mouth.

"I recognized you at once, y'know, Gigìn! At once! But what's this? Already a patriarch? Tee hee! Snowy locks! Vouchsafe me another kiss, Gigione, dear fellow, in honour of your sainted old age! . . . I spotted you here, standing stock-still, and it looked as if you were expecting me. When I saw you reach up to climb on to that devilish conveyance, it felt like a betrayal, so it did!"

"Well, as it happens," said Mear, forcing a smile, "I was on my way to the office . . ."

"Kindly do me the favour not to speak of such dross at a moment like this!"

"How's that?"

"Do as I say! I order you not to!"

"Indeed, indeed! Why should one always say 'please'? You're a fine fellow, I *must* say!"

"Yes, I know. But you weren't expecting me, were you. I can see it in your face: you weren't expecting me."

"No . . . To tell the truth . . ."

"I got in yesterday evening. And I bring you greetings from your brother who – this'll make you laugh – suggested giving me a letter of introduction to you. 'What!' said I. 'To Gigione? I'd have you know I knew him before you did, so to speak. Childhood friends, for heaven's sake! How many times we've played at fisticuffs . . . Buddies at university and after . . . Ah Padua, Padua. Gigione, do you remember? The great bell you never heard, as you were always sleeping like a . . . let's say dormouse, eh?, though like a pig is what you deserve. You only heard it the once, and you thought it was the fire-alarm! Ah, those were the days! Your brother's in fine fettle, by the way, thanks be to God. We've got a little bit of business going. That's what brought me here. But for goodness' sake, what's up with you? You've a face like a funeral! Don't say you've married!"

"My dear chap, no!" exclaimed Gigi Mear, rallying.

"On the brink, then?"

"Are you out of your mind? At past forty? I wouldn't dream of it!"

"Forty? Ha ha, and what would you say to fifty years already rung up? But of course you made a speciality of not hearing anything ring, bells, years, or what you will. I'd forgotten. Me, fifty, *fifty* years already rung up, I assure you dear fellow. Alas and alack, things begin to take a serious turn. You were born . . . now let's see . . . April 1851. True or false? The 12th of April."

"*May*, with your permission. And 1852, *with* your permission." Gigi spelt out the words with pedantic vexation. "Or do you now claim to know better than I do? May the Twelfth 1852. Therefore, so far, forty-nine years and a month or so."

"And no wife? Good work! Me yes, didn't you know. Ah, the tragedy of it! It'll make you die laughing. In the meantime we assume you've invited me to lunch, eh, eh? Where do you scoff your nosh these days? Still at old Barba's?"

"Good Lord!" blurted Gigi Mear with mounting astonishment. "You even know about old Barba's? Don't tell me you went *there* as well!"

"What, me? Barba's? How do'you think I could've, seeing as I live in Padua? Word's got round and I've heard tell of the wondrous feats you achieve, you and your fellow scoffers, in that old . . . what should I call it . . . eating-house, chop-shop, dive?"

"Dive," returned Mear. "Low dive. But these days . . . Well, if you intend lunching with me I must give notice at home, to the maid . . ."

"Young?"

"Ah, no! Old, my dear fellow, old! As for Barba's, I'll have you know I don't go there any more, and as for feats of gluttony, no more of those for three years now. When you reach a certain age . . ."

"Past forty!"

"Yes, past forty you have to have spirit enough to turn your back on a path which, if pursued, would lead you to the brink of the pit. The downward toddle is all very well, taken little by little, little by little, so as not to come a cropper. Ah, here we are! Please step upstairs. I'll show you how I've made a pretty little thing of my tiny home . . ."

"Toddle! Little by little! Pretty little thing! Tiny home!" snorted the friend as he followed Gigi Mear up the stairs. "So you talk to me in diminutives now, do you, and you yourself such a robust, superlative fellow? My poor Gigione! What have they been doing to you? Twisting your tail? D'you want to make me weep?"

"Hummph!" grunted Gigi Mear, as he waited on the landing for the maid to come and open the door. "At our age you have to butter up this rotten life. You have to flatter and caress her with pet names, otherwise she'll diddle you! I have no desire to creep to the grave on all-fours!"

"Ah, so you conceive of man as a *biped*, do you?" retorted the other. "Gigione, don't tell me, don't tell me! All too well I know what an effort I make at times to stand upright on only two legs. Believe me friend, if it were left up to nature we'd all prefer to be quadrupeds. Best thing! More comfy, firm-set, well-balanced . . . Many's the time I long to get down on all-fours, hands splayed, like a great cat. This rotten 'civilization' is our ruin! On four legs I'd be a beautiful wild animal, on four legs I'd lash you out a couple of kicks in the belly for the tomfoolery you've been talking. If I were four-legged I'd have no wife, no debts, no worries. Do you really want to make me weep? I'm off!"

Gigi Mear, dazed by the buffooneries of this friend out of the blue, looked him up and down and racked his brains to conjecture what the devil his name was, and when and how he had met him there in Padua, as child or as undergraduate. Over and over again he passed in review all his erstwhile good friends. In vain! Not one of them corresponded to this fellow's physiognomy. Meanwhile he dared not demand an explanation. The intimacy professed was so great and of such a kind that he was fearful of giving offence. He resolved to succeed by stealth.

The maidservant took her time in opening the door, not having expected her master home so soon. Gigi pressed the bell again, and at last she arrived, flapping in her slippers.

"My dear old thing," said Mear. "I'm back again already, and what's more in company. Lay the table for two, would you, and do your very best. There's no joking, I can tell you, with this friend of mine, who has the most curious name . . ."

"Anthropophagus Capribarbicorniped!" asserted the stranger, pulling a face and leaving the old woman at a loss whether to giggle or to cross herself. "And no one, old dear, can any longer stand the sound of this grandiose name of mine. Bank managers turn up their noses, loan sharks are wrong-footed. My wife, my wife alone was delighted to take it – but mind you! only the name. That's all I allowed her to take. Me not! O no, not me! I'm too handsome a young feller, Christ alive! . . . Gigione, since you have this foible, take me on a tour of your trifles. And you, old dame, jump to it and fork out some fodder!"

Gigi Mear, defeated, escorted him round the five little rooms of the flatlet, each furnished with loving care: with the care of one who no longer wishes to find anything to hanker after outside his own little shell, having already made up his mind to pull in his horns. A little sitting-room, a tiny bedroom, a dinky bathroom, a dining-room, a wee study.

In the little sitting-room Mear's agonized astonishment knew no bounds as he hearkened to his friend discussing the most personal and intimate family matters while scanning the photographs displayed on the shelf.

"Gigione! I wish to God I had a brother-in-law like this one of yours. You can't imagine how devilish mine is!"

"Don't tell me he mistreats your sister!"

"No, he mistreats *me*! It'd be so easy for him to give me a helping hand in my present predicament . . . But does he?!"

"Do forgive me," put in Mear, "but I don't recall your brother-in-law's name . . ."

"Not to worry, you couldn't possibly. You've never met him. He's been less than two years in Padua. You know what he did to me? Your brother, who is kindness itself to me, promised to lend me a hand if that cad would underwrite my promissory notes. And would you believe it? The cad refused to sign! Whereupon your brother, who when it comes down to it (though a bosom friend) is not one of the family, got so indignant that he'd have no more to do with him! The business is on a firm footing, that yes. But if I were to tell you the reason why my brother-in-law refused to sign! . . . Gosh, I'm still a good-looking fellow, that goes without saying. A magnetic personality, though I say it myself. Well, my brother-in-law's sister, poor dear, unfortunately took it into her head to fall in love with me. Long on taste but short on wisdom! Just imagine, as if I . . . Anyway she took poison."

"Dead?" queried Mear, aghast.

"No. She threw up a bit and recovered. But I scarcely have to tell you there's been small chance of my setting foot in my brother-in-law's house since the tragedy. But God in heaven! When are we going to eat? I'm famished. Ah well, down the hatch!"

A while later, at table, Gigi Mear, bowed down by the effusions of affection of this friend, which filled his head with such bad language he could scarcely refrain from socking him one, decided to ask for news of Padua, of this and of that, in the hope of dragging the man's name from his lips if only by a stroke of luck. Or hoping at least, with exasperation mounting moment by moment, that he might take his mind off his fixation with the problem by changing the subject.

"What news of that fellow Valverde, the Director of the Bank of Italy, with his beautiful wife and that huge hulk of a sister – cross-eyed into the bargain, if I mistake not. Still in Padua?"

At this enquiry his friend laughed fit to bust.

"What's so funny?" queried Mear, his curiosity aroused. "*Isn't* she cross-eyed?"

"Stop it, stop it," implored the other, unable to check his convulsive laughter. "Cross-eyed as they come! And so snub-nosed, God save us, that she can see all the way round back into her brain. The very lady!"

"What lady?"

"My wife!"

Gigi Mear was thunderstruck, barely able to babble some witless apology. The friend burst into even longer and louder laughter. Finally he quietened down, knitted his brows and heaved a mighty sigh.

"My dear fellow," he said. "There are acknowledged acts of heroism in life, which the most unbridled poetic imagination is unlikely ever to conceive of!"

"Yes indeed . . ." muttered Mear. "How right you are . . . Er . . . I see . . ."

"You haven't seen a sodding thing!" came the instant rebuttal. "Do you think I allude to myself? What me, a hero? The most I might claim to be is the victim. But scarcely that. No, the heroine was my sister-in-law, Lucio Valverde's wife. Listen to this – blind, stupid, imbecile . . ."

"What, me?"

"No, no! Me, me! In that I could have flattered myself that Lucio Valverde's wife had fallen for me . . . to the point of doing him the dirty (because believe me, Gigìn, in all conscience he'd have deserved it). Not the case! Not the case at all! D'you know what it was?

Altruistic spirit of self-sacrifice! Get an earful of this, now. Off goes Valverde. Or rather, he makes a pretence (in cahoots with his wife, of course) of going off as he does every day. Thereupon she invites me in. Come the tragic moment of the 'discovery' and she shoos me into the bedroom of her cross-eyed sister-in-law who, greeting me all of a tremble and smothered with blushes, also gives the impression of immolating herself for the peace of mind and honour of her brother. I scarcely have time to cry out, 'Don't worry, dear lady, it cannot be possible that Lucio thinks . . .' No time to finish! Lucio, in a towering rage, bursts into the bedroom . . . And the rest you may well imagine."

"Why so?" exclaimed Gigi Mear. "You, with your indomitable spirit . . ."

"And what about my promissory notes?" bellowed the other. "My unpaid bills of exchange that Valverde agreed to renew because of the fake good graces of his wife? Now he would protest them *ipso facto*, don't you see? And he'd ruin me! Iniquitous blackmail! Let us speak not of it! In the last analysis, in view of the fact that I have not so much as a penny of my own and never will have, and in view of the fact that I have no intention of taking a wife . . ."

"What!" broke in Gigi Mear. "But you already married!"

"Ah no! Not me, I assure you! She married *me*! She did it all by herself. For my part I told her as much from the word go. 'Do as you would be done by.' That's my motto. 'Madam,' I said, 'you wish to bear my name? Then take it. Personally speaking I don't know what to do with it. But that's all you get, see?'"

"So," ventured Gigi Mear, crowing with jubilation, "that's it then! First she was called Valverde and now she's called . . ."

"Yea, woe is me!" cried the other, rising from the table.

"Ah no! Hold on a moment!" exclaimed Gigi Mear, able to bear it no longer and taking his courage in both hands. "You've given me a most enjoyable morning, and I have bade you welcome like a brother. Now you must do me a favour . . ."

"Were you thinking, perchance, of the loan of my wife?"

"Many thanks, but no! My only demand is that you should tell me your name!"

"Me? Tell you my name?" blurted out the friend, as if suddenly coming down from the clouds, and stabbing a finger into his chest as though questioning his own existence. "What's this now? You don't know it? You don't remember?"

"No I don't," confessed Mear, utterly mortified. "Forgive me! Call me the most scatter-brained man on earth, but I could virtually swear to never even having met you."

"Is that so! Excellent! Excellent!" returned the other. "My dear Gigione, let me shake you by the hand. I thank you with all my heart for your luncheon and your company, and I depart without revealing it. Just imagine!"

Gigi Mear leapt to his feet and flew off the handle. "You are *going* to tell me, by God! I've been racking my brains for a whole morning! I won't let you leave this place unless you tell me."

"Kill me, then!" replied the friend impassively. "Hack me to pieces! I will not tell you."

"Come on, now, there's a good fellow," pleaded Mear, changing his tone. "I've never until now – you must believe me – suffered from this loss of memory, and I swear to you it makes a very painful impression on me. For me, at this moment, you personify a nightmare. Tell me your name for pity's sake!"

"Your guess is as good as mine."

"I beseech you! Look here, my forgetfulness has not prevented me from inviting you to my table, and even supposing I had never met you, even supposing you had never been a friend of mine, you have now become one, and a very dear friend, believe me! Towards you I feel the fondness of a brother, I admire you, I would wish you ever at my side! Therefore, tell me your name!"

"It's no use, you know," concluded the other. "You're not going to inveigle me. Be reasonable: do you now ask me to forfeit the unexpected pleasure of leaving you completely thwarted without knowing whom you've treated to lunch? No, come off it. You're asking too much, and it's quite plain you no longer recognize me. Unless you want me to bear you a grudge for your disgraceful forgetfulness, let me leave things as they stand."

"Get out at once then, I abjure you!" cried Gigi Mear at the end of his tether. "I can't bear the sight of you a moment longer!"

"All right, I'll be off. But first – a kiss, Gigione! I'll be away again on the morrow . . ."

"Not on your life," shrieked Mear, "unless you tell me . . ."

The other cut him short: "No, no, enough of that! So it's goodbye, eh?"

And off he went, chuckling and turning back to give one last flourish of the hand on his way down the stairs.

Translated from the Italian by Patrick Creagh

John Ryder

THE CASE FOR LEGIBILITY

IN THE MAKING OF BOOKS the agent of communication between the author and the reader is the designer, and from the appearance of printed books it is not always clear that designers understand and practise what is required of them in order to establish this communication. For me this is 'the case for legibility', which implies not just a readable page but a complete book produced in such a way that it is easy to use and to read.

With all the new developments in the printing industry (like computer-assisted filmsetting and cathode-ray tube font development) we need designers wedded to the pursuit of legibility, for it must never be taken for granted that legibility is universally desired. To some it is detestable. New alphabets are drawn in ways which make them difficult to read. Advertisements are designed and printed to the bewilderment of all who notice them and then avert their eyes without receiving the message. In the process of book design legibility becomes important as soon as the author's work is taken seriously, or as soon as the effect of design upon the eye of the reader is considered.

Since 1935 I have devoted much time to written and printed images on paper, and so have come to know something about the process of book design and about typographical matters in general. Recent startling changes in techniques have not invalidated the canons of good typographical arrangement, though they have made sympathetic understanding between designer and printer more difficult to establish and maintain.

Once legibility is accepted as the objective, the urge to achieve it may be expressed in many ways: for instance in the act of making the eye of an e open enough to be read *(1)*. Such careful attention to detail must be applied to every written and printed letter, and not only to the letter itself but also to how and where it appears on the page – in relation to adjacent letters, words, lines of letters, margins.

Fig 1: Michael Harvey's drawing of a normal e aside low-legibility characters

The process of design for legibility can be described in three stages:
1. knowing and understanding the author's and editor's intention,
2. translating this intention into typographical signs and instructions so that setting and proofing may be done,
3. arranging the typographical material on proof into a sequence of pages which, to the best of the designer's skill and experience, reflects the author's intention.

This process begins with the choice of an alphabet for the text setting. At the same time format and paper must be considered. Then the text is arranged into typographical material which will make a sequence of pages, taking account of illustration, decoration and space wherever applicable. Now a specification and schedule of work and materials is made and this involves 'finishing' – not just details of binding, but the whole process of imposition and printing as well.

Throughout this procedure the designer can only achieve coherence and unity by subjecting every detail to the test of suitability – suitability to subject, author, publisher, market, mechanical processes of origination and reproduction, and, of course, to costing – closely controlled costs are part of each stage of design.

These statements imply freedom of choice but in practice the designer's choice is restricted. For many books, the economics of publishing have already chosen the typesetter. The choice of typeface is therefore narrowed. Then speed of production may exclude some faces whose matrices or keybars or discs are not immediately available. If we try to be positive and choose Baskerville, we soon find a need to be more specific, for that simple type name may refer to:

> Monotype Series 169 metal letters
> or Monophoto film images
> or Lino or Intertype metal slugs
> or Linotype VIP film
> or Linotron CRT scanned lines
> or Autologic (APS4) CRT scanned dots
> or IBM golfball electronic typewriting.

A complex of considerations will make the choice. Moreover, the closest attention will have to be paid to proofing, plate-making and inking controls if the designer's intentions are not to be frustrated, even by presses of good reputation.

If you cannot choose and control the apparent typeface, how can you choose a suitable paper for it?

Perhaps the imposition of the type area on the page, the margins, can be exactly given? No. These details are not constant because of the variation in machine folding of large sheets, and in any case often not precise because of the economic necessity of producing sewn and perfect-bound copies from one and the same imposition.

Type size sounds like a detail within the designer's control but it lacks precision and objectivity when we have to talk in terms of linear percentages of an original which may itself be an image projected to film by a light source; or dots or lines scanned electronically, projected photographically; or a proof from hot metal setting reduced or enlarged by camera. Only print from type carries the certainly of measurable type size.

Face, size, impression, paper, imposition – is there normally such lack of precision as to blur the designer's intention? I think there is. Therefore if we are striving for legibility we must get back to first principles and accept the control that these principles impose.

The prognosis is not good. Discipline is needed to save the eyesight of the human race. If that sounds like overstatement, just reflect that the adoption of dry transfer lettering *(2)* and CRT typesetting have given the designer scope beyond his knowledge and experience, for lettering design is not taught in most colleges of art, and this sad state of affairs will continue as long as attention to the roman alphabet is thought unnecessary once we are out of the nursery.

Appeal
illiterate
HOCKEY
SLAVISH

PUNCH-DRUNK
FAVOUR
OGRE
STICK

Fig 2: Misused spacing of dry-transfer lettering and computerised type setting

When my connections with typography began in 1935, I had left school and begun work in a London bookshop. At this time I bought a typewriter and started to make books in typescript; bought a hand-press and a miniature font of Gill Sans, and began to print. Then in 1940 I was reluctantly joined to the Army and remained for a long time as much bewildered by typographical points as by the violence of political volcanoes erupting in Europe. Enforced travels abroad put an end to all studies except that I learnt to milk a parachute and to assist surgeons.

The theatre of war was sometimes terrifying; but the present terror of being overcome by illiteracy and blinded by illegibility is just as real. Before the war my knowledge of typography was too slight for me to know what I was really doing. I now know that whatever is to be done must be done for the reader's benefit and for maximum legibility.

So the heart of the matter is that if writing is to be read, then problems of legibility must be solved. You must present an author's work to the reader without fuss and with design techniques as invisible as possible. This concept surely requires no defence.

A page in a book must not look like a collection of letters. At least it should look like a collection of words, at best a collection of phrases. To achieve this, not only must the right letter-design for the language and text and format be chosen, but it must also be used in a way which allows the easy flow, and therefore recognition, of phrases. That is the basis of designing a page for the printer to print for the reader to read.

The image shown here *(3)* of a Latin text impressed into the mat surface of well-woven, rag paper is a tribute to past techniques in legibility – an affirmation of suitability. The printing from Caslon types was done in 1912 at the Chiswick Press. At the same time the printed pages of Nicolas Jenson *(4)* and Aldus Manutius *(5)* should be compared with this Caslon example, since it was these Italian models which influenced Caslon through Garamond and the Dutch types of van Dyck.

What are the factors in this kind of legibility? Sir Cyril Burt gave us a clue to personal preference based on familiarity – choice of type according to reading habits, implying maximum legibility in the most familiar letter-forms. Perhaps I should have re-read Sir Cyril – and the Medical Research Council's report on the legibility of print, Pyke's government paper of 1926. One reason why I have not done so is that these factors I want to identify and describe are not based on preferences for the familiar way in which mathematical or legal papers or the classics have been printed. The factors I wish to draw your attention to are basic to any language, any text, any age, and the critical moderator is the human eye. They are, and I dare to say it, instinctive, genetic, though perhaps also teachable, and implicit in the roman alphabet. All we need to know in order to make these factors self-apparent is how to use the alphabet.

So consider the transcription of a typescript into a sequence of printed pages – a process which should become increasingly simple as the designer's experience grows. Ideally, when shown a typescript, the designer should also have a *précis* of its contents so that, as he turns the pages looking for divisions and breaks, insertions and notes and quotations of one

tius in eadem miseria vivant tardiusque moriantur.
Procul dubio ergo indicant, inmortalitatem, saltem
talem quae non habeat finem mendicitatis, quanta
gratulatione susciperent. Quid? animalia omnia
etiam inrationalia, quibus datum non est ista cogi-
tare, ab inmensis draconibus usque ad exiguos ver-
miculos nonne se esse velle atque ob hoc interitum
fugere omnibus quibus possunt motibus indicant?
Quid? arbusta omnesque frutices, quibus nullus
est sensus ad vitandam manifesta motione perni-
ciem, nonne ut in auras tutum cacuminis germen
emittant, aliud terrae radicis adfigunt, quo alimen-
tum trahant atque ita suum quodam modo esse
conservent? Ipsa postremo corpora, quibus non
solum sensus, sed nec ulla saltem seminalis est vita,
ita tamen vel exiliunt in superna vel in ima descen-
dunt vel librantur in mediis, ut essentiam suam,
ubi secundum naturam possunt esse, custodiant.

Iam vero nosse quantum ametur quamque falli
nolit humana natura, vel hinc intellegi potest, quod
lamentari quisque sana mente mavult quam laetari
in amentia. Quae vis magna atque mirabilis mor-
talibus praeter homini animantibus nulla est, licet
eorum quibusdam ad istam lucem contuendam
multo quam nobis sit acrior sensus oculorum; sed
lucem illam incorpoream contingere nequeunt,
qua mens nostra quodam modo radiatur, ut de his
omnibus recte iudicare possimus. Nam in quantum eam capimus, in tantum id possumus. Verum
tamen inest in sensibus inrationalium animantium,
etsi scientia nullo modo, at certe quaedam scientiae
similitudo; cetera autem rerum corporalium, non

Fig 3: Caslon types set and printed by the Chiswick Press in 1912

qui omnibus ui aquarum fubmerſis cum fi
mirabili quodā modo quaſi ſemen huāni ge
utinā quaſi uiuam quandam imaginem imi
quidem ante diluuium fuerunt:poſt diluui
altiſſimi dei ſacerdos iuſtitiæ ac pietatis mir
bræorū appellatus eſt:apud quos nec circun
ulla mentio erat . Quare nec iudæos(poſteris
gentiles:quoniam non ut gentes pluralitater
hebræos proprie noīamus aut ab Hebere ut
tranſitiuos ſignificat.Soli qppe a creaturis n
nō ſcripta ad cognitionē ueri dei trāſiere:& u
ad rectam uitam pueniſſe ſcribunt:cum qui
totius generis origo Habraam numerādus eſ
iuſtitiā quā non a moſaica lege(ſeptima eīm
Moyſes naſcitur)ſed naturali fuit ratione co
atteſtatur.Credidit enim Habraam deo & re
Quare multarum quoqȝ gentium patrem di
ipſo benedicēdas oēs gentes hoc uidelic& ipſ
aperte prædictum eſt:cuius ille iuſtitiæ perfe
ſed fide cōſecutus eſt:qui poſt multas dei ui
filium:quem primum omnium diuino pſu
cæteris qui ab eo naſcerétur tradidit:uel ad
eorum futuræ ſignum:uel ut hoc quaſi pate
tinétes maiores ſuos imitari conaret͈:aut qbu

Fig 4: A detail from a page of Jenson's fifteenth-century types

fieri poffe uix puto : fed plane quia ita de-
bemus inter nos: neq; enim arbitror cario
rem fuiffe ulli quenquam ;q̃ tu fis mihi.
Sed de his et diximus aliâs fatis multa ; et
faepe dicemus:nũc autem ;quoniam iam
quotidie ferè accidit poftea,q̃ e Sicilia ego,
et tu reuerfi fumus ; ut de Aetnae incendi-
is interrogaremus ab iis, quibus notum
eft illa nos fatis diligenter perfpexiffe ; ut
ea tandem moleftia careremus; placuit mi
hi eum fermonem confcribere ; quem
cum Bernardo parente habui paucis poft
diebus, q̃ rediiffemus; ad quem reiicien-
di effent ii, qui nos deinceps quippiam
de Aetna poftularent. Itaq; confeci librũ;
quo uterq; noftrum cõmuniter uteretur:
nã cum effemus in Noniano ; et pater fe
(ut folebat) ante atrium in ripam Pluuici
contuliffet ;acceffi ad eũ progreffo iam in
meridianas horas die:ubi ea , quae locuti
sum? inter nos,ferè ifta fũt.Tibi uero nũc
orationé utriufq; noftrũ,tanq̃ habeatur,
A ii

Fig 5: A page printed by Manutius of Griffo's fifteenth-century types

sort or another which may require special settings, he will have some idea of the construction and development of the text. He should also know, or be told, the age of the intended reader. With experience most of the work can be done without layouts.

In forming a clear idea of what the proposed book will look like, the first factor is the letter. By this I mean all that is implied by the choice of a type-face, or series of related faces which may include condensed or expanded letters, light or bold letters.

This choice involves a knowledge of the ratios of widths of main strokes to the height of letters, in addition to ratios of main stroke widths to cross-bars, diagonals and thin strokes; stress of curves; types of serif; slant of ital-ic and variation of slant; relation of x-height to extruders; presence or absence of irregularities of certain letters in the font; and the origin of the finally printed letters, that is to say, origin from metal types directly impressed, or repro-pulls photographed for lithographic plate-making, or from any of the various film matrix or CRT images.

The next three factors are:

> the size of the letter,
> the length of the line of letters,
> the space between the lines of letters.

These are closely linked and should naturally be considered together. The size of the letter relates directly to the length of the line of letters (measure). The space between the lines of letters depends on the chosen letter, and the size of letter, and the measure.

The fifth factor relates to the space between the words – an important measurement closely inter-related with these first four factors. If spaces between words are not close, the eye reads slowly; if uneven, jerkily; but nevertheless the word-spacing has to be related to the character spacing, to the fit of the letters. The appearance of loose-fitting characters, as in the malpractice of letterspacing lowercase, reduces legibility, whilst tight-fit-ting characters may easily destroy the identity of the letters.

Next is the size of page, or format, which will take into account the length of the typescript, the kind of text that it is, and its use and market – respecting at least some of the conventions, adopted by the printing and publishing trades, which have evolved and lasted for centuries.

The seventh factor, the printed area of the page, will largely be determined by the six preceding factors.

The eighth factor relates to margins surrounding the printed area on the page; this again will be affected by all decisions so far taken.

There is a subordinate consideration between factors seven and eight – belonging to both type-area and margins. I refer to extrusions beyond the regular printed area. These include folios, headlines, running headlines, shoulder titles, footnotes, catchlines, and possibly antiwidow lines. It is convenient to consider at this stage half-titles and chapter headings and all forms of sub-headings, and we must not ignore the presence of signature marks and collating marks.

The ninth factor might be described as a visual or even mechanical aid to continuity of design and may vary from the simplicity of almost invisible pin-pricks in a mediaeval scribe's sheet of vellum, to a printed complex of guide-lines for text and picture areas in various relationships on the page – the grid. When designing a book the grid emerges naturally as requirements are put upon the designer by the nature of the text.

My tenth and last factor is 'finishing', already briefly mentioned, which includes how the work is imposed, printed and bound – giving details of paper folding, collating, plating, sewing, trimming, blocking, covering, labelling, wrappering. Here marketing imposes itself because many buyers of the package are not the author's market, that is the reader, but intermediaries. They are the publishers' market, perhaps booksellers or librarians, or teachers, and in this process a more or less strong influence may be exerted by literary editors and their chosen reviewers.

The designer must work from the beginning with the finishing clearly in mind – all considerations, choices, decisions must support the total plan, but the plan is not inflexible; indeed it will often evolve as the answers are sought to the problems that arise along the way.

From the consideration of all these typographical factors will emerge a simple formula intended to answer the problems posed by the particular text in the interests of reader, author, editor, publisher, designer and printer. This formula, if successful, will provide legibility.

Whilst these details show something of the process of design, there is as yet no mention of style. In thinking about this I would like to propose a simple classification not by century or printer, not by divisions like symmetrical and asymmetrical, not by punchcutter or kind of letter, and not by its relationship to other arts of the period, but by analysis of the intentions of the designers. All typographical styles might be said to fall within five broad categories:

Full or Empty
Ornamental or Artifical
Natural.

Such a classification is valuable because it helps to simplify a complicated subject and may even influence some designers who show concern for the reader.

A series of title-pages will show what I mean. The title-page for William Morris' *Coleridge (6)* exemplifies *full* and is as full as any two-dimensional

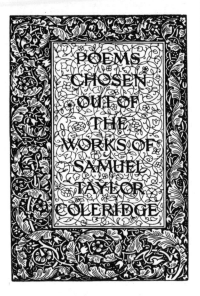

Fig 6: Style example: Full   Fig 7: Style example: Empty

image can be. It leaves no doubt about stylistic intent. The opposite, or *empty* style, is well shown in a title-page *(7)* from the middle period of Tschichold. John Bell's Shakespeare of 1774 demonstrates *ornamental (8)* where the desire to decorate is more than evident.

Of course ornamentation takes many different forms. *Artificial,* in this sense meaning contrived, is aptly shown in J. H. Mason's title-page *(9)* for Lawrence's *The Man Who Died.* Each line is made of uniform length irrespective of its relative value on the page by using a size of letter which will meet this demand – both word and letter-spacing are grotesquely manipulated.

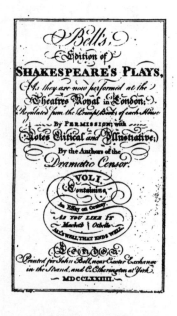

Fig 8: *Style example: Ornamental*   Fig 9: *Style example: Artificial*

Finally, the opposite of *artificial* emerges as *natural,* a typographical style in which the items on the page are arranged in a sequence of related editorial values which may be read vertically and where no item is too big or too small or over-spaced or without adequate space. The University Press at Oxford has sometimes excelled in this style *(10).*

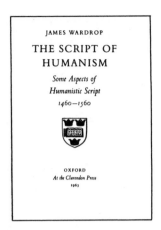

JAMES WARDROP

THE SCRIPT OF
HUMANISM

*Some Aspects of
Humanistic Script*
1460—1560

OXFORD
At the Clarendon Press
1963

Fig 10: Style example: Natural

A semblance of style might be learnt easily enough, but I suspect that an understanding in depth is genetic, instinctive, and that natural style belongs to the organic make-up of a highly, visually, literate person, is as much a part of the natural order of sophisticated life as are the golden mean and other modules of proportional relationships. The discovery that masterpieces of the past relate to the golden mean, not accidentally but inevitably, is an important lesson for any designer, and it is particularly valuable for the typographer. Walter Kaech in his *Rhythm and Proportion in Lettering* gives an analytical descriptions of, for instance, the Neptune temple *(11)* of the sixth century at Paestum and an inscribed tombstone *(12)* from Chieti of the first century AD.

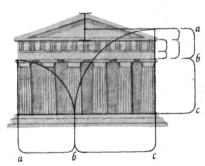

Fig 11: Golden mean analysis of the temple of Neptune, sixth century BC

Fig 12: Golden mean analysis of an inscription from Chieti first century A D.

The study of style is fascinating, and it stimulates creativity: but having glanced at it, we must get back to practical matters.

With design experience and a superficial knowledge of the typescript, the ten factors for legibility will have been weighed and a basic formula produced. The following example may be typical of well-made, general books:

> Demy octavo, Monotype Series 169, eleven on thirteen, by nineteen ems by thirty-two lines plus folios in spaced parentheses centred at foot. Headlines centred in small caps spaced two units.

> Margins: inner, 4 ems; head, 5 ems. Chapter drop, five lines.

Qualifying details and even layouts may be needed to complete the plan and to indicate what stylistic approach is being used, but the main structure of the book is established by that brief specification.

At least some of the many books on the setting and spacing and arrangement of type should be read; studying other people's ideas is a great help in working out our own. The exchanges of typographical ideas between Harold Curwen and J.H. Mason must at least be sampled by reading Leslie Owen's *J.H. Mason*, even though Leslie Owen's book is indulgent. B. H. Newdigate deserves some attention: the publication of his typographical principles in a literary magazine may well be unique. Joseph Thorp's *B.H. Newdigate* reprints many of these notes. The 1917 report on Cambridge typography by Bruce Rogers also merits a careful reading. It was made available to friends of the University Printer in 1950 and to the members of the Wynkyn de Worde Society in 1968. Eric Gill's *An Essay on Typography*, first issued in 1931, has points to compare with, for instance, Stanley Morison's *First Principles of Typography*, 1936, and with Oliver Simon's *Introduction to Typography* of 1945, and with Geoffrey Dowding's *Finer Points in the Spacing and Arrangement of Type*, 1954. Mardersteig, Rogers, Tschichold and Meynell have all published notes on the making of books which merit our attention.

In short, a comparative analysis of the way these designers have handled the ten factors I have enumerated, in theory as well as in practice, would be as valuable an exercise as one could devise for the aspiring typographer. Equally important in this process of laying the foundations of one's skills is an understanding of roots. Such an understanding is to be found in Harry Carter's *A View of Early Typography*, 1969. This introduction may give you a fresh insight into the period of incunable printing and certainly reveal the greatness of the Renaissance of printing at Paris in the 1520s. And if the past is important, there is the present to consider. An analytical approach to current work will also prove formative and will soon show that designer and editor must function neither separately nor in opposition but together if valid results are to be achieved.

However, some textual legibility problems remain, and an attempt to establish a touchstone for those of us involved in perpetuating the written word may be helpful. Myfanwy Piper once wrote of Reynolds Stone: '. . . he had a responsibility towards each letter each time he cut it so that its full dignity and character was brought out.' Such responsibility can hardly be claimed for dry-transfer lettering manufacturers who promote student lettering of maximum illegibility. Between these two extremes we have to maintain visual excellence in the wake of computer-organised filmsetting which includes font development or the making of new alphabets by electronic methods. It is important for us to pursue legibility rather than be forced to join a society for the prevention of cruelty to human eyesight.

We must see to it that our editors re-arrange copy which might result in confusion *(13)* so that it can be presented ready for reading vertically *(14)* like the cover to a booklet printed at the Oxford University Press.

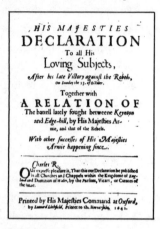 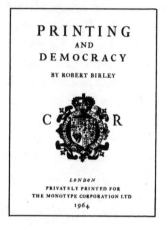

Fig 13: Title-page printed at Oxford in 1641   Fig 14: Booklet printed at Oxford in 1964

Also we must encourage designers to employ their freedom in the pursuit of legibility. Printing with capital letters can be done sufficiently well to arouse interest *(15)*, *(16)* and, with short lines, reading at a slowed speed is possible – but in principle too many factors of low legibility are involved.

CAPVT III.

PLERIQVE EORVM, QVI VETERIS POE-
TICAE HISTORIAE FASTOS NON SATIS
ACCVRATE DISPICIVNT, IN EVM DELA-
BVNTVR ERROREM, VT CREDANT, AT-
QVE AFFIRMENT, ANACREONTA MISE-

Fig 15: Part of a page printed by G. B. Bodoni at Parma in 1784

OF THE TRUE GREATNESSE OF KINGDOM^{ES} AND ESTATE^S

THE SPEECH OF THEMISTOCLES THE ATHENIAN, WHICH WAS HAUGHTIE AND ARROGANT, IN TAK-ING SO MUCH TO HIMSELFE, HAD BEEN A GRAVE AND WISE OBSERVATION & CENSURE, APPLIED AT LARGE TO OTHERS. DESIRED AT A FEAST TO TOUCH A LUTE, HE SAID; HE COULD NOT FIDDLE, BUT YET HE COULD MAKE A SMALL TOWNE, A GREAT CITTY THESE WORDS (HOLPEN A LITTLE WITH A META-PHORE) MAY EXPRESSE TWO DIFFERING ABILITIES, IN THOSE THAT DEALE IN BUSINESSE OF ESTATE. FOR IF A TRUE SURVEY BE TAKEN, OF COUNSELL-OURS AND STATESMEN, THERE MAY BE FOUND (THOUGH RARELY) THOSE, WHICH CAN MAKE A SMALL STATE GREAT, AND YET CANNOT FIDDLE: AS

Fig 16: Text page (detail) printed at The Shakespeare Head Press, 1927

When we think of the triumphant collection of twenty-six unaccented roman letters – the simplest known key to literacy ? – we realise that there is an overwhelming advantage inherent in the roman alphabet and partic-ularly for us in the English language. We have miraculously avoided the oriental policy that has forced millions of readers to live in a maze of pic-tographs. We have even avoided the legacy of Gutenberg's 290 separately cast characters. So why do we join letters, fuse them together and add unwise spaces that can only distress the reader's eye ? We even print words in unacceptable colours reversed out of screaming back-grounds. Instead of straining for effect in such ways, we should be examining every detail of legibility with the discrimination that results from understanding the roman alphabet.

I have tried to suggest that it is time to pause, to give some fresh thought to the major changes that have occurred in typography.

I am hinting at the addition of sloped roman capitals to the font of italic, and this, I think, was a mistake. The use of small upright roman capitals with italic lowercase provided the perfect amount of irregularity the eye needs for maximum legibility. Add to this, minimal changes in slant and restrained flourishes as we see in a page *(17)* printed by Castellione of Milan in 1541 and you have all the contrast needed when used with a text set in roman letters.

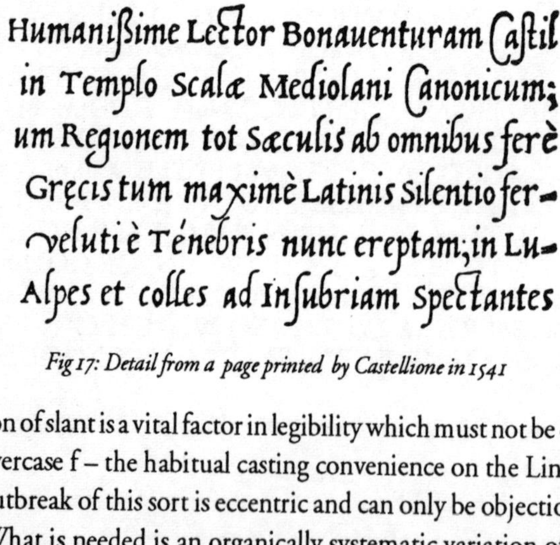

Humanißime Lector Bonauenturam Castil
in Templo Scalæ Mediolani Canonicum;
um Regionem tot Sæculis ab omnibus ferè
Grecis tum maximè Latinis Silentio fer-
veluti è Ténebris nunc ereptam; in Lu-
Alpes et colles ad Insubriam Spectantes

Fig 17: Detail from a page printed by Castellione in 1541

Variation of slant is a vital factor in legibility which must not be confined to the lowercase f – the habitual casting convenience on the Linotype. A solitary outbreak of this sort is eccentric and can only be objectionable to the eye. What is needed is an organically systematic variation of slant in italic lowercase. In other words, we must avoid such typographical mistakes as resulted from the recutting of Griffo's 1501 italics in which all mainstrokes were made exactly parallel. A similar loss of identity and legibility occurred in the recutting of Anton Janson's italics. The three illustrations *(18)* – *(20)* show how one version of Janson with its several angles of slant has been mis-cut with a single, constant nineteen degrees slope.

The attention of the reader is drawn to the fact that in the facsimile the calligraphic specimens are numbered in pencil by hand to allow the reader to follow the references made in the text to individual plates.

Fig 18: Janson italic printed by Giovanni Mardesteig

Both these recuttings of italics, Bembo and Janson, suffer from the lack of variation of slant. As a result they have become less legible.

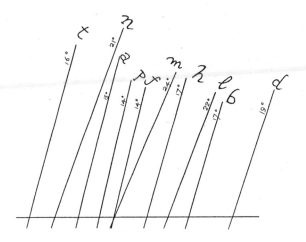

Fig 19: Slant analysis of the Janson italic shown in Fig 15

abcdefghijklmn opqrstuvwxyz

Fig 20: Janson italic with uniform slant of nineteen degrees

Let us introduce Nicolas Jenson of Venice and Francesco Griffo of Bologna and the Parisian Simon de Colines with his young successor Robert Estienne to the computers before it's too late. Let us programme with the few golden canons of typography we believe in.

This article is an abbreviated form of John Ryder's book *The Case For Legibility* which was first published by The Bodley Head in 1979. It is here typeset by the Libanus Press in 11/14pt Adobe Garamond on a measure marginally narrower than the one used in the rest of the book.

NOTES ON THE AUTHORS

ANNA AKHMATOVA was born in 1889. "The greatest Russian poetess of the twentieth century" (Joseph Brodsky), she was for many years prevented from publishing her work in the Soviet Union. In 1935 her son, Lev Gumilev, and second husband, Nikolay Punin, were arrested, released, and subsequently rearrested. Punin died in a camp in 1953; Gumilev was released to fight for his country in the Second World War, then imprisoned again until 1956. During the years of his imprisonment Akhmatova was forced to write "patriotic" verse in an effort to protect her son. In 1965 a substantial but censored edition of her work, *The Flight of Time*, finally appeared, and that same year she was permitted to travel to Oxford to receive an honorary D. Litt. She died in Leningrad in 1966.

ANDREI BITOV (1937–), an architect's son, was born in Leningrad, and studied at the Institute of Mining there; an expulsion forced him to spend some time in compulsory military service, but he graduated in 1962. Immediately upon graduating he signed a contract for his first book, a collection of short stories under the title *The Big Balloon* (1963), which gained him wide recognition. In the 1970s and early '80s his work came under official criticism ostensibly for its "excessive subjectivity", but in reality partly because of the publication of his novel *Pushkin House* in the West and also because of his involvement in the *Metropol* affair (an attempt to found an uncensored literary almanac). *Pushkin House* appeared in the Soviet Union only in 1987. *A Captive of the Caucasus* will be published by Harvill in autumn 1993.

LYDIA CHUKOVSKAYA was born in St Petersburg in 1907. She worked in the Leningrad office of Detizdat (the state publishing house for children's literature) until its entire editorial staff was purged in 1937. She was expelled from the Writers' Union in 1974 for writing an article in support of Alexander Solzhenitsyn and Andrei Sakharov. In addition to *The Akhmatova Journals*, her many books include two novellas, *Sofia Petrovna* and *Going Under*, a book of childhood memoirs, and two volumes of poetry. In 1976 she was awarded the first PEN Club Freedom Prize on the publication of the *Journals* in Russian in Paris, and in 1990 she was awarded the first Sakharov Prize for the courage displayed in her life's work. She lives in Moscow.

YURY DOMBROVKSY (1909–78) was born and brought up in Moscow. After graduating in 1932 he worked in a museum in Alma-Ata. His earliest publications were of poetry, but in 1939 he brought out a novel, *Derzhavin*. Immediately on its appearance he was arrested; he then spent fifteen years in prisons, labour camps and in exile. On being rehabilitated he returned to Moscow and in 1964 (the year of Khrushchev's downfall) he published *The Keeper of Antiquities*. In the year of his death its sequel, *The Faculty of Useless Knowledge*, was first published in the West. These two books form his major work.

RICHARD FORD was born in Jackson, Mississippi, in 1944. He is the author of four novels, all published to wide critical acclaim on both sides of the Atlantic: *Wildlife, The Sportswriter, The Ultimate Good Luck* and *A Piece of My Heart*, and a collection of short stories, *Rock Springs*.

GEORGE MACDONALD FRASER served in the Border Regiment in Burma during the Second World War, and in the Gordon Highlanders. He is author of the internationally popular Flashman novels and of the Private McAuslan stories. His other novels include *Mr American* and *The Pyrates*, and he has written a history of the Anglo-Scottish Border Reivers, *The Steel Bonnets*. His film scripts include those for "The Three Musketeers" and "Octopussy".

NADINE GORDIMER was awarded the Nobel Prize for Literature in 1991. Among her other awards are the MLA, the Malaparte Prize, Aigle d'Or, James Tait Black Memorial Prize, the Booker Prize (joint winner) and the CNA Literary Award. Educated in South Africa, she has been nominated to honorary fellowships at universities including Harvard, Yale and Leuven. She lives in Johannesburg.

ROBERT HUGHES, art critic of *Time* magazine and twice winner of the American College Art Associations F. J. Mather Award for distinguished criticism, is author of *The Shock of the New, Heaven and Hell in Western Art*, and of the history of the transportation of convicts to Australia, *The Fatal Shore*. His most recent publication is the acclaimed cultural history of *Barcelona*.

YASHAR KEMAL was born in 1923 in a village on the cotton-growing plain of Chukurova, Turkey. He started life as an agricultural labourer and factory-worker, but succeeded in improving his education and became a journalist. In 1952 he published a volume of short stories and three years later his first novel, *Memed, My Hawk*, won the Varlik Prize and laid the foundations of Kemal's international reputation as a great storyteller and the voice of the oppressed people among whom he grew up. In the words of Elia Kazan, Kemal is "a storyteller in the oldest tradition, that of Homer, spokesman for a people who had no other voice".

LEOPARD II

JAAN KROSS was born in Tallinn, Estonia, in 1920. He studied Law at the University of Tartu and worked for two years as a teacher until his arrest and deportation, with countless other Estonians, to Siberia in 1946. In 1954 he was released and returned to Tallinn, where he devoted himself to poetry and to translating the classics, including Shakespeare, Balzac and Stefan Zweig, for he had taught himself fluency in several languages during his imprisonment. Later he turned his attention to the historical novel, and has established his reputation as a world-class practitioner in this genre. Harvill are publishers of his novel set in the Baltic provinces of the Russian Empire at the time of Alexander I, *The Czar's Madman*.

ALEKSANDR KUSHNER, [1936—] poet and translator of Philip Larkin into Russian, was one of a group of young Petersburg poets which included the Nobel Laureate, Joseph Brodsky, whose mentors included the poet Anna Akhmatova and the literary critic and theorist Lidiya Ginzburg. A selection of his poems, *Apollo in the Snow*, is published by Harvill. He lives in St Petersburg.

GIUSEPPE TOMASI DI LAMPEDUSA (1896–1957), Prince of Lampedusa and a notable survivor into our own day of the great Sicilian landed aristocracy, is best remembered as author of *The Leopard*, "perhaps the greatest novel of the century" (L. P. Hartley). The short story reproduced here amply demonstrates that he was also a master of this difficult form. A man of broad culture, his acquaintance with English literature surpassed that of many a well-read Englishman.

CLAUDIO MAGRIS was born in Trieste in 1939. After graduating from the University of Turin, he lectured there in German Language and Literature from 1970 to 1978, before moving to the faculty of Literature and Philosophy at the University of Trieste. He has translated works by Ibsen, Kleist and Schnitzler and written many works of literary criticism. He is internationally recognized as author of *Danube*. His novel *A Different Sea* is a remarkable work of reflective philosophy which, like *Danube*, awakens many echoes in the reader.

OSIP MANDELSTAM (1892–1938). A major figure in twentieth-century Russian poetry, Mandelstam published three books of poems in his lifetime: *Stone* (1913), *Tristia* (1922) and *Poems* (1928). In 1934 he read a satirical poem about Stalin to a small group of friends. Within days he was arrested and sentenced to be "isolated but preserved". His wife, Nadezhda, went with him into exile in Voronezh, where his last great poems were written. In 1938 he was arrested for a second time and died in a labour camp near Vladivostok in the winter of that year.

JAVIER MARIAS was born in Madrid in 1951 and published his first novel at the age of nineteen. He has held academic posts in Spain, the United

States (visiting professor at Wellesley College) and at Oxford (Lecturer in Spanish Literature). He has written more than half a dozen novels, several of which have won prizes, including *All Souls*, based on his period at Oxford. "An Epigram of Loyalty" features an English eccentric man of letters who plays a significant role in *All Souls*.

JULIAN MAZOR was born in Baltimore in 1929. He studied Law at Yale, but instead of practicing law when he graduated, he joined the Air Force, where he remained until 1957. His first collection of fiction *Washington and Baltimore* was published to huge acclaim in 1968. He was awarded a grant by the Rockefeller Foundation and used the money to support a long stay in England and Ireland. In 1975 he disappeared from the literary world as completely as J. D. Salinger. "The Munster Final" marks his welcome return.

YUNNA MORITZ was born on 2 June 1937 in Kiev. A poet, she has been a member of the Union of Writers since 1962. She has published eight books of lyric verse and six books of poetry for children. Her poetry has been translated into English by Lidya Pasternak Slater, Elaine Feinstein, Stanley Kunitz and Daniel Weissbort. She lives in Moscow and is a member of the Russian PEN Centre.

BORIS PASTERNAK (1890–1960) was one of Russia's great twentieth-century poets. He made his reputation in 1917 with the collection, *My Sister, Life*, but as the Communist regime established its control over all areas of Russian life, Pasternak, like many of his contemporaries, found it increasingly difficult to write. In 1958 he published his novel, *Doctor Zhivago*, in the West and was awared the Nobel Prize for Literature, which he was forced to renounce. He died a broken man in 1960.

GEORGES PEREC (1936–82) was a Frenchman of Polish-Jewish descent. His ambition was constantly to break new ground in the field of literature – he was perhaps the most radical writer France has produced this century. His first novel, *Things. A Story of the Sixties*, won the Prix Renaudot. He combined fiction and autobiography in *W or The Memory of Childhood*, and triumphantly achieved the challenge of writing a full-length novel without once using the letter e, in *A Void* (shortly to be published in an equally triumphant translation by Gilbert Adair). His last novel, which he died leaving unfinished, was the mystery story, *"53 Days"*. But his fame principally rests on his dissection of an apartment block and its inhabitants, *Life A User's Manual*, considered to be "one of the great novels of the century" *T.L.S.* These works are all published, or about to be, by Harvill, who are also to publish the definitive biography, *Georges Perec: A Life in Words* by his principal translator, David Bellos.

LUIGI PIRANDELLO (1867–1936) is one of this century's greatest play-wrights (*Six Characters in Search of an Author*), as well as a prolific writer of novels and short stories. He won the Nobel Prize for Literature in 1934. His short stories were collected into *Novelle per un Anno* between 1922 and 1937. The two stories reproduced in this anthology give some idea of his range, from the world of the Sicilian peasant to that of the urban *bourgeoisie*.

EVGENY POPOV was born in Krasnoyarsk Region, Siberia. His first short story was published in 1976. He was a co-editor of the *Metropol* almanac (see under BITOV). Popov's books include *Merry-making in Old Russia* (1981), *The Beauty of Life* (1989), *I Await a Love that's True* (1989), and *The Soul of a Patriot* (1989). He lives in Moscow.

YULIA PYATNITSKAYA was a young Communist activist when she met and married Osip Pyatnitsky, a leading *apparatchik* eighteen years her senior. After a university education she worked as an engineer in an industrial-planning institute. The couple had two sons, Igor and Volodya (Vova). After the arrest of her husband and elder son, she scraped a living to support herself and her schoolboy son for a painful year and a half until her own arrest late in 1938. She died in the labour camps in 1940; her husband had by then been executed, but her son was eventually released. Her diary was preserved by the K.G.B.

JOHN RYDER was head of Design at the Bodley Head for thirty years, during which period he imparted to that imprint a quite distinctive stylishness allied with excellent legibility. A leading authority in the field of book design and typography, he is author of a number of books, including the popular manual *Printing for Pleasure*. In 1974 his own typographical work was honoured with a special exhibition at the Bodleian Library, Oxford. His *Intimate Leaves from a Designer's Notebook* is due to be published by Signal in 1993.

JOSE SARAMAGO was born in Portugal in 1922. Employed variously as a mechanic, technical designer and literary editor, since 1979 he has devoted himself entirely to writing. His many publications include works of non-fiction, plays, poetry, short stories and several novels which have been translated into more than twenty languages. The author of *Baltasar and Blimunda* (1982) and the award-winning *The Year of the Death of Ricardo Reis* (1984), Saramago is considered to be Portugal's most influential novelist.

RAIJA SIEKKINEN was born in 1953. Her first collection of short stories, *Talven tulo* (Arrival of Winter) was published in 1978. Since then she has written four collections of short stories, a novel and three books for children. Her most recent short story collection won the prestigious

Runeberg prize for literature 1993. "A Small Lie" is taken from the collection of the same name published in 1986 by Otava, Helsinki.

MARINA TSVETAEVA (1892–1941) was a contemporary of Pasternak, Mandelstam and Akhmatova. Tsvetaeva's fate was perhaps the most tragic of all. Her husband, Sergey Efron, served during the Civil War as an officer in the White Army. From 1925 till 1939 they lived in exile in Paris, but were forced to flee France when Efron was suspected of being a Soviet secret service agent. Shortly after her return to Moscow, her husband and daughter were arrested. Efron died or was executed in prison; her daughter was released in 1955. When war broke out Tsvetaeva was evacuated to the town of Elabuga, where in August 1941 she hanged herself.

JOY WILLIAMS is the author of three novels, including *Breaking and Entering* published by Harvill, and several collections of short stories, the most recent of which was *Escapes*. Her fiction has appeared in *Esquire*, *Granta*, and the *Paris Review*. She has just been honoured by the American Academy of Arts and Letters with a Strauss Living Award.

NOTES ON THE TRANSLATORS

SUSAN BROWNSBERGER holds degrees from Radcliffe and from Boston College. In addition to Andrei Bitov's novel, *Pushkin House*, she has translated *The Fur Hat* by Vladimir Voinovich, *The Hand* by Yuz Aleshovsky and *Sandro of Chegem* by Fazil Iskander.

MARGARET JULL COSTA took a degree in Spanish and Portuguese at the University of Bristol and went on to achieve an MA at Stanford University, California. Her translations from the Spanish include works by Alvaro Pombo, Juan José Saer, Bernardo Atxaga, Vlady Kociancich, as well as Javier Marías's novel, *All Souls*. She is also the translator of the great Portuguese writer, Fernando Pessoa.

PATRICK CREAGH has translated Italian poets and prose-writers from Dante and Leopardi to Calvino. His translation of Salvatore Satta's *The Day of Judgment* won the Lewis Galantière Prize, and he was awarded the John Florio Prize for his translations of Gesualdo Bufalino's *Blind Argus* and Claudio Magris's *Danube*.

ERIC DICKENS lived in Finland, Sweden and Poland before settling in Holland. He has a remarkable range of languages at his command, including Swedish, Finnish, Polish, Estonian, Dutch, German and French. He has translated works of non-fiction from Swedish and poetry from Finnish.

DAVID FLOYD, journalist and broadcaster, was for many years correspondent of the *Daily Telegraph* on Soviet and East European affairs. He has translated a great number of books from Russian; among the more recent ones are *Sofia Petrovna* by Lydia Chukovskaya and *I Hope* by Raisa Gorbachev.

MAX HAYWARD was the leading Russian translator of his generation, translating *Dr Zhivago* (with Manya Harari), *Hope against Hope* and works by Babel, Mayakovsky, Sinyavsky and Voznesensky.

STINA KATCHADOURIAN translates from Swedish, Finnish, Spanish, German and Armenian. Her translation of *Love and Solitude*, Selected Poems by Edith Södergran, won the Pushcart Prize in 1987.

THILDA KEMAL is the wife of the novelist Yashar Kemal; practically all Kemal's work that has been published in English is translated by her. The most recent novel published by Harvill, in her translation, was *To Crush the Serpent*.

STANLEY KUNITZ has received numerous awards for his poetry, including Harvard's Garrison Medal for Poetry, a Guggenheim Fellowship and the Pulitzer Prize.

MILENA MICHALSKI, a graduate of the School of Slavonic and East European Studies, University of London, is most recently the translator (with Sylva Rubashova) of stories by Alexander Lavrin and Dmitry Bakin, published in *Leopard I: Dissonant Voices, The New Russian Fiction*.

IAN MONK studied Classics at Bristol University, and has lived in France for the past seven years. He divides his time between teaching and translating, with a preference for the most challenging texts.

ALAN MYERS has translated a wide variety of contemporary Russian prose and verse texts, including *You Live and Love* by Valentin Rasputin. His translations of Joseph Brodsky include poetry and prose collected in *A Part of Speech* and *Less than One*, as well as his plays, *Marble* and *Democracy*. He has recently completed translations of *Behind the Lines* by Lydia Ginzburg and *The Faculty of Useless Knowledge* by Yury Dombrovsky for Harvill.

PETER NORMAN is the translator of poetry by Arseny Tarkovsky and most recently that of Marina Tsvetaeva in Viktoria Schweitzer's definitive biography *Tsvetaeva* (Harvill 1992).

GIOVANNI PONTIERO is a Reader in Latin American Literature at the University of Manchester. The translator of numerous works from the Portuguese, including José Saramago's *The Year of the Death of Ricardo Reis*, he is also the author of various books and critical works on Portuguese and Brazilian art and literature.

ROBERT PORTER is Senior Lecturer in Russian Studies at Bristol University. He studied Russian and Czech at Leeds University. He taught in the University of Wales, Aberystwyth for three years, before taking up his present post in 1974. His books include *Understanding Soviet Politics through Literature* with Martin Crouch (1984) and *Four Contemporary Russian Writers* (1989). He has published translations from Russian, Czech and Danish, and has recently completed a translation of Evgeny Popov's novel, *The Soul of a Patriot*, for Harvill.

CRAIG RAINE is the author of three books of poetry, a verse play, an opera libretto and a collection of essays, *Haydn and the Brass Trumpet*. Formerly Poetry editor at Faber & Faber, he is now a Fellow in English at New College, Oxford.

SYLVA RUBASHOVA came to the West from Leningrad in 1965, worked for the BBC Russian Service until 1987, and is the author of an autobiography, *A Sparrow in the Snow*, published under the pen-name Sylva Darel.

STEPHEN SPURR teaches Classics at Eton College.

ROBERT TRACY has published a bilingual edition of Osip Mandelstam's *Stone* (Harvill, 1991).

GUIDO WALDMAN edited *The Penguin Book of Italian Short Stories*, some of which he translated. Modern authors whose work he has translated include Gadda, Marotta and Calvino.

FRANK WILLIAMS used to work for the Russian Service of the BBC World Service in London and now works for Radio Liberty in Munich. He is the translator of Leonid Borodin's *The Story of a Strange Time* (Harvill, London, 1990), which won the London *Independent*'s Foreign Fiction award in its month of publication. He specialises in new Russian fiction.

Harvill editions by contributors to this volume

ANNA AKHMATOVA
Selected Poems

ANDREI BITOV
Pushkin House
A Captive of the Caucasus

LYDIA CHUKOVSKAYA
Sofia Petrovna
The Akhmatova Journals

RICHARD FORD
A Piece of My Heart
The Ultimate Good Luck
The Sportswriter
Rock Springs
Wildlife

GEORGE MACDONALD FRASER
"The Flashman Papers" ~ in nine volumes
"The McAuslan Stories" ~ in three volumes
The Steel Bonnets
Mr American
The Pyrates
Quartered Safe out Here
The Candlemass Road

ROBERT HUGHES
The Fatal Shore
Nothing If Not Critical
Barcelona

YASHAR KEMAL
Memed, My Hawk
The Wind from the Plain

Iron Earth, Copper Sky
The Undying Grass
To Crush the Serpent

JAAN KROSS
The Czar's Madman

ALEKSANDR KUSHNER
Apollo in the Snow

GIUSEPPE TOMASI DI LAMPEDUSA
The Leopard

CLAUDIO MAGRIS
Danube
A Different Sea

OSIP MANDELSTAM
Stone
The Collected Critical Prose and Letters

JAVIER MARIAS
All Souls

BORIS PASTERNAK
Doctor Zhivago
Poems 1955–1959 *with* An Essay in Autobiography

EVGENY POPOV
The Soul of a Patriot

JOSE SARAMAGO
The Year of the Death of Ricardo Reis
The Gospel According to Jesus Christ

JOY WILLIAMS
Breaking and Entering

Leopard I, Dissonant Voices: The New Russian Fiction

Edited by Oleg Chukhontsev, formerly poetry editor of *Novy Mir*

Vladimir Zazubrin: *The Chip*
Arseny Tarkovsky: *Frostbitten Hands*
Vladimir Tendryakov: *On the Blessed Island of Communism*
Andrei Bitov: *The Doctor*
Vladimir Makanin: *Those Who Did Not Get into the Choir*
Vasily Belov: *A War Like That*
Irina Povolskaya: *The Rosy-Fingered Dawn*
Yury Kazakov: *You Cried So Bitterly in Your Sleep*
Leonid Borodin: *The Visit*
Yury Dombrovsky: *An Arm, a Leg, a Gherkin Too . . .*
Larisa Vaneeva: *Lame Pigeons*
Dmitry Bakin: *Lagopthalmos*
Oleg Ermakov: *Safe Return*
Izrael Metter: *Ryabov and Kozhin*
Viktor Erofeev: *Sludge-gulper*
Evgeny Popov: *The Situation*
Fazil Iskander: *Broadbrow*
Alexander Lavrin: *The Death of Igor Ilich*
Valery Popov: *Dreams on an Upper Berth*
Viktor Astafiev: *The Blind Fisherman*
Serafim Chetverukhin: *Tsarevich Dmitry*
Yury Trifonov: *Archetypal Themes*
Elena Rzhevskaya: *On the Tarmac*
Vyacheslav Pietsukh: *Anamnesis and Epicrisis*
Lyudmila Petrushevskaya: *A Modern Family Robinson*
Pavel Petrov: *A Bit of Winter*

Harvill Paperbacks are published by Harvill,
an Imprint of HarperCollins*Publishers*

1. Giuseppe Tomasi di Lampedusa *The Leopard*
2. Boris Pasternak *Doctor Zhivago*
3. Alexander Solzhenitsyn *The Gulag Archipelago*
4. Jonathan Raban *Soft City*
5. Alan Ross *Blindfold Games*
6. Joy Adamson *Queen of Shaba*
7. Vasily Grossman *Forever Flowing*
8. Peter Levi *The Frontiers of Paradise*
9. Ernst Pawel *The Nightmare of Reason*
10. Patrick O'Brian *Joseph Banks*
11. Mikhail Bulgakov *The Master and Margarita*
12. Leonid Borodin *Partings*
13. Salvatore Satta *The Day of Judgment*
14. Peter Matthiessen *At Play in the Fields of the Lord*
15. Alexander Solzhenitsyn *The First Circle*
16. Homer, translated by Robert Fitzgerald *The Odyssey*
17. George MacDonald Fraser *The Steel Bonnets*
18. Peter Matthiessen *The Cloud Forest*
19. Theodore Zeldin *The French*
20. Georges Perec *Life A User's Manual*
21. Nicholas Gage *Eleni*
22. Eugenia Ginzburg *Into the Whirlwind*
23. Eugenia Ginzburg *Within the Whirlwind*
24. Mikhail Bulgakov *The Heart of a Dog*
25. Vincent Cronin *Louis and Antoinette*
26. Alan Ross *The Bandit on the Billiard Table*
27. Fyodor Dostoyevsky *The Double*
28. Alan Ross *Time was Away*
29. Peter Matthiessen *Under the Mountain Wall*
30. Peter Matthiessen *The Snow Leopard*
31. Peter Matthiessen *Far Tortuga*
32. Jorge Amado *Shepherds of the Night*
33. Jorge Amado *The Violent Land*